MATH
ADVANTAGE

TEST
COPYING
MASTERS

- **Multiple-Choice (Standardized) Format Tests**
- **Free-Response Format Tests**
- **Answer Keys**
- **Management Forms**

Harcourt Brace & Company
Orlando • Atlanta • Austin • Boston • San Francisco • Chicago • Dallas • New York • Toronto • London

http://www.hbschool.com

Y0-CDP-790

CONTENTS

▶ Formal Assessment

▶ Management Forms

Harcourt Brace School Publishers

Multiple-Choice Format Tests
(Standardized)

The multiple-choice format is provided to assess mastery of the learning goals of the program. These tests assess concepts, skills, and problem solving. The use of these tests helps prepare students for standardized achievement tests.

There is an Inventory Test which tests the learning goals from the previous grade level. This can be used at the beginning of the year or as a placement test when a new student enters your class.

There is a Chapter Test for each chapter and a Multi-Chapter Test to be used as review after several chapters in a content cluster. Also, there are Cumulative Tests at the same point as the Multi-Chapter Tests. The Cumulative Test reviews content from Chapter 1 through the current chapter.

Math Advantage also provides free-response format tests that parallel the multiple-choice tests. You may wish to use one form as a pretest and one form as a posttest.

Name _____

Choose the correct answer.

1. ▢▢▢▢▨▨

$$4 + 2 = \underline{\hspace{1cm}}$$

(A) 3   (B) 4

(C) 5   (D) 6

2. ▢▢▢▢☒

$$5 - 1 = \underline{\hspace{1cm}}$$

(A) 3   (B) 4

(C) 5   (D) 6

3.

(A) 7   (B) 8

(C) 9   (D) 10

4.
$$\begin{array}{r} 6 \\ + 2 \\ \hline \end{array}$$

(A) 7   (B) 8

(C) 9   (D) 10

5. 🍐🍐🍐🍐🍐🍐🍐✗✗

$$9 - 2 = \underline{\hspace{1cm}}$$

(A) 7   (B) 8

(C) 9   (D) 10

6.
$$\begin{array}{r} 5 \\ - 0 \\ \hline \end{array}$$

(A) 0   (B) 4

(C) 5   (D) 16

7. Which one is the same shape?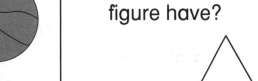

(A)   (B)

(C)   (D)

8. How many sides does this figure have?

(A) 1 side   (B) 3 sides

(C) 4 sides   (D) 5 sides

9. Which is an **open** figure?

Ⓐ

Ⓑ

Ⓒ

Ⓓ

10. Which shape comes next in the pattern?

Ⓐ ☐   Ⓑ △

Ⓒ ○

11.
$$\begin{array}{r} 5 \\ +5 \\ \hline \end{array}$$

Ⓐ 9   Ⓑ 10
Ⓒ 11   Ⓓ not here

12.
$$\begin{array}{r} 6 \\ +5 \\ \hline 11 \end{array} \qquad \begin{array}{r} 11 \\ -5 \\ \hline \end{array}$$

Ⓐ 7   Ⓑ 8
Ⓒ 9   Ⓓ not here

13. How many?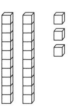

Ⓐ 5   Ⓑ 13
Ⓒ 23   Ⓓ 32

14. Which number comes **between** 83 and 85?

83, ___, 85

Ⓐ 82   Ⓑ 84
Ⓒ 86   Ⓓ 87

15. Count by fives. Which number comes after 15?

5, 10, 15, ___

Ⓐ 16   Ⓑ 20
Ⓒ 25   Ⓓ 30

16. How much money?

Ⓐ 3¢   Ⓑ 7¢
Ⓒ 11¢   Ⓓ 30¢

17. Which coins are the same amount as  ?

Ⓐ 5 pennies Ⓑ 10 pennies
Ⓒ 20 pennies Ⓓ 25 pennies

18. What time is it?

Ⓐ 4:30 Ⓑ 5:30
Ⓒ 6:30 Ⓓ 7:30

Use the calendar to answer questions 19 and 20.

May

Sunday	Monday	Tuesday	Wednesday	Thursday	Friday	Saturday
					1	2
3	4	5	6	7	8	9

19. On which day does this month begin?

Ⓐ Sunday Ⓑ Tuesday
Ⓒ Friday Ⓓ Saturday

20. On which day is May 4?

Ⓐ Sunday Ⓑ Monday
Ⓒ Wednesday Ⓓ Thursday

21. How many inches long is the paper clip?

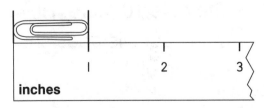
inches

Ⓐ 1 inch Ⓑ 2 inches
Ⓒ 3 inches Ⓓ 4 inches

22. About how many  does the ▨ hold?

Ⓐ 1 Ⓑ 2
Ⓒ 4 Ⓓ 8

23. Which picture has $\frac{1}{3}$ colored?

 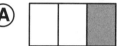

24. How many stars are red?

Stars	
red	IIII III
gold	IIII

(A) 4 stars (B) 5 stars
(C) 6 stars (D) 7 stars

Use the graph to answer questions 25 and 26.

Farm Animals						Total
pig	🐷	🐷	🐷			3
cow	🐄					1
chick	🐤	🐤	🐤	🐤	🐤	5

25. How many pigs are there?
(A) 1 pig (B) 3 pigs
(C) 4 pigs (D) 5 pigs

26. How many animals in all?
(A) 1 animal (B) 3 animals
(C) 9 animals (D) 10 animals

27.
$$\begin{array}{r} 3 \\ 7 \\ +2 \\ \hline \end{array}$$

(A) 10 (B) 12
(C) 13 (D) 19

28. Jane has 13 pencils. Then she gets 10 more. How many pencils does she have in all?

(A) 3 pencils (B) 10 pencils
(C) 23 pencils (D) 130 pencils

Choose the correct answer.

1. Which addition sentence tells about the picture?

(A) 6 + 4 = 10
(B) 6 + 6 = 12
(C) 6 + 7 = 13
(D) 6 + 6 = 66

2. Which addition sentence tells about the picture?

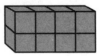 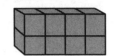

(A) 8 + 8 = 88
(B) 8 + 8 = 15
(C) 8 + 8 = 16
(D) 8 + 8 = 17

3.
$$7$$
$$+8$$

(A) 13
(B) 14
(C) 15
(D) not here

4.
$$7$$
$$+6$$

(A) 13
(B) 14
(C) 15
(D) not here

5.
$$9$$
$$+2$$

(A) 10
(B) 11
(C) 12
(D) 13

6.
$$9$$
$$+8$$

(A) 14
(B) 15
(C) 16
(D) 17

7.
$$5$$
$$+9$$

(A) 14
(B) 15
(C) 16
(D) not here

8.
$$3$$
$$+9$$

(A) 9
(B) 10
(C) 11
(D) not here

Name _____

9.

$$\begin{array}{r} 7 \\ +3 \\ \hline \end{array}$$

Ⓐ 8   Ⓑ 9
Ⓒ 10   Ⓓ not here

10.

$$\begin{array}{r} 8 \\ +4 \\ \hline \end{array}$$

Ⓐ 11   Ⓑ 12
Ⓒ 13   Ⓓ not here

11. Carl has 6 red stars and 6 gold stars. How many stars does he have?

Ⓐ 9 stars   Ⓑ 10 stars
Ⓒ 11 stars   Ⓓ 12 stars

12. Sara spent 9¢ for a pen and 5¢ for paper. How much money did she spend?

Ⓐ 14¢   Ⓑ 55¢
Ⓒ 16¢   Ⓓ 17¢

13.

$$\begin{array}{r} 3 \\ 7 \\ +6 \\ \hline \end{array}$$

Ⓐ 13   Ⓑ 14
Ⓒ 15   Ⓓ 16

14.

$$\begin{array}{r} 4 \\ 9 \\ +4 \\ \hline \end{array}$$

Ⓐ 15   Ⓑ 16
Ⓒ 17   Ⓓ 18

15. Nan has 6 red pens, 6 blue pens, and 2 black pens. How many pens does she have?

Ⓐ 13 pens   Ⓑ 14 pens
Ⓒ 15 pens   Ⓓ 16 pens

16. Cody has 8 red cars, 9 green cars, and 1 yellow car. How many cars does he have?

Ⓐ 15 cars   Ⓑ 16 cars
Ⓒ 17 cars   Ⓓ 18 cars

Harcourt Brace School Publishers

Choose the correct answer.

1.

$$\begin{array}{r} 8 \\ +5 \\ \hline 13 \end{array} \qquad \begin{array}{r} 13 \\ -8 \\ \hline \end{array}$$

(A) 4   (B) 5
(C) 6   (D) 7

2.

$$15 - 6 = 9$$
$$9 + 6 = \underline{}$$

(A) 12   (B) 13
(C) 14   (D) 15

3.

$$\begin{array}{r} 7 \\ +8 \\ \hline 15 \end{array} \qquad \begin{array}{r} 15 \\ -8 \\ \hline \end{array}$$

(A) 4   (B) 5
(C) 6   (D) 7

4.

$$17 - 9 = 8$$
$$8 + 9 = \underline{}$$

(A) 15   (B) 16
(C) 17   (D) 18

Use the number line to answer questions 5 and 6.

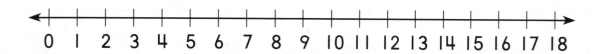

0 1 2 3 4 5 6 7 8 9 10 11 12 13 14 15 16 17 18

5.

$$14 - 7 = \underline{}$$

(A) 7   (B) 8
(C) 9   (D) 10

6.

$$16 - 8 = \underline{}$$

(A) 6   (B) 7
(C) 8   (D) 9

7. Which number sentence belongs in this fact family?

$$7 + 9 = 16$$
$$9 + 7 = 16$$
$$16 - 9 = 7$$

(A) $19 - 6 = 13$
(B) $16 - 7 = 9$
(C) $7 + 6 = 13$
(D) $9 + 9 = 18$

8. Which number sentence belongs in this fact family?

$$8 + 6 = 14$$
$$6 + 8 = 14$$
$$14 - 6 = 8$$

(A) $14 - 7 = 7$
(B) $14 - 5 = 9$
(C) $14 - 8 = 6$
(D) $7 + 7 = 14$

Which is the missing addend?

9.

$$9 + \underline{} = 15$$

(A) 4   (B) 5
(C) 6   (D) not here

10.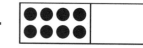

$$8 + \underline{} = 11$$

(A) 1   (B) 2
(C) 3   (D) not here

11. There were 9 boys and 5 girls playing ball. How many children were playing ball?

(A) 4 children
(B) 14 children
(C) 16 children
(D) 18 children

12. There were 15 birds in a tree. Then 7 birds flew away. How many birds were left?

(A) 8 birds   (B) 9 birds
(C) 12 birds   (D) 22 birds

Choose the correct answer.

1.
$$\begin{array}{r} 9 \\ +6 \\ \hline \end{array}$$

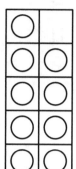

- Ⓐ 14
- Ⓑ 15
- Ⓒ 16
- Ⓓ 17

2.
$$\begin{array}{r} 5 \\ +5 \\ \hline \end{array}$$

- Ⓐ 10
- Ⓑ 11
- Ⓒ 12
- Ⓓ not here

3. Bill has 8 red fish and 8 gold fish. How many fish does he have?

- Ⓐ 15 fish
- Ⓑ 16 fish
- Ⓒ 17 fish
- Ⓓ 18 fish

4. Cora spent 7¢ for an orange and 6¢ for grapes. How much money did she spend?

- Ⓐ 11¢
- Ⓑ 12¢
- Ⓒ 13¢
- Ⓓ 14¢

5.
$$\begin{array}{r} 6 \\ 2 \\ +4 \\ \hline \end{array}$$

- Ⓐ 9
- Ⓑ 10
- Ⓒ 11
- Ⓓ 12

6.
$$\begin{array}{r} 3 \\ 8 \\ +3 \\ \hline \end{array}$$

- Ⓐ 14
- Ⓑ 15
- Ⓒ 16
- Ⓓ 17

Form A • Multiple-Choice

Go on.

7.
$$8 \qquad 15$$
$$\underline{+7} \qquad \underline{-\ 8}$$
$$15$$

Ⓐ 4   Ⓑ 5
Ⓒ 6   Ⓓ 7

8. $11 - 4 = 7$
$$7 + 4 = \underline{\qquad}$$

Ⓐ 9   Ⓑ 10
Ⓒ 11   Ⓓ 12

Use the number line to answer questions 9 and 10.

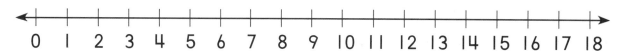

0 1 2 3 4 5 6 7 8 9 10 11 12 13 14 15 16 17 18

9. $16 - 7 = \underline{\qquad}$

Ⓐ 7   Ⓑ 9
Ⓒ 11   Ⓓ 12

10. $14 - 9 = \underline{\qquad}$

Ⓐ 5   Ⓑ 6
Ⓒ 7   Ⓓ 8

11. Which is the missing addend?

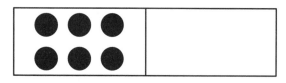

$$6 + \underline{\qquad} = 11$$

Ⓐ 3   Ⓑ 4
Ⓒ 5   Ⓓ not here

12. There were 7 boys and 5 girls in the contest. How many children were in the contest?

Ⓐ 12 children
Ⓑ 13 children
Ⓒ 14 children
Ⓓ 15 children

Form A • Multiple-Choice   A10   **Stop!**

Harcourt Brace School Publishers

Name _____

Choose the correct answer.

---

1. Which addition sentence tells about the picture?

- Ⓐ 4 + 4 = 8
- Ⓑ 4 + 5 = 9
- Ⓒ 4 + 8 = 12

2. Which addition sentence tells about the picture?

- Ⓐ 7 + 7 = 77
- Ⓑ 7 + 9 = 16
- Ⓒ 7 + 7 = 14

3.
$$\begin{array}{r} 8 \\ +9 \\ \hline \end{array}$$

- Ⓐ 16
- Ⓑ 17
- Ⓒ 18
- Ⓓ not here

4.
$$\begin{array}{r} 6 \\ +5 \\ \hline \end{array}$$

- Ⓐ 9
- Ⓑ 10
- Ⓒ 11
- Ⓓ not here

5.
$$\begin{array}{r} 7 \\ +8 \\ \hline \end{array}$$

- Ⓐ 14
- Ⓑ 15
- Ⓒ 16
- Ⓓ not here

6.
$$\begin{array}{r} 3 \\ +2 \\ \hline \end{array}$$

- Ⓐ 6
- Ⓑ 7
- Ⓒ 8
- Ⓓ not here

7.
$$\begin{array}{r} 9 \\ +3 \\ \hline \end{array}$$

- Ⓐ 10
- Ⓑ 11
- Ⓒ 12
- Ⓓ 13

8.
$$\begin{array}{r} 2 \\ +9 \\ \hline \end{array}$$

- Ⓐ 10
- Ⓑ 11
- Ⓒ 12
- Ⓓ 13

---

9. Use the picture to find the sum.

$$\begin{array}{r} 8 \\ +5 \\ \hline \end{array}$$

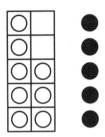

Ⓐ 13 Ⓑ 14
Ⓒ 15 Ⓓ not here

10. Use the picture to find the sum.

$$\begin{array}{r} 5 \\ +7 \\ \hline \end{array}$$

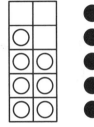

Ⓐ 11 Ⓑ 12
Ⓒ 13 Ⓓ not here

11. Davey has 7 blue cars and 9 red cars. How many cars does he have?

Ⓐ 9 cars Ⓑ 10 cars
Ⓒ 16 cars Ⓓ 18 cars

12. Kris has 6 pink bows, 5 green bows, and 6 red bows. How many bows does she have?

Ⓐ 17 bows Ⓑ 18 bows
Ⓒ 19 bows Ⓓ 20 bows

13.
$$\begin{array}{r} 5 \\ 8 \\ +5 \\ \hline \end{array}$$

Ⓐ 17 Ⓑ 18
Ⓒ 19 Ⓓ 20

14.
$$\begin{array}{r} 7 \\ 3 \\ +5 \\ \hline \end{array}$$

Ⓐ 15 Ⓑ 16
Ⓒ 17 Ⓓ 18

Harcourt Brace School Publishers

Name _____

Choose the correct answer.

1. How many ones are there?

4 tens = __ ones

Ⓐ 14   Ⓑ 40
Ⓒ 44   Ⓓ 140

2. How many ones are there?

2 tens = __ ones

Ⓐ 2   Ⓑ 12
Ⓒ 20   Ⓓ 22

3. How many tens and ones are there?

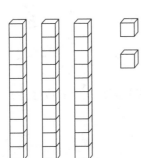

Ⓐ 2 tens 3 ones = 23
Ⓑ 3 tens 2 ones = 32
Ⓒ 4 tens 3 ones = 43
Ⓓ 4 tens 4 ones = 44

4. How many tens and ones are there?

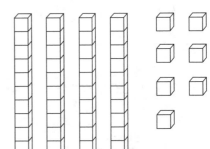

Ⓐ 7 tens 4 ones = 74
Ⓑ 7 tens 7 ones = 77
Ⓒ 10 tens 4 ones = 104
Ⓓ 4 tens 7 ones = 47

5. Which is the number?

9 tens 6 ones = __

Ⓐ 3   Ⓑ 69
Ⓒ 96   Ⓓ 906

6. Which is the number?

8 tens 0 ones = __

Ⓐ 8   Ⓑ 18
Ⓒ 80   Ⓓ 88

Harcourt Brace School Publishers

Name _____

7. Which is the number?

7 tens 9 ones = __

(A) 19   (B) 79

(C) 97   (D) not here

8. Which is the number?

5 tens 1 one = __

(A) 6   (B) 15

(C) 51   (D) not here

9. Which number is shown?

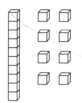

(A) 8   (B) 18

(C) 81   (D) 88

10. Which number is shown?

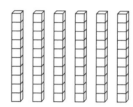

(A) 6   (B) 16

(C) 60   (D) 66

Use these groups to help you answer questions 11 and 12.

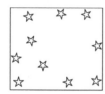   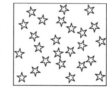   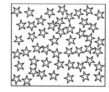

10 stars   25 stars   50 stars

11. Which is the best estimate?

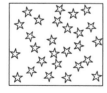

(A) about 10 stars

(B) about 25 stars

(C) about 50 stars

12. Which is the best estimate?

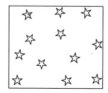

(A) about 10 stars

(B) about 25 stars

(C) about 50 stars

Form A • Multiple-Choice   A16   **Stop!**

Name _____

CHAPTER 4 TEST
PAGE 1

Choose the correct answer.

1. Count by fives. Which number comes next?

5, 10, 15, 20, ___

(A) 21 (B) 22
(C) 25 (D) 30

2. Count by tens. Which number comes next?

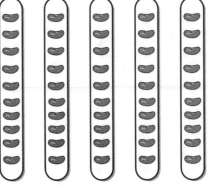

10, 20, 30, 40, ___

(A) 41 (B) 42
(C) 45 (D) 50

3. Count by fives. Which number comes next?

55, 60, 65, 70, ___

(A) 71 (B) 75
(C) 77 (D) 80

4. Count by tens. Which number comes next?

50, 60, 70, 80, ___

(A) 81 (B) 85
(C) 89 (D) not here

5. Count by twos. Which number comes next?

28, 30, 32, 34, ___

(A) 35 (B) 36
(C) 37 (D) not here

6. Count by threes. Which number comes next?

9, 12, 15, 18, ___

(A) 21 (B) 22
(C) 23 (D) not here

Harcourt Brace School Publishers

Form A • Multiple-Choice   A17   **Go on.**

Name _____

7. Even or odd?

5

Ⓐ even   Ⓑ odd

8. Even or odd?

12

Ⓐ even   Ⓑ odd

9. Count on by tens. Which number comes next?

34, 44, 54, 64, ___

Ⓐ 66   Ⓑ 70
Ⓒ 74   Ⓓ 75

10. Count back by tens. Which number comes next?

81, 71, 61, 51, ___

Ⓐ 41   Ⓑ 45
Ⓒ 49   Ⓓ 50

11. Which rule will help you find the missing number?

20, 30, ___, 50

Ⓐ Count by twos.
Ⓑ Count by threes.
Ⓒ Count by fives.
Ⓓ Count by tens.

12. Which rule will help you find the missing number?

30, 32, ___, 36

Ⓐ Count by twos.
Ⓑ Count by threes.
Ⓒ Count by fives.
Ⓓ Count by tens.

Harcourt Brace School Publishers

Form A • Multiple-Choice   A18   Stop!

Name _____

Choose the correct answer.

1. Which number is **greater**?

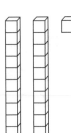 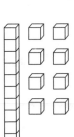

(A) 21   (B) 18

2. Which number is **less**?

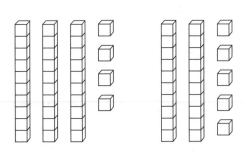

(A) 34   (B) 25

---

3. Which sign goes in the circle?

17 ◯ 9

(A) <   (B) >

4. Which sign goes in the circle?

35 ◯ 53

(A) <   (B) >

---

5. Which number is just after 49?

(A) 40   (B) 47
(C) 50   (D) 51

6. Which number is between 12 and 14?

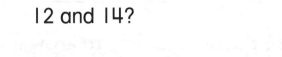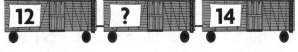

(A) 8   (B) 11
(C) 15   (D) not here

Form A • Multiple-Choice   A19   Go on. ➡

Harcourt Brace School Publishers

7. Which number is just before?

__, 17

Ⓐ 16   Ⓑ 18
Ⓒ 19   Ⓓ not here

8. Which number is between?

79, __, 81

Ⓐ 74   Ⓑ 75
Ⓒ 78   Ⓓ not here

Use the pictures to answer questions 9 and 10.

| first | second | third | fourth | fifth | sixth | seventh | eighth |
| 1st | 2nd | 3rd | 4th | 5th | 6th | 7th | 8th |

9. Which is the position of the ?

Ⓐ second   Ⓑ fifth
Ⓒ sixth   Ⓓ eighth

10. Which is the position of the ?

Ⓐ 4th   Ⓑ 5th
Ⓒ 6th   Ⓓ 7th

Use the number line to answer questions 11 and 12.

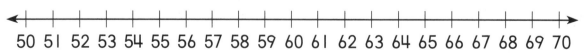

50 51 52 53 54 55 56 57 58 59 60 61 62 63 64 65 66 67 68 69 70

11. Is 66 closer to 60 or 70?

Ⓐ 60   Ⓑ 70

12. Is 52 closer to 50 or 60?

Ⓐ 50   Ⓑ 60

Name _____

Choose the correct answer.

1. How many tens and ones are there?

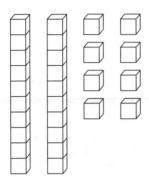

(A) 2 tens 2 ones = 22
(B) 2 tens 8 ones = 28
(C) 3 tens 8 ones = 38
(D) 8 tens 2 ones = 82

2. How many tens and ones are there?

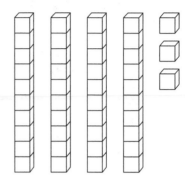

(A) 3 tens 3 ones = 33
(B) 3 tens 4 ones = 34
(C) 4 tens 3 ones = 43
(D) 4 tens 4 ones = 44

3. Which is the number?

7 tens 1 one = ____

(A) 6   (B) 8
(C) 17   (D) 71

4. Which is the number?

6 tens 4 ones = ____

(A) 64   (B) 46
(C) 20   (D) 2

5. Count by fives. Which number comes next?

35, 40, 45, 50, ____

(A) 51   (B) 52
(C) 55   (D) 60

6. Count back by tens. Which number comes next?

73, 63, 53, 43, ____

(A) 33   (B) 44
(C) 45   (D) 50

Form A • Multiple-Choice   A21   **Go on.**

7. Even or odd?

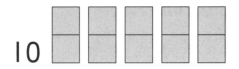

10

Ⓐ even   Ⓑ odd

8. Which rule will help you find the missing numbers?

10, 13, __, 19, 22

Ⓐ Count by twos.

Ⓑ Count by threes.

Ⓒ Count by fives.

Ⓓ Count by tens.

9. Which number is just before?

__, 82

Ⓐ 79   Ⓑ 80

Ⓒ 81   Ⓓ not here

10. Which number is between?

95, __, 97

Ⓐ 90   Ⓑ 92

Ⓒ 93   Ⓓ not here

Use the number line to answer questions 11 and 12.

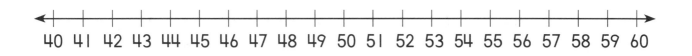

40 41 42 43 44 45 46 47 48 49 50 51 52 53 54 55 56 57 58 59 60

11. Is 54 closer to 50 or 60?

Ⓐ 50   Ⓑ 60

12. Is 47 closer to 40 or 50?

Ⓐ 40   Ⓑ 50

Stop!

Harcourt Brace School Publishers

Name _____

Choose the correct answer.

1.
   $$\begin{array}{r} 4 \\ +5 \\ \hline \end{array}$$

   (A) 8   (B) 9
   (C) 10   (D) not here

2. $16 - 7 = 9$

   $9 + 7 = \underline{\ ?\ }$

   (A) 15   (B) 16
   (C) 17   (D) 18

3. How many ones are there?

   3 tens = __?__ ones

   (A) 3   (B) 13
   (C) 30   (D) 130

4. How many tens and ones are there?

   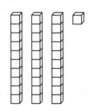

   (A) 1 ten 3 ones = 13
   (B) 1 ten 4 ones = 14
   (C) 2 tens 3 ones = 23
   (D) 3 tens 1 one = 31

5. Which is the number?

   7 tens 4 ones = __?__

   (A) 4   (B) 7
   (C) 47   (D) 74

6. Which number is shown?

   (A) 13   (B) 30
   (C) 31   (D) 33

Name _____

Use these groups to help you answer questions 7 and 8.

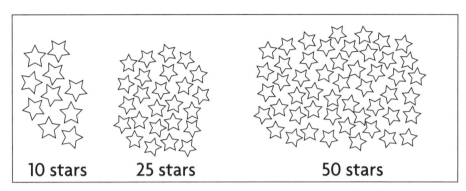

10 stars   25 stars   50 stars

---

7. Which is the best estimate?

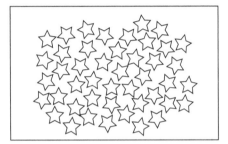

(A) about 10 stars
(B) about 25 stars
(C) about 50 stars

8. Which is the best estimate?

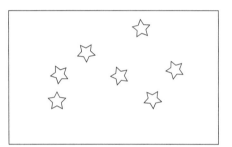

(A) about 10 stars
(B) about 25 stars
(C) about 50 stars

---

9. Count by twos. Which number comes next?

32, 34, 36, 38, ___

(A) 40   (B) 41
(C) 42   (D) not here

10. Count back by tens. Which number comes next?

62, 52, 42, 32, ___

(A) 35   (B) 31
(C) 30   (D) 22

---

11. Even or odd?

6

(A) even   (B) odd

12. Which rule will help you find the missing numbers?

15, 20, 25, 30, ___

(A) Count by twos.
(B) Count by threes.
(C) Count by fives.
(D) Count by tens.

13. Which number is **greater**?

(A) 16   (B) 22

14. Which number is **less**?

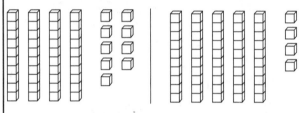

(A) 49   (B) 54

15. Which sign goes in the circle?

6 ◯ 11

(A) <   (B) >

16. Which number is between?

59, ___, 61

(A) 58   (B) 65
(C) 71   (D) not here

Use the pictures below to answer questions 17 and 18.

| first
1st | second
2nd | third
3rd | fourth
4th | fifth
5th | sixth
6th | seventh
7th | eighth
8th |

17. Which is the position of the

(A) third (B) fifth
(C) sixth (D) seventh

18. Which is the position of the

(A) 1st (B) 3rd
(C) 4th (D) 6th

Use the number line to answer questions 19 and 20.

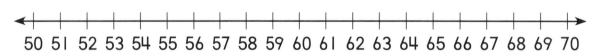

50 51 52 53 54 55 56 57 58 59 60 61 62 63 64 65 66 67 68 69 70

19. Is 37 closer to 30 or 40?

(A) 30 (B) 40

20. Is 41 closer to 40 or 50?

(A) 40 (B) 50

Name _____

Choose the correct answer.

1. Count on. Which is the total amount?

(A) 27¢   (B) 31¢
(C) 8¢   (D) 13¢

2. Count on. Which is the total amount?

(A) 8¢   (B) 16¢
(C) 31¢   (D) 35¢

3. Count on. Which is the total amount?

(A) 5¢   (B) 12¢
(C) 22¢   (D) 25¢

4. Count on. Which is the total amount?

(A) 26¢   (B) 40¢
(C) 42¢   (D) 45¢

5. Count on. Which is the total amount?

(A) 27¢   (B) 31¢
(C) 35¢   (D) 36¢

6. Count on. Which is the total amount?

(A) 25¢   (B) 30¢
(C) 35¢   (D) 40¢

7. Which answer shows the coins in order from greatest to least value?

(A)

(B)

(C)

8. Which answer shows the coins in order from greatest to least value?

(A)

(B)

(C)

9. Which is the total amount?

(A) 30¢   (B) 31¢
(C) 32¢   (D) not here

10. Which is the total amount?

(A) 37¢   (B) 45¢
(C) 50¢   (D) not here

Harcourt Brace School Publishers

Name _____

11. Which is the total amount?

(A) 55¢   (B) 62¢

(C) 67¢   (D) not here

12. Which is the total amount?

(A) 40¢   (B) 78¢

(C) 80¢   (D) not here

13. Which group of coins will buy  ?

(A)

(B)

(C)

(D)

14. Which group of coins will buy  ?

(A)

(B)

(C)

(D)

Form A • Multiple-Choice   A29   **Stop!**

1. Which group of coins has the same value as

 ?

Ⓐ

Ⓑ

2. Which group of coins has the same value as

   ?

Ⓐ

Ⓑ

Which group uses fewer coins to show the same amount?

3.

Ⓐ

Ⓑ

4.

Ⓐ

Ⓑ

Harcourt Brace School Publishers

5. Which toy could you buy with this group of coins?

(A) 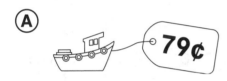 79¢

(B)  95¢

(C) 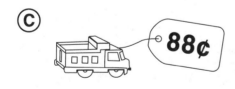 88¢

(D)  85¢

6. Which toy could you buy with this group of coins?

(A)  75¢

(B)  91¢

(C)  83¢

(D)  68¢

7. You have 50¢.
You buy  .

48¢ ___¢ ___¢
Your change is ___.

(A) 2¢   (B) 3¢
(C) 4¢   (D) 6¢

8. You have 35¢.
You buy  .

32¢ ___¢ ___¢ ___¢
Your change is ___.

(A) 2¢   (B) 3¢
(C) 4¢   (D) 5¢

9. Adam saved 1 half-dollar, 2 dimes, and 5 pennies. How much money did he save in all?

(A) 50¢   (B) 57¢
(C) 70¢   (D) 75¢

10. Kari saved 1 half-dollar, 1 quarter, 1 nickel, and 1 penny. How much money did she save in all?

(A) 71¢   (B) 76¢
(C) 81¢   (D) 86¢

11. Which coins give you enough money to buy  ?

(A) 4 dimes, 1 nickel
(B) 2 quarters
(C) 1 quarter, 3 nickels
(D) 3 dimes, 3 nickels, 3 pennies

12. Which coins give you enough money to buy  ?

(A) 1 quarter, 5 nickels
(B) 2 quarters, 5 pennies
(C) 1 half-dollar, 1 dime, 1 nickel
(D) 6 nickels, 5 pennies

Harcourt Brace School Publishers

Name _____

Choose the correct answer.

1. Which time does the clock show?

Ⓐ 12:00   Ⓑ 1:00
Ⓒ 6:00   Ⓓ not here

2. Which time does the clock show?

Ⓐ 3:30   Ⓑ 4:00
Ⓒ 4:30   Ⓓ not here

3. Which time does the clock show?

Ⓐ 10:00   Ⓑ 10:05
Ⓒ 10:10   Ⓓ 10:15

4. Which time does the clock show?

Ⓐ 4:15   Ⓑ 4:20
Ⓒ 4:25   Ⓓ 4:30

5. Which time does the clock show?

Ⓐ 1:45   Ⓑ 2:00
Ⓒ 2:15   Ⓓ 2:45

6. Which time does the clock show?

Ⓐ 8:15   Ⓑ 8:30
Ⓒ 9:00   Ⓓ 9:15

Form A • Multiple-Choice   A33   **Go on.**

7. Which clock shows 7:05?

Ⓐ

Ⓑ

Ⓒ

Ⓓ not here

8. Which clock shows 11:40?

Ⓐ

Ⓑ

Ⓒ

Ⓓ not here

9. Elva starts her homework at

It takes her 30 minutes. What time does she finish her homework?

Ⓐ at 6:45   Ⓑ at 7:00
Ⓒ at 7:30   Ⓓ at 7:45

10. Bart had a party. It started at

It ended 2 hours later. What time was the party over?

Ⓐ at 4:00   Ⓑ at 5:00
Ⓒ at 6:00   Ⓓ at 7:00

Stop!

Harcourt Brace School Publishers

Name _____

CHAPTER 9 TEST
PAGE 1

Choose the correct answer.
Use the calendar to answer questions 1 and 2.

June						
Sunday	Monday	Tuesday	Wednesday	Thursday	Friday	Saturday
		1	2	3	4	5
6	7	8	9	10	11	12
13	14	15	16	17	18	19
20	21	22	23	24	25	26
27	28	29	30			

1. Which is the date of the second Thursday?
(A) June 3   (B) June 10
(C) June 16   (D) June 25

2. On which day does this month end?
(A) Sunday   (B) Monday
(C) Tuesday   (D) Wednesday

Use the calendar to answer questions 3 and 4.

January	February	March	April
S M T W T F S	S M T W T F S	S M T W T F S	S M T W T F S
1 2 3 4	1	1	1 2 3 4 5
5 6 7 8 9 10 11	2 3 4 5 6 7 8	2 3 4 5 6 7 8	6 7 8 9 10 11 12
12 13 14 15 16 17 18	9 10 11 12 13 14 15	9 10 11 12 13 14 15	13 14 15 16 17 18 19
19 20 21 22 23 24 25	16 17 18 19 20 21 22	16 17 18 19 20 21 22	20 21 22 23 24 25 26
26 27 28 29 30 31	23 24 25 26 27 28	23 24 25 26 27 28 29 30 31	27 28 29 30

May	June	July	August
S M T W T F S	S M T W T F S	S M T W T F S	S M T W T F S
1 2 3	1 2 3 4 5 6 7	1 2 3 4 5	1 2
4 5 6 7 8 9 10	8 9 10 11 12 13 14	6 7 8 9 10 11 12	3 4 5 6 7 8 9
11 12 13 14 15 16 17	15 16 17 18 19 20 21	13 14 15 16 17 18 19	10 11 12 13 14 15 16
18 19 20 21 22 23 24	22 23 24 25 26 27 28	20 21 22 23 24 25 26	17 18 19 20 21 22 23
25 26 27 28 29 30 31	29 30	27 28 29 30 31	24 25 26 27 28 29 30 31

September	October	November	December
S M T W T F S	S M T W T F S	S M T W T F S	S M T W T F S
1 2 3 4 5 6	1 2 3 4	1	1 2 3 4 5 6
7 8 9 10 11 12 13	5 6 7 8 9 10 11	2 3 4 5 6 7 8	7 8 9 10 11 12 13
14 15 16 17 18 19 20	12 13 14 15 16 17 18	9 10 11 12 13 14 15	14 15 16 17 18 19 20
21 22 23 24 25 26 27	19 20 21 22 23 24 25	16 17 18 19 20 21 22	21 22 23 24 25 26 27
28 29 30	26 27 28 29 30 31	23 24 25 26 27 28 29 30	28 29 30 31

3. Which is the fifth month in the year?
(A) May   (B) June
(C) July   (D) not here

4. Which month follows September?
(A) July   (B) August
(C) October   (D) not here

Harcourt Brace School Publishers

Form A • Multiple-Choice   A35   **Go on.**

Name _____

5. School starts at

.

Lily gets there at

.

Is Lily early or late?

(A) early   (B) late

6. The game starts at

.

Ben gets there at

.

Is Ben early or late?

(A) early   (B) late

7. Use the clocks. Which event comes first?

(A)

(B)

(C)

8. Use the clocks. Which event comes third?

(A)

(B)

(C)

Harcourt Brace School Publishers

5. You have 25¢.
You buy

 22¢

23¢ _____ ¢ _____ ¢
Your change is_____.
Ⓐ 3¢   Ⓑ 4¢
Ⓒ 5¢   Ⓓ 6¢

6. Tina saved 1 half-dollar, 1 dime, and 2 pennies. How much money did she save in all?

Ⓐ 37¢   Ⓑ 52¢
Ⓒ 62¢   Ⓓ 77¢

7. Which time does the clock show?

Ⓐ 6:10   Ⓑ 6:15
Ⓒ 6:20   Ⓓ 6:25

8. Which time does the clock show?

Ⓐ 3:45   Ⓑ 4:45
Ⓒ 5:00   Ⓓ 5:15

9. Lil went to a picnic. It started at

It ended 3 hours later. What time was the picnic over?
Ⓐ at 3:00   Ⓑ at 4:00
Ⓒ at 5:00   Ⓓ at 6:00

10. The class starts at

 2:00 .

Dave gets there at

 1:30 .

Is Dave early or late?
Ⓐ early   Ⓑ late

Name _____

Use the schedule to answer questions 11 and 12.

Team Sports Day

8:30 – 10:00	Soccer
10:30 – 12:00	Kickball
12:00 – 1:00	Lunch
1:30 – 2:00	Rest
2:30 – 3:30	Baseball

---

11. What time does kickball start?

Ⓐ 8:30

Ⓑ 10:00

Ⓒ 10:30

Ⓓ not here

12. How long is the baseball game?

Ⓐ 30 minutes

Ⓑ 1 hour

Ⓒ 2 hours

Ⓓ not here

13. How long is the rest period?

Ⓐ 30 minutes

Ⓑ 1 hour

Ⓒ 2 hours

Ⓓ not here

14. What time does baseball end?

Ⓐ 8:30

Ⓑ 10:00

Ⓒ 1:30

Ⓓ 3:30

Choose the correct answer.

1.
$$\begin{array}{r} 5 \\ 7 \\ +5 \\ \hline \end{array}$$

 Ⓐ 16 Ⓑ 17
 Ⓒ 18 Ⓓ 19

2.
$$\begin{array}{r} 6 \\ 4 \\ +5 \\ \hline \end{array}$$

 Ⓐ 15 Ⓑ 16
 Ⓒ 17 Ⓓ 18

3. $14 - 6 =$ ___
 Ⓐ 7 Ⓑ 8
 Ⓒ 9 Ⓓ 10

4. $18 - 9 =$ ___
 Ⓐ 8 Ⓑ 9
 Ⓒ 10 Ⓓ 11

5. There were 3 big cats and 9 little cats in a barn. How many cats were in the barn?
 Ⓐ 6 cats Ⓑ 11 cats
 Ⓒ 12 cats Ⓓ 13 cats

6. There were 11 birds in a tree. Then 7 birds left. How many birds were still in the tree?
 Ⓐ 7 birds Ⓑ 6 birds
 Ⓒ 5 birds Ⓓ 4 birds

7. Count by fives. Which number comes next?

25, 30, 35, 40, ___

 Ⓐ 41 Ⓑ 45
 Ⓒ 46 Ⓓ 50

8. Which rule will help you find the missing numbers?

33, 36, ___, 42, 45

 Ⓐ Count by twos.
 Ⓑ Count by threes.
 Ⓒ Count by fives.
 Ⓓ Count by tens.

9. Count back by tens. Which number comes next?

64, 54, 44, 34, ___

(A) 35   (B) 32
(C) 30   (D) 24

10. Even or odd?

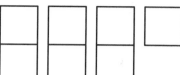

7

(A) even   (B) odd

11. Which sign goes in the circle?

12 ◯ 9

(A) <   (B) >

12. Which number is between?

69, ___, 71

(A) 68   (B) 72
(C) 81   (D) not here

Use the pictures below to answer questions 13 and 14.

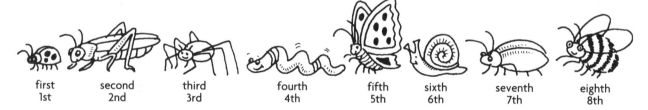

| first | second | third | fourth | fifth | sixth | seventh | eighth |
| 1st | 2nd | 3rd | 4th | 5th | 6th | 7th | 8th |

13. Which is the position of the

 ?

(A) first   (B) third
(C) fifth   (D) seventh

14. Which is the position of the

 ?

(A) 1st   (B) 2nd
(C) 4th   (D) not here

15. Count on. Which is the total amount?

(A) 7¢   (B) 12¢

(C) 25¢   (D) 27¢

16. You have 50¢. You buy

Your change is ___?___.

(A) 1¢   (B) 2¢

(C) 3¢   (D) 4¢

17. Which group of coins will buy

 ?

(A)

(B)

(C)

18. Which toy could you buy with this group of coins?

(A)  90¢

(B)  89¢

(C)  85¢

19. Which time does the clock show

- (A) 11:00
- (B) 11:05
- (C) 11:10
- (D) 11:15

20. Which time does the clock show

- (A) 5:15
- (B) 5:30
- (C) 6:10
- (D) 6:15

Use the calendar to answer questions 21 and 22.

May						
Sunday	Monday	Tuesday	Wednesday	Thursday	Friday	Saturday
				1	2	3
4	5	6	7	8	9	10
11	12	13	14	15	16	17
18	19	20	21	22	23	24
25	26	27	28	29	30	31

21. On which day does this month begin?

- (A) Sunday
- (B) Monday
- (C) Tuesday
- (D) Thursday

22. Which is the date of the third Friday?

- (A) May 9
- (B) May 16
- (C) May 23
- (D) May 30

Use the schedule to answer questions 23 and 24.

Camp Schedule
9:30 – 10:30   Hike
10:30 – 11:30 Swim
11:30 – 12:00 Art
12:00 – 1:00   Lunch

23. What time does the hike end?

- (A) 9:30
- (B) 10:30
- (C) 11:30
- (D) not here

24. How long is lunch?

- (A) 30 minutes
- (B) 45 minutes
- (C) 1 hour
- (D) 2 hours

Harcourt Brace School Publishers

Name _____

Choose the correct answer.
Use base-ten blocks to answer questions 1 and 2.

1. $9 + 4 = 13$ ones

How many tens and ones?
(A) I ten   3 ones
(B) I ten   4 ones
(C) 3 tens   4 ones
(D) 3 tens   9 ones

2. $5 + 3 = 8$ ones

How many tens and ones?
(A) 0 tens 5 ones
(B) 0 tens 8 ones
(C) 8 tens 3 ones
(D) 8 tens 5 ones

3. $15 + 6$

How many in all?
(A) II   (B) 19
(C) 21   (D) 29

4. $13 + 7$

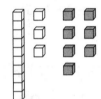

How many in all?
(A) 10   (B) 20
(C) 23   (D) 30

5. $12 + 14$

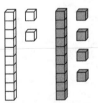

How many in all?
(A) 26   (B) 28
(C) 30   (D) 36

6. $17 + 18$

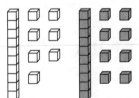

How many in all?
(A) II   (B) 25
(C) 29   (D) 35

7.

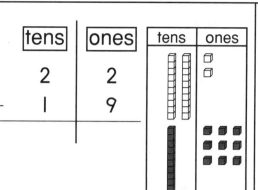

tens	ones
2	2
+ 1	9

Ⓐ 31 Ⓑ 37
Ⓒ 41 Ⓓ 47

8.

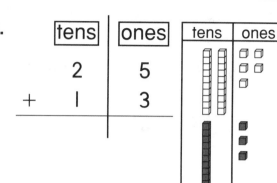

tens	ones
2	5
+ 1	3

Ⓐ 38 Ⓑ 42
Ⓒ 48 Ⓓ 52

Make a model to answer questions 9 and 10.

9. The library has 18 books on trains and 14 books on airplanes. How many books does the library have about trains and airplanes?

tens	ones
1	8
+ 1	4

Ⓐ 22 books Ⓑ 31 books
Ⓒ 32 books Ⓓ 42 books

10. There are 16 boys and 13 girls in Ms. Wong's class. How many children are in Ms. Wong's class?

tens	ones
1	6
+ 1	3

Ⓐ 3 children Ⓑ 19 children
Ⓒ 23 children Ⓓ not here

Choose the correct answer.
Use base-ten blocks to answer questions 1 and 2.
Add. Regroup if you need to.

1.

tens	ones
☐	
2	5
+	6

Ⓐ 29
Ⓑ 30
Ⓒ 31
Ⓓ 32

2.

tens	ones
☐	
1	4
+1	6

Ⓐ 20
Ⓑ 28
Ⓒ 29
Ⓓ 30

3.

tens	ones
☐	
1	9
+	3

Ⓐ 22
Ⓑ 23
Ⓒ 32
Ⓓ not here

4.

tens	ones
☐	
3	6
+	8

Ⓐ 34
Ⓑ 36
Ⓒ 44
Ⓓ not here

5.

tens	ones
5	3
+ 1	5

Ⓐ 62   Ⓑ 68
Ⓒ 72   Ⓓ not here

6.

tens	ones
4	7
+ 1	9

Ⓐ 56   Ⓑ 59
Ⓒ 62   Ⓓ not here

7.
$$\begin{array}{r} 45 \\ +28 \\ \hline \end{array}$$

Ⓐ 53   Ⓑ 63
Ⓒ 68   Ⓓ 73

8.
$$\begin{array}{r} 22 \\ +39 \\ \hline \end{array}$$

Ⓐ 51   Ⓑ 61
Ⓒ 71   Ⓓ not here

Form A • Multiple-Choice

Go on.

9. 66
  +9

Ⓐ 75   Ⓑ 77
Ⓒ 85   Ⓓ not here

10. 59
   +24

Ⓐ 73   Ⓑ 75
Ⓒ 83   Ⓓ not here

11. The children in two classes collected cans. One class collected 27 cans. The other class collected 38 cans. How many cans did the two classes collect?

Ⓐ 11 cans
Ⓑ 55 cans
Ⓒ 65 cans
Ⓓ 515 cans

12. On Saturday, Fred made 28 cookies. On Sunday, he made 21 cookies. How many cookies did he make in all?

Ⓐ 49 cookies
Ⓑ 51 cookies
Ⓒ 59 cookies
Ⓓ 61 cookies

13. Rosie planted 16 flowers in her garden. It took her 10 minutes on Monday and 25 minutes on Tuesday. How many minutes did she work?

Ⓐ 26 minutes
Ⓑ 35 minutes
Ⓒ 41 minutes
Ⓓ 51 minutes

14. Mr. Allen's class planted 31 corn seeds and 39 bean seeds. They raked for 20 minutes. How many seeds did they plant?

Ⓐ 59 seeds
Ⓑ 60 seeds
Ⓒ 70 seeds
Ⓓ 90 seeds

Choose the correct answer.

1. 17 + 11

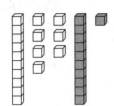

How many in all?
Ⓐ 18   Ⓑ 28
Ⓒ 37   Ⓓ 38

2. 16 + 15

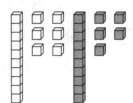

How many in all?
Ⓐ 21   Ⓑ 26
Ⓒ 31   Ⓓ 41

Make a model to answer questions 3 and 4.

3. Troy saw one train with 19 boxcars and another train with 16 boxcars. How many boxcars did Troy see?

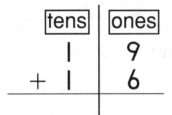

tens	ones
1	9
+ 1	6

Ⓐ 35 boxcars
Ⓑ 36 boxcars
Ⓒ 45 boxcars
Ⓓ 96 boxcars

4. There are 17 blue marbles and 12 green marbles in Julie's bag. How many marbles are in Julie's bag?

tens	ones
1	7
+ 1	2

Ⓐ 5 marbles
Ⓑ 19 marbles
Ⓒ 29 marbles
Ⓓ not here

5.

tens	ones
□	
3	8
+	3

Ⓐ 41
Ⓑ 57
Ⓒ 61
Ⓓ not here

6.

tens	ones
□	
5	8
+2	6

Ⓐ 74
Ⓑ 76
Ⓒ 84
Ⓓ not here

7.
```
  43
+  8
```

Ⓐ 45   Ⓑ 48
Ⓒ 61   Ⓓ not here

8.
```
  68
+ 27
```

Ⓐ 85   Ⓑ 95
Ⓒ 96   Ⓓ not here

9. Luis played with his new game 25 minutes on Friday and 17 minutes on Monday. He did not play on Saturday. How many minutes did Luis play the game?

Ⓐ 30 minutes
Ⓑ 32 minutes
Ⓒ 40 minutes
Ⓓ 42 minutes

10. Lynn baked 49 chocolate cookies and 29 sugar cookies. It took her 3 hours. Lynn ate 2 of the cookies. How many cookies did she bake?

Ⓐ 20 cookies
Ⓑ 60 cookies
Ⓒ 78 cookies
Ⓓ 88 cookies

Name _____

Choose the correct answer.

1.
```
    3
    6
  + 3
  ____
```
(A) 9   (B) 10
(C) 11   (D) 12

2. Which is the missing addend?

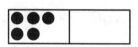

5 + __ = 12

(A) 5   (B) 6
(C) 7   (D) not here

3. How many tens and ones are there?

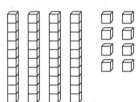

(A) 2 tens 6 ones = 26
(B) 4 tens 8 ones = 48
(C) 6 tens 8 ones = 68
(D) 8 tens 4 ones = 84

4. Count back by tens. Which number comes next?

95, 85, 75, 65, __

(A) 55   (B) 56
(C) 64   (D) 66

5. Which number is between?

34, __, 36

(A) 33   (B) 37
(C) 45   (D) not here

6. Count on. Which is the total amount?

(A) 3¢   (B) 20¢
(C) 25¢   (D) 30¢

Harcourt Brace School Publishers

7. Dave saved 1 half-dollar, 1 nickel, and 4 pennies. How much money did he save in all?

(A) 55¢   (B) 57¢

(C) 59¢   (D) 90¢

8. Suzi went to a party. It started at

It ended 2 hours later. What time was the party over?

(A) at 3:00   (B) at 4:00

(C) at 5:00   (D) at 6:00

9. The movie starts at

Lucy gets there at

Is Lucy early or late?

(A) early   (B) late

10. Lunch starts at

Billy gets there at

Is Billy early or late?

(A) early   (B) late

Use base-ten blocks to answer questions 11 and 12.

11. $9 + 6 = 15$ ones

How many tens and ones?

(A) 1 ten   4 ones
(B) 1 ten   5 ones
(C) 7 tens   5 ones
(D) 8 tens   7 ones

12. $13 + 8$

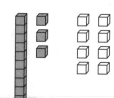

How many in all?

(A) 15
(B) 18
(C) 21
(D) 23

13.

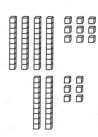

tens	ones
4	9
+ 2	6

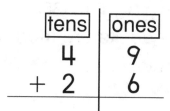

(A) 55   (B) 64
(C) 65   (D) 75

14. Renee has 25 baseball cards and 13 football cards. How many cards does Renee have?

tens	ones
2	5
+ 1	3

(A) 12 cards   (B) 28 cards
(C) 38 cards   (D) 39 cards

Name _____

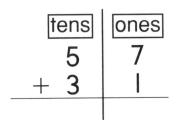
15.

tens	ones
☐	
3	6
+	5

- (A) 31
- (B) 37
- (C) 41
- (D) not here

16.

tens	ones
5	7
+ 3	1

- (A) 26
- (B) 58
- (C) 88
- (D) not here

17.
```
  45
+ 28
```
- (A) 53
- (B) 54
- (C) 73
- (D) 83

18.
```
  24
+  7
```
- (A) 14
- (B) 31
- (C) 41
- (D) not here

19. Donnie sold 23 boxes of cards. Ronnie sold 48 boxes. How many boxes of cards did the two boys sell?

- (A) 25 boxes
- (B) 35 boxes
- (C) 41 boxes
- (D) 71 boxes

20. There are 21 desks in Mrs. Snow's class and 49 desks in Mr. Troy's class. How many desks are there in both classes?

- (A) 50 desks
- (B) 60 desks
- (C) 70 desks
- (D) 80 desks

Choose the correct answer.
Subtract. Regroup if you need to.

1.

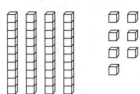

Subtract 6 ones. How many tens and ones are left?

Ⓐ 3 tens 3 ones
Ⓑ 3 tens 13 ones
Ⓒ 4 tens 0 ones
Ⓓ 4 tens 1 one

2.

Subtract 8 ones. How many tens and ones are left?

Ⓐ 1 ten 5 ones
Ⓑ 1 ten 8 ones
Ⓒ 2 tens 1 one
Ⓓ 3 tens 1 one

3.

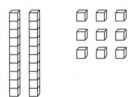

29 – 7 = _____

Ⓐ 12   Ⓑ 18
Ⓒ 21   Ⓓ 22

4.

21 – 4 = _____

Ⓐ 7   Ⓑ 14
Ⓒ 17   Ⓓ 18

5.

tens	ones
3	2
−	6

tens	ones

Ⓐ 24   Ⓑ 26
Ⓒ 28   Ⓓ 29

6.

tens	ones
4	0
−	8

tens	ones

Ⓐ 22   Ⓑ 28
Ⓒ 32   Ⓓ 48

Use base-ten blocks. Subtract.

7.

tens	ones
5	2
− 2	6

Ⓐ 26 Ⓑ 34
Ⓒ 36 Ⓓ 38

8.

tens	ones
2	8
−	7

Ⓐ 9 Ⓑ 10
Ⓒ 11 Ⓓ 21

9.

tens	ones
4	0
− 1	5

Ⓐ 15 Ⓑ 20
Ⓒ 25 Ⓓ 35

10.

tens	ones
3	8
− 2	9

Ⓐ 7 Ⓑ 9
Ⓒ 11 Ⓓ 19

Use base-ten blocks.
Choose the operation and solve. Write + or −.

11. Carla invites 16 girls and 15 boys to her party. How many children does Carla invite?

tens	ones
1	6
◯ 1	5

Ⓐ 21 children
Ⓑ 25 children
Ⓒ 31 children
Ⓓ 46 children

12. Kip has 55¢. He buys a  .

How much money does Kip have left?

tens	ones
5	5
◯ 1	9

Ⓐ 34¢ Ⓑ 36¢
Ⓒ 64¢ Ⓓ 74¢

Harcourt Brace School Publishers

Name _____

Choose the correct answer.
Subtract. Regroup if you need to.

1.

tens	ones
3	2
−	7

Ⓐ 19   Ⓑ 23
Ⓒ 25   Ⓓ 29

2.

tens	ones
8	1
−	9

Ⓐ 70   Ⓑ 72
Ⓒ 75   Ⓓ 78

3.

tens	ones
7	7
− 2	7

Ⓐ 40   Ⓑ 45
Ⓒ 47   Ⓓ 50

4.

tens	ones
5	3
− 2	5

Ⓐ 22   Ⓑ 28
Ⓒ 32   Ⓓ 38

5.

$$82$$
$$-43$$

Ⓐ 31   Ⓑ 39
Ⓒ 41   Ⓓ 49

6.

$$56$$
$$-48$$

Ⓐ 8   Ⓑ 12
Ⓒ 14   Ⓓ 18

Harcourt Brace School Publishers

Form A • Multiple-Choice   **A57**   **Go on.**

7.
$$\begin{array}{r} 41 \\ -18 \\ \hline \end{array}$$

Ⓐ 23　　Ⓑ 27
Ⓒ 37　　Ⓓ 59

8.
$$\begin{array}{r} 79 \\ -37 \\ \hline \end{array}$$

Ⓐ 32　　Ⓑ 36
Ⓒ 38　　Ⓓ 42

9. Which numbers should you add to check this subtraction problem?

$$\begin{array}{r} 73 \\ -57 \\ \hline 16 \end{array}$$

Ⓐ
$$\begin{array}{r} 16 \\ +57 \\ \hline \end{array}$$

Ⓑ
$$\begin{array}{r} 16 \\ +73 \\ \hline \end{array}$$

Ⓒ
$$\begin{array}{r} 73 \\ +57 \\ \hline \end{array}$$

Ⓓ
$$\begin{array}{r} 57 \\ +57 \\ \hline \end{array}$$

10. Which numbers should you add to check this subtraction problem?

$$\begin{array}{r} 42 \\ -18 \\ \hline 24 \end{array}$$

Ⓐ
$$\begin{array}{r} 24 \\ +42 \\ \hline \end{array}$$

Ⓑ
$$\begin{array}{r} 42 \\ +18 \\ \hline \end{array}$$

Ⓒ
$$\begin{array}{r} 24 \\ +18 \\ \hline \end{array}$$

Ⓓ
$$\begin{array}{r} 24 \\ +24 \\ \hline \end{array}$$

Choose the operation and solve. Write $+$ or $-$.

11. You have 65¢. You buy 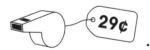 . How much do you have left?

$$\begin{array}{r} 65¢ \\ \bigcirc 29¢ \\ \hline \end{array}$$

Ⓐ 36¢　　Ⓑ 46¢
Ⓒ 84¢　　Ⓓ 94¢

12. How much money would you need to buy and  ?

$$\begin{array}{r} 58¢ \\ \bigcirc 12¢ \\ \hline \end{array}$$

Ⓐ 46¢　　Ⓑ 60¢
Ⓒ 70¢　　Ⓓ 76¢

Harcourt Brace School Publishers

Name _____

Choose the correct answer.

1.

tens	ones
4	3
−	7

Ⓐ 34   Ⓑ 35
Ⓒ 36   Ⓓ 46

2.

tens	ones
2	0
−	6

Ⓐ 14   Ⓑ 16
Ⓒ 24   Ⓓ 26

3.

tens	ones
5	5
− 3	8

Ⓐ 16   Ⓑ 17
Ⓒ 23   Ⓓ 27

4.

tens	ones
3	9
−	4

Ⓐ 5   Ⓑ 25
Ⓒ 33   Ⓓ 35

Choose the operation and solve. Write + or −.

5. Dan sees 15 blue birds and 17 red birds in a tree. How many birds does Dan see?

tens	ones
1	5
○ 1	7

Ⓐ 22 birds   Ⓑ 32 birds
Ⓒ 33 birds   Ⓓ 42 birds

6. Lily has 41¢. She buys a  .

How much money does Lily have left?

tens	ones
4	1
○ 1	8

Ⓐ 3¢   Ⓑ 13¢
Ⓒ 23¢   Ⓓ 49¢

Form A • Multiple-Choice   A59   Go on.

7.

tens	ones
☐	☐
6	6
− 3	6

Ⓐ 20   Ⓑ 30
Ⓒ 31   Ⓓ 36

8.

tens	ones
☐	☐
5	2
− 2	3

Ⓐ 21   Ⓑ 25
Ⓒ 26   Ⓓ 29

9.   75
   −67

Ⓐ 8   Ⓑ 12
Ⓒ 17   Ⓓ 22

10.   77
    −32

Ⓐ 35   Ⓑ 39
Ⓒ 44   Ⓓ 45

Choose the operation and solve. Write + or −.

11. You have 97¢. You buy a

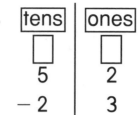

How much do you have left?

   97¢
○ 49¢

Ⓐ 25¢   Ⓑ 48¢
Ⓒ 49¢   Ⓓ 52¢

12. How much money would you need to buy

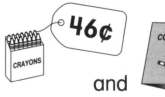

and   ?

   46¢
○ 14¢

Ⓐ 32¢   Ⓑ 50¢
Ⓒ 59¢   Ⓓ 60¢

Choose the correct answer.

1. Which group uses fewer coins to show the same amount?

Ⓐ

Ⓑ

2. Which group uses fewer coins to show the same amount?

Ⓐ

Ⓑ

3. Which coins give you enough money to buy

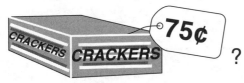
75¢
CRACKERS CRACKERS
?

Ⓐ 2 quarters, 1 dime
Ⓑ 5 dimes, 3 nickels
Ⓒ 3 quarters
Ⓓ 2 quarters, 4 nickels, 3 pennies

4. Which coins give you enough money to buy

40¢
?

Ⓐ 1 quarter, 5 pennies
Ⓑ 3 dimes, 1 nickel
Ⓒ 4 nickels, 10 pennies
Ⓓ 1 quarter, 1 dime, 1 nickel

5. Which time does the clock show?

Ⓐ 4:30   Ⓑ 5:00
Ⓒ 5:30   Ⓓ not here

6. Subtract 4 ones. How many tens and ones are left?

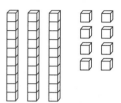

Ⓐ 3 tens 12 ones
Ⓑ 3 tens 4 ones
Ⓒ 4 tens 3 ones
Ⓓ 4 tens 4 ones

7.

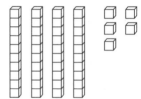

45 − 3 = ___

Ⓐ 15   Ⓑ 23
Ⓒ 41   Ⓓ 42

8.

tens	ones
2	0
−	6

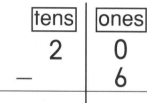

Ⓐ 4   Ⓑ 8
Ⓒ 14   Ⓓ 26

9.

tens	ones
4	1
− 1	4

Ⓐ 27   Ⓑ 35
Ⓒ 37   Ⓓ 55

10.

tens	ones
6	0
− 2	5

Ⓐ 25   Ⓑ 35
Ⓒ 45   Ⓓ 85

● **Choose the operation and solve. Write + or − .**

11. There are 18 girls and 13 boys in Mara's class. How many children are in Mara's class?

tens	ones
1	8
○ 1	3

Ⓐ 15 children
Ⓑ 25 children
Ⓒ 31 children
Ⓓ 35 children

12. Alice has 75¢. She buys a

59¢

How much money does Alice have left?

tens	ones
7	5
○ 5	9

Ⓐ 16¢   Ⓑ 24¢
Ⓒ 34¢   Ⓓ 54¢

Subtract. Regroup if you need to.

13.

tens	ones
□	□
3	4
−	5

Ⓐ 21   Ⓑ 29
Ⓒ 31   Ⓓ 39

14.

tens	ones
□	□
7	1
− 5	3

Ⓐ 18   Ⓑ 22
Ⓒ 24   Ⓓ 28

15.
$$62$$
$$-25$$

Ⓐ 47 Ⓑ 43
Ⓒ 37 Ⓓ 33

16.
$$87$$
$$-43$$

Ⓐ 44 Ⓑ 43
Ⓒ 40 Ⓓ 34

17. Which numbers should you add to check this subtraction problem?

$$91$$
$$-65$$
$$26$$

Ⓐ
$$26$$
$$+91$$

Ⓑ
$$26$$
$$+65$$

Ⓒ
$$65$$
$$+91$$

Ⓓ
$$26$$
$$+26$$

18. Which numbers should you add to check this subtraction problem?

$$62$$
$$-26$$
$$36$$

Ⓐ
$$62$$
$$+36$$

Ⓑ
$$26$$
$$+26$$

Ⓒ
$$62$$
$$+26$$

Ⓓ
$$26$$
$$+36$$

Choose the operation. Write $+$ or $-$.

19. You have 75¢. You buy

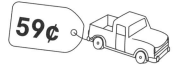
59¢

. How much do you have left?

$$75¢$$
$$\bigcirc 59¢$$

Ⓐ 14¢ Ⓑ 16¢
Ⓒ 24¢ Ⓓ 26¢

20. How much money would you need to buy?

 and ?

$$36¢$$
$$\bigcirc 24¢$$

Ⓐ 12¢ Ⓑ 60¢
Ⓒ 62¢ Ⓓ 70¢

Name _____

Choose the correct answer.
Use the picture to answer questions 1 and 2.

  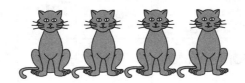 

1. Which tally marks show how many dogs there are? (A) ‖ (B) ‖‖ (C) ‖‖‖‖ (D) ‖‖‖‖ ‖	**2.** Which tally marks show how many bears there are? (A) ‖ (B) ‖‖ (C) ‖‖‖‖ (D) ‖‖‖‖ ‖

Max asked classmates about their pets.
The tally table shows what he found.
Use the table to answer questions 3 and 4.

Kinds of Pets	Tally Marks	Totals
dogs	‖	2
cats	‖‖‖‖	5
fish	‖	2
birds	‖	1

3. How many children have fish for pets? (A) 2 (B) 7 (C) 9 (D) 10	**4.** Which animal do most children have as a pet? (A) cats (B) dogs (C) fish (D) birds

Form A • Multiple-Choice   A65   **Go on.**

Use the table to answer questions 5 to 8.

Number of Children Absent on Monday	Tally Marks	Totals
Ms. Wilson's Class	IIII	4
Mr. Wang's Class	II	2
Ms. Johnson's Class	HHt	5
Ms. King's Class	IIII	4

5. In which two classes were the same number of children absent?

Ⓐ Ms. Wilson's and Mr. Wang's

Ⓑ Mr. Wang's and Ms. Johnson's

Ⓒ Ms. Johnson's and Ms. King's

Ⓓ Ms. Wilson's and Ms. King's

6. How many more children were absent from Ms. Johnson's class than from Mr. Wang's?

Ⓐ 1 more child

Ⓑ 2 more children

Ⓒ 3 more children

Ⓓ 5 more children

7. How many children in all were absent?

Ⓐ 12 children
Ⓑ 13 children
Ⓒ 14 children
Ⓓ 15 children

8. In which class were the most children absent?

Ⓐ Ms. King's class
Ⓑ Ms. Johnson's class
Ⓒ Mr. Wang's class
Ⓓ Ms. Wilson's class

Use the tables to answer questions 9 to 12.

Favorite Seasons in Room 21	Tally Marks	Totals
fall	‖‖‖ ‖	7
winter	‖‖‖ ‖‖	8
spring	‖‖‖ ‖	6
summer	‖‖‖ ‖‖‖	10

Favorite Seasons in Room 22	Tally Marks	Totals
fall	‖‖‖ ‖	7
winter	‖‖‖ ‖‖‖	9
spring	‖‖‖	5
summer	‖‖‖ ‖‖‖	10

9. In which room do more children like spring best?

   Ⓐ Room 21
   Ⓑ Room 22
   Ⓒ Both rooms are the same.

10. In which room do more children like fall best?

   Ⓐ Room 21
   Ⓑ Room 22
   Ⓒ Both rooms are the same.

11. Which season got the most votes in both rooms?

   Ⓐ summer
   Ⓑ fall
   Ⓒ winter
   Ⓓ spring

12. Which season got more votes in Room 22 than in Room 21?

   Ⓐ fall
   Ⓑ winter
   Ⓒ spring
   Ⓓ summer

Name _____

Choose the correct answer.
Use the graph to answer questions 1 to 4.

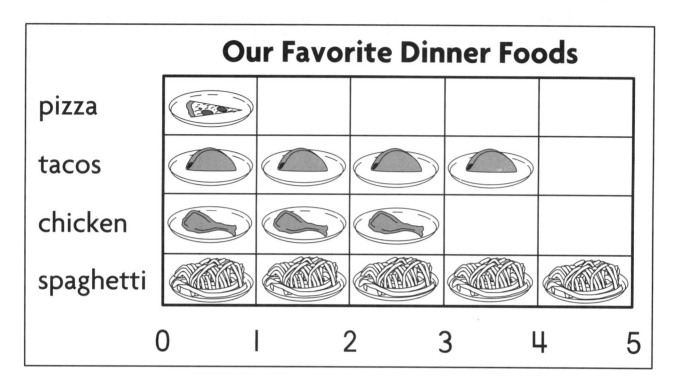

Our Favorite Dinner Foods

	0	1	2	3	4	5
pizza						
tacos						
chicken						
spaghetti						

1. Which is the favorite dinner food of the most people?

   Ⓐ pizza
   Ⓑ tacos
   Ⓒ chicken
   Ⓓ spaghetti

2. Which is the favorite dinner food of the fewest people?

   Ⓐ pizza
   Ⓑ tacos
   Ⓒ chicken
   Ⓓ spaghetti

3. How many more people like spaghetti than like pizza?

   Ⓐ 1 more   Ⓑ 2 more
   Ⓒ 3 more   Ⓓ 4 more

4. How many fewer people like chicken than like tacos?

   Ⓐ 1 fewer   Ⓑ 2 fewer
   Ⓒ 3 fewer   Ⓓ 4 fewer

Use the graph to answer questions 5 to 8.

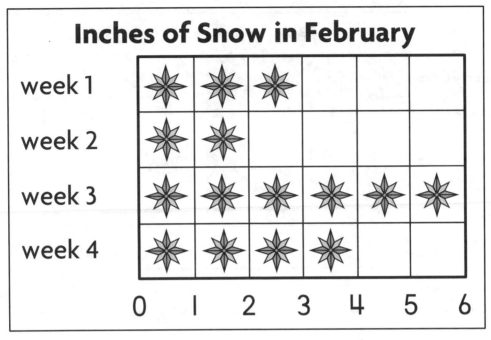

Inches of Snow in February

Each ✳ stands for 2 inches of snow.

5. Which week had 6 inches of snow?

   Ⓐ week 1
   Ⓑ week 2
   Ⓒ week 3
   Ⓓ week 4

6. Which week had the fewest inches of snow?

   Ⓐ week 1
   Ⓑ week 2
   Ⓒ week 3
   Ⓓ week 4

7. Which week had the most inches of snow?

   Ⓐ week 1
   Ⓑ week 2
   Ⓒ week 3
   Ⓓ week 4

8. How many inches of snow were there in week 4?

   Ⓐ 4 inches
   Ⓑ 6 inches
   Ⓒ 7 inches
   Ⓓ 8 inches

Use the graph to answer questions 9 to 14.

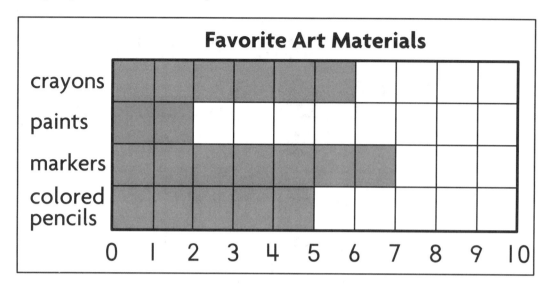

Favorite Art Materials

9. How many people like colored pencils the best?
   (A) 2 people (B) 3 people
   (C) 4 people (D) 5 people

10. How many people like crayons the best?
    (A) 5 people (B) 6 people
    (C) 7 people (D) 8 people

11. Which art materials do the most people like the best?
    (A) crayons
    (B) paints
    (C) markers
    (D) colored pencils

12. Which art materials do the fewest people like the best?
    (A) crayons
    (B) paints
    (C) markers
    (D) colored pencils

13. How many more people like crayons than like paints the best?
    (A) 1 more (B) 2 more
    (C) 3 more (D) 4 more

14. How many fewer people like colored pencils than like markers the best?
    (A) 1 fewer (B) 2 fewer
    (C) 3 fewer (D) 4 fewer

Name _____

Choose the correct answer.
Use the picture to answer questions 1 to 4.

1. Which group of coins are you certain to find on the tray?

Ⓐ

Ⓑ

Ⓒ

2. Which group of coins is impossible to find on the tray?

Ⓐ

Ⓑ

Ⓒ

3. Which group of coins are you certain to find on the tray?

Ⓐ

Ⓑ

Ⓒ

4. Which group of coins is impossible to find on the tray?

Ⓐ

Ⓑ

Ⓒ

Form A • Multiple-Choice

A71

Go on.

Use the table to answer questions 5 and 6.
This table shows the outcomes of 10 pulls from the bag.

Shape	Tally Marks	Totals
triangle	ⅢⅠⅡ	7
circle	Ⅲ	3

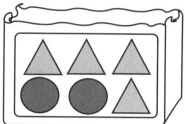

---

5. Which shape was pulled out more often?
   Ⓐ triangle
   Ⓑ circle

6. How many times was a circle pulled out?
   Ⓐ 2 times   Ⓑ 3 times
   Ⓒ 5 times   Ⓓ 10 times

---

7. In a bag there are 5 yellow tiles, 5 blue tiles, and 15 red tiles. Which color do you think will be pulled out most often?
   Ⓐ yellow
   Ⓑ blue
   Ⓒ red

8. This spinner can stop on stripes, dots, or zigzags. Which do you think it will stop on most often?
   Ⓐ stripes
   Ⓑ dots
   Ⓒ zigzags

---

9. From which bag do you think a cube will be pulled least often?
   Ⓐ   Ⓑ
   Ⓒ   Ⓓ

10. This spinner can stop on stripes, dots, or zigzags. Which do you think it will stop on least often?
   Ⓐ stripes
   Ⓑ dots
   Ⓒ zigzags

Name _____

Choose the correct answer.
Use the tables to answer questions 1 to 4.

Favorite Story in Room 28	Tally Marks	Totals
Snow White	JHT IIII	
Bambi	JHT JHT	
Three Little Pigs	JHT	
Peter Rabbit	IIII	

Favorite Story in Room 29	Tally Marks	Totals
Snow White	JHT II	
Bambi	JHT JHT	
Three Little Pigs	JHT I	
Peter Rabbit	IIII	

1. In which room do more children like Snow White best?

   Ⓐ Room 29
   Ⓑ Room 28
   Ⓒ Both rooms are the same.

2. In which room do more children like Peter Rabbit best?

   Ⓐ Room 29
   Ⓑ Room 28
   Ⓒ Both rooms are the same.

3. Which story got the most votes in both rooms?

   Ⓐ Snow White
   Ⓑ Bambi
   Ⓒ Three Little Pigs
   Ⓓ Peter Rabbit

4. Which story got more votes in Room 29 than in Room 28?

   Ⓐ Snow White
   Ⓑ Bambi
   Ⓒ Three Little Pigs
   Ⓓ Peter Rabbit

Name _____

Use the graph to answer questions 5 to 8.

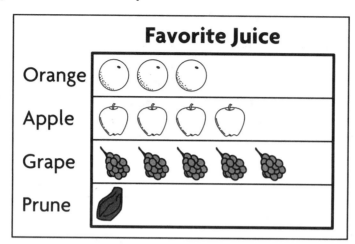

Favorite Juice

5. Which is the favorite juice of the most people?
   Ⓐ orange   Ⓑ apple
   Ⓒ grape   Ⓓ prune

6. How many more like apple than orange juice best?
   Ⓐ 1 more   Ⓑ 2 more
   Ⓒ 3 more   Ⓓ 4 more

Use the picture to answer questions 7 and 8.

7. Which group of coins are you certain to find on the tray?
   Ⓐ
   Ⓑ

8. Which group of coins is impossible to find on the tray?
   Ⓐ
   Ⓑ

Choose the correct answer.

1.

   $$\begin{array}{r} 8 \\ +7 \\ \hline \end{array}$$

   Ⓐ 8   Ⓑ 10
   Ⓒ 15   Ⓓ 17

2. Which rule will help you find the missing numbers?

   10, 20, ___, 40, 50

   Ⓐ Count by twos.
   Ⓑ Count by threes.
   Ⓒ Count by fives.
   Ⓓ Count by tens.

3. Jill went to a play. It started at

   It ended 2 hours later. What time was the play over?

   Ⓐ at 3:00   Ⓑ at 4:00
   Ⓒ at 5:00   Ⓓ at 6:00

4. Mia found 16 cans on Monday and 27 cans on Friday. Mia read 2 books on Tuesday. How many cans did Mia find?

   Ⓐ 39 cans
   Ⓑ 43 cans
   Ⓒ 48 cans
   Ⓓ 52 cans

The principal asked children how many would buy lunch on Monday.
The tally table shows what she found.
Use the table to answer questions 5 to 8.

Number of Children Buying Lunch	Tally Marks	Totals
Mr. King's class	‖‖‖		6
Mrs. Cobb's class	‖‖‖ ‖‖‖	10
Mrs. Sanchez's class	‖‖‖ ‖‖‖ ||	12
Mr. Wright's class	‖‖‖ |||	8

5. How many children in Mr. King's class will buy lunch?

Ⓐ 6
Ⓑ 8
Ⓒ 10
Ⓓ 12

6. In which class will the most children buy lunch?

Ⓐ Mr. King's class
Ⓑ Mrs. Cobb's class
Ⓒ Mrs. Sanchez's class
Ⓓ Mr. Wright's class

7. In which class will 8 children buy lunch?

Ⓐ Mr. King's class
Ⓑ Mrs. Cobb's class
Ⓒ Mrs. Sanchez's class
Ⓓ Mr. Wright's class

8. How many more children will buy lunch in Mrs. Sanchez's class than in Mrs. Cobb's class?

Ⓐ 1 more
Ⓑ 2 more
Ⓒ 10 more
Ⓓ 12 more

Use the graph to answer questions 9 and 10.

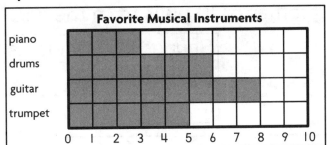

9. How many fewer people like drums than like guitar?

Ⓐ 1 fewer Ⓑ 2 fewer
Ⓒ 3 fewer Ⓓ 5 fewer

10. How many people like the trumpet the best?

Ⓐ 3 people Ⓑ 5 people
Ⓒ 6 people Ⓓ 8 people

Use the graph to answer questions 11 and 12.

Our Favorite Pets

bird	🐦	🐦				
cat	🐱	🐱	🐱	🐱		
dog	🐶	🐶	🐶	🐶	🐶	🐶
hamster	🐹	🐹	🐹			

11. How many fewer people like hamsters than like cats?

Ⓐ 1 fewer Ⓑ 2 fewer
Ⓒ 3 fewer Ⓓ 4 fewer

12. Which is the favorite pet of the most people?

Ⓐ bird Ⓑ cat
Ⓒ dog   Ⓓ hamster

Name _____

Use the table to answer questions 13 and 14.
This table shows the outcomes of 10 pulls from the bag.

Shape	Tally Marks
squares	IIII I
triangles	IIII

13. Which shape was pulled out more often?

Ⓐ square

Ⓑ triangle

14. How many times was a triangle pulled out?

Ⓐ 2 times   Ⓑ 3 times

Ⓒ 4 times   Ⓓ 6 times

15. In a bag there are 2 dimes, 2 pennies, and 10 nickels. Which coin do you think will be pulled out most often?

Ⓐ dime

Ⓑ penny

Ⓒ nickel

16. This spinner can stop on stripes, dots, or zigzags. Which do you think it will stop on most often?

Ⓐ dots

Ⓑ stripes

Ⓒ zigzags

17. From which bag do you think a ball will be pulled most often?

Ⓐ   Ⓑ

Ⓒ   Ⓓ

18. This spinner can stop on stripes, dots, or zigzags. Which do you think it will stop on least often?

Ⓐ stripes

Ⓑ dots

Ⓒ zigzags

Harcourt Brace School Publishers

Name _____

Choose the correct answer.

1. Which object is shaped like this solid figure?

   Ⓐ   Ⓑ

   Ⓒ   Ⓓ

2. Which object is shaped like this solid figure?

   Ⓐ   Ⓑ

   Ⓒ   Ⓓ

3. Which object is shaped like this solid figure?

   Ⓐ   Ⓑ

   Ⓒ   Ⓓ

4. Which solid figure is the same shape as this solid figure?

   Ⓐ   Ⓑ

   Ⓒ   Ⓓ

5. Which solid figure has only two flat faces and can be stacked?

   Ⓐ   Ⓑ

   Ⓒ  Ⓓ

6. Which solid figure has six flat faces and can be stacked?

   Ⓐ   Ⓑ

   Ⓒ   Ⓓ

7. Which solid figure has no flat faces and can roll?

Ⓐ   Ⓑ

Ⓒ   Ⓓ

8. Which solid figure can stack and roll?

Ⓐ   Ⓑ

Ⓒ   Ⓓ

9. Which solid figure is missing in the pattern?

Ⓐ   Ⓑ

10. Which solid figure is missing in the pattern?

Ⓐ   Ⓑ

Ⓒ

11. Which plane figure could you trace from the solid figure?

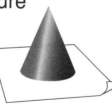

Ⓐ   Ⓑ ◯

Ⓒ ▢   Ⓓ ▭

12. Which plane figure could you trace from the solid figure?

Ⓐ △   Ⓑ ◯

Ⓒ ▢   Ⓓ ▭

Name _____

Choose the correct answer.

1. Which figure is a circle?

Ⓐ    Ⓑ

Ⓒ   Ⓓ

2. Which figure is a square?

Ⓐ   Ⓑ

Ⓒ   Ⓓ

3. How many sides does this figure have?

Ⓐ 3 sides   Ⓑ 4 sides
Ⓒ 5 sides   Ⓓ 6 sides

4. How many corners does this figure have?

Ⓐ 0 corners   Ⓑ 3 corners
Ⓒ 4 corners   Ⓓ 5 corners

5. Which figure has 4 sides and 4 corners?

Ⓐ 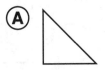   Ⓑ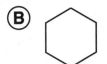

Ⓒ   Ⓓ

6. Which figure has 6 sides and 6 corners?

Ⓐ    Ⓑ

Ⓒ   Ⓓ

Form A • Multiple-Choice   A81   Go on.

7. Which drawing shows how you can cut this figure to make 4 triangles?

Ⓐ   Ⓑ

Ⓒ   Ⓓ

8. Which drawing shows how you can cut this figure to make 2 squares?

Ⓐ   Ⓑ

Ⓒ   Ⓓ

9. Which shows figures that are the same size and shape?

Ⓐ   Ⓑ

Ⓒ 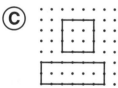   Ⓓ

10. Which figure is the same size and shape as this figure?

Ⓐ   Ⓑ

Ⓒ   Ⓓ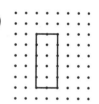

11. Which figure will fit?

Ⓐ   Ⓑ

Ⓒ   Ⓓ

12. Which figure will fit?

Ⓐ   Ⓑ

Ⓒ   Ⓓ

Name _____

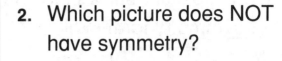
Choose the correct answer.

1. Which picture has symmetry?

Ⓐ   Ⓑ

Ⓒ   Ⓓ

2. Which picture does NOT have symmetry?

Ⓐ   Ⓑ

Ⓒ    Ⓓ

3. Which picture has symmetry?

Ⓐ   Ⓑ

Ⓒ    Ⓓ

4. Which picture does NOT have symmetry?

Ⓐ   Ⓑ

Ⓒ    Ⓓ

Harcourt Brace School Publishers

Form A • Multiple-Choice   **A83**

5. Which picture shows the line of symmetry for this glass?

Ⓐ   Ⓑ

Ⓒ   Ⓓ

6. Which picture shows the line of symmetry for the letter C?

Ⓐ   Ⓑ

Ⓒ   Ⓓ

7. Which word names the move?

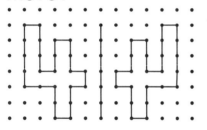

Ⓐ turn   Ⓑ flip
Ⓒ slide

8. Which word names the move?

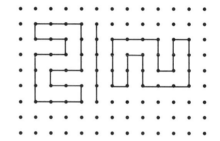

Ⓐ turn   Ⓑ flip
Ⓒ slide

9. Which word names the move?

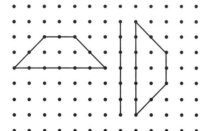

Ⓐ turn   Ⓑ flip
Ⓒ slide

10. Which word names the move?

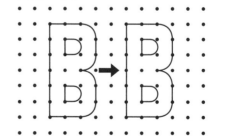

Ⓐ turn   Ⓑ flip
Ⓒ slide

Harcourt Brace School Publishers

Name _____

Choose the correct answer.

1. Which object is shaped like this solid figure?

Ⓐ   Ⓑ

Ⓒ   Ⓓ

2. Which solid figure can slide and roll?

Ⓐ   Ⓑ

Ⓒ   Ⓓ

3. Which solid figure is missing in the pattern?

Ⓐ   Ⓑ

Ⓒ   Ⓓ

4. Which plane figure could you trace from the solid figure?

Ⓐ   Ⓑ

Ⓒ   Ⓓ

5. Which figure has 5 sides and 5 corners?

Ⓐ   Ⓑ

Ⓒ Ⓓ

6. Which drawing shows how you can cut this figure to make 4 triangles?

Ⓐ   Ⓑ

Ⓒ   Ⓓ

Form A • Multiple-Choice   A85   **Go on.** ▶

7. Which figure will fit?

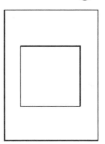

    Ⓑ

Ⓒ    Ⓓ

8. Which picture shows the line of symmetry for the letter M?

Ⓐ 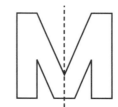   Ⓑ

Ⓒ    Ⓓ

9. Which word names the move?

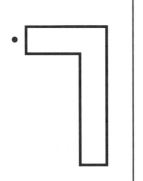

Ⓐ turn   Ⓑ flip   Ⓒ slide

10. Which word names the move?

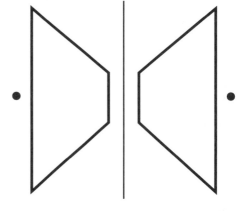

Ⓐ turn   Ⓑ flip   Ⓒ slide

Harcourt Brace School Publishers

Name _____

Choose the correct answer.

1. Which is the total amount?

Ⓐ 28¢   Ⓑ 40¢
Ⓒ 45¢   Ⓓ not here

2. Which is the total amount?

Ⓐ 53¢   Ⓑ 57¢
Ⓒ 75¢   Ⓓ not here

Use the tables to answer questions 3 and 4.

Favorite Colors in Room 24	Tally Marks	Totals
red	卌 卌	
blue	卌 l	
yellow	卌 lll	
green	卌 ll	

Favorite Colors in Room 25	Tally Marks	Totals
red	卌 lll	
blue	卌 llll	
yellow	卌 l	
green	卌 ll	

3. In which room do more children like red best?

Ⓐ Room 24
Ⓑ Room 25
Ⓒ Both rooms are the same.

4. In which room do more children like green best?

Ⓐ Room 24
Ⓑ Room 25
Ⓒ Both rooms are the same.

Name _____

5. Which clock shows 9:05?

Ⓐ

Ⓑ

Ⓒ

Ⓓ not here

6. Which clock shows 2:40?

Ⓐ

Ⓑ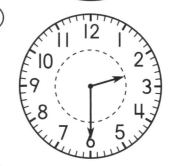

Ⓒ

Ⓓ not here

7. Which solid figure has only two flat faces and can be rolled?

Ⓐ   Ⓑ

Ⓒ    Ⓓ

8. Which solid figure has no flat faces and can be rolled?

Ⓐ    Ⓑ

Ⓒ   Ⓓ

Harcourt Brace School Publishers

9. Which solid figure is missing in the pattern?

Ⓐ

Ⓑ

Ⓒ

10. Which plane figure could you trace from the solid figure?

Ⓐ   Ⓑ

Ⓒ   Ⓓ

11. Which object is shaped like this solid figure?

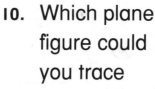

Ⓐ   Ⓑ

Ⓒ   Ⓓ

12. How many sides does this figure have?

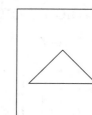

Ⓐ 3 sides   Ⓑ 4 sides
Ⓒ 5 sides   Ⓓ 6 sides

13. Which drawing shows how you can cut this figure to make 2 triangles?

Ⓐ   Ⓑ

Ⓒ   Ⓓ

14. Which figure will fit?

Ⓐ   Ⓑ

Ⓒ   Ⓓ

15. Which figure is a triangle?

Ⓐ   Ⓑ

Ⓒ   Ⓓ

16. Which figure is a rectangle?

Ⓐ   Ⓑ

Ⓒ    Ⓓ

17. Which picture has symmetry?

Ⓐ   Ⓑ

Ⓒ   Ⓓ

18. Which picture shows the line of symmetry for this butterfly?

Ⓐ    Ⓑ

Ⓒ   Ⓓ

19. Which word names the move?

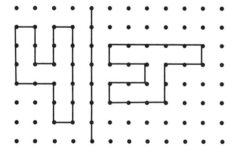

Ⓐ turn   Ⓑ flip
Ⓒ slide

20. Which word names the move?

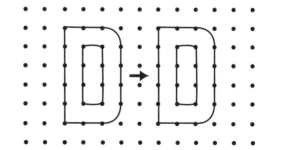

Ⓐ turn   Ⓑ flip
Ⓒ slide

Harcourt Brace School Publishers

Name _____

Choose the correct answer.
Use an inch ruler.

1. About how many paper clips long is this bean?

(A) about 1 paper clip
(B) about 3 paper clips
(C) about 4 paper clips
(D) about 6 paper clips

2. About how many paper clips long is this eraser?

(A) about 1 paper clip
(B) about 3 paper clips
(C) about 4 paper clips
(D) about 5 paper clips

3. Which is the best estimate for how long this pencil is?

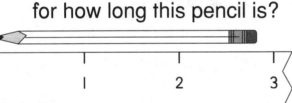

(A) about 3 inches
(B) about 5 inches
(C) about 6 inches
(D) about 8 inches

4. About how long is this peanut?

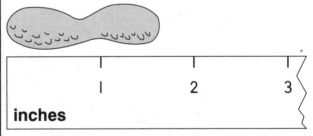

(A) about 1 inch
(B) about 2 inches
(C) about 3 inches
(D) about 4 inches

5. How long is this ribbon?

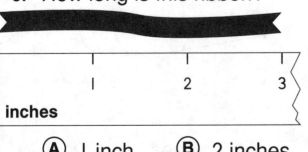

(A) 1 inch   (B) 2 inches
(C) 3 inches   (D) 4 inches

6. How long is this bandage?

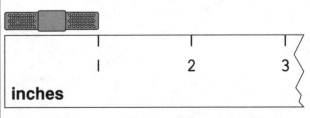

(A) 1 inch   (B) 2 inches
(C) 3 inches   (D) 4 inches

Harcourt Brace School Publishers

7. About how long is a bed?

Ⓐ less than 1 foot
Ⓑ about 1 foot
Ⓒ more than 1 foot

8. About how long is a toothbrush?

Ⓐ less than 1 foot
Ⓑ about 1 foot
Ⓒ more than 1 foot

9. Which object is about 1 foot long?

Ⓐ
Ⓑ
Ⓒ
Ⓓ

10. Which object is more than 1 foot long?

Ⓐ ⊂⊃
Ⓑ ◁█▶
Ⓒ ▭═▷
Ⓓ ▱

11. How long is this path?

Ⓐ 2 inches Ⓑ 4 inches
Ⓒ 8 inches Ⓓ 10 inches

12. How long is this path?

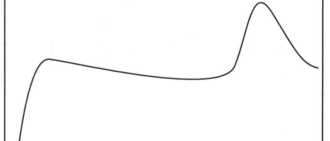

Ⓐ 2 inches Ⓑ 7 inches
Ⓒ 5 inches Ⓓ 10 inches

Stop!

Harcourt Brace School Publishers

Name _____

Choose the correct answer.
Use a centimeter ruler.

1. How long is this paper clip?

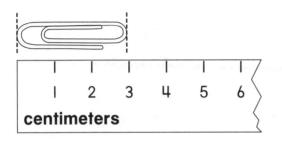

Ⓐ about 3 centimeters
Ⓑ about 4 centimeters
Ⓒ about 5 centimeters
Ⓓ about 6 centimeters

2. How long is this ticket?

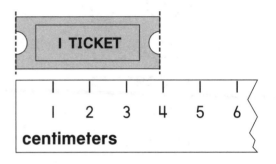

Ⓐ about 1 centimeter
Ⓑ about 2 centimeters
Ⓒ about 3 centimeters
Ⓓ about 4 centimeters

3. How long is this key?

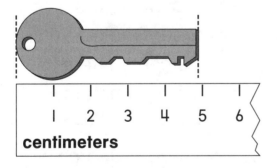

Ⓐ about 2 centimeters
Ⓑ about 4 centimeters
Ⓒ about 5 centimeters
Ⓓ about 7 centimeters

4. How long is this line?

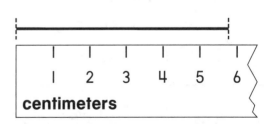

Ⓐ about 1 centimeter
Ⓑ about 3 centimeters
Ⓒ about 4 centimeters
Ⓓ about 6 centimeters

Form A • Multiple-Choice   A93   **Go on.**

Name _____

For questions 5 and 6, use a decimeter ruler.

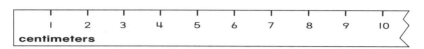

```
  1    2    3    4    5    6    7    8    9   10
centimeters
```

5. Which object is about a decimeter long?

   (A) a desk
   (B) a paper clip
   (C) a crayon
   (D) an airplane

6. Which object is more than a decimeter long?

   (A) an eraser
   (B) a ladybug
   (C) a desk
   (D) a paper clip

7. How many centimeters is it around the figure?

   (A) 2 centimeters
   (B) 4 centimeters
   (C) 6 centimeters
   (D) 10 centimeters

8. How many centimeters is it around the figure?

   (A) 3 centimeters
   (B) 9 centimeters
   (C) 10 centimeters
   (D) 12 centimeters

9. How many squares will fit in the figure?

   (A) 3 squares
   (B) 6 squares
   (C) 9 squares
   (D) 12 squares

10. How many squares will fit in the figure?

    (A) 4 squares
    (B) 6 squares
    (C) 8 squares
    (D) 10 squares

Form A • Multiple-Choice   A94   **Stop!**

Harcourt Brace School Publishers

Name _____

Choose the correct answer.

1. How many cups fill 1 quart?

- Ⓐ 2 cups
- Ⓑ 4 cups
- Ⓒ 8 cups
- Ⓓ 10 cups

2. How many cups fill 1 pint?

- Ⓐ 2 cups
- Ⓑ 4 cups
- Ⓒ 8 cups
- Ⓓ 10 cups

3. How many cups fill 2 quarts?

- Ⓐ 2 cups
- Ⓑ 4 cups
- Ⓒ 8 cups
- Ⓓ 16 cups

4. Which object weighs more than 1 pound?

- Ⓐ a crayon
- Ⓑ a pencil
- Ⓒ a desk

5. About how much does this dog weigh?

- Ⓐ less than 1 pound
- Ⓑ more than 1 pound

6. About how much does this sandwich weigh?

- Ⓐ less than 1 pound
- Ⓑ more than 1 pound

Form A • Multiple-Choice A95 **Go on.**

Name _____

7. What is the temperature?

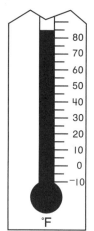

(A) 30° F
(B) 65° F
(C) 70° F
(D) 85° F

8. What is the temperature?

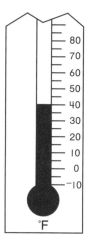

(A) 10° F
(B) 35° F
(C) 40° F
(D) 55° F

9. What is the temperature?

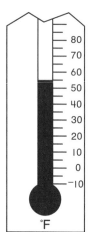

(A) 55° F
(B) 65° F
(C) 70° F
(D) 85° F

10. Which tool should you use to find out how much juice is in a bottle?

(A) cup
(B) ruler
(C) thermometer

11. Which tool should you use to find out how cold it is outside?

(A) cup
(B) ruler
(C) thermometer

12. Which tool should Gus use to find out how tall his bean plant is?

(A) cup
(B) ruler
(C) thermometer

Harcourt Brace School Publishers

Choose the correct answer.

1. How many equal parts are there?

(A) 1   (B) 2
(C) 3   (D) 4

2. How many equal parts are there?

(A) 1   (B) 2
(C) 3   (D) 4

3. What part is colored?

(A) $\frac{1}{2}$ (B) $\frac{1}{3}$

(C) $\frac{1}{4}$ (D) $\frac{1}{6}$

4. Which picture shows $\frac{1}{4}$ colored?

(A)    (B)

(C) 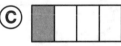   (D)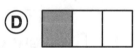

5. Which fraction tells what part is colored?

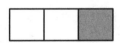

(A) $\frac{1}{6}$ (B) $\frac{1}{4}$

(C) $\frac{1}{3}$ (D) $\frac{1}{2}$

6. Which fraction tells what part is colored?

(A) $\frac{1}{2}$ (B) $\frac{1}{3}$

(C) $\frac{1}{4}$ (D) $\frac{1}{6}$

Name _____

7. What fraction of the figure is colored?

(A) $\frac{3}{4}$ (B) $\frac{2}{3}$

(C) $\frac{1}{2}$ (D) $\frac{2}{6}$

8. Which figure shows $\frac{3}{6}$ colored?

(A)   (B)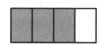

(C)  (D)

9. What fraction of the group of circles is colored?

(A) $\frac{3}{4}$ (B) $\frac{1}{2}$

(C) $\frac{1}{4}$ (D) $\frac{1}{6}$

10. What fraction of the group of cupcakes is white?

(A) $\frac{2}{3}$ (B) $\frac{1}{2}$

(C) $\frac{1}{3}$ (D) $\frac{1}{6}$

11. Thea cut a pie in sixths. Then she ate one piece. What part did Thea eat?

(A) $\frac{1}{2}$

(B) $\frac{1}{3}$

(C) $\frac{1}{4}$

(D) $\frac{1}{6}$

12. Four children share 8 cookies. Each gets an equal part of the group. What part does one child get?

(A) $\frac{1}{6}$

(B) $\frac{1}{4}$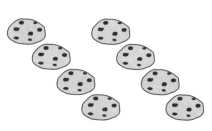

(C) $\frac{1}{3}$

(D) $\frac{1}{2}$

Form A • Multiple-Choice   A98   **Stop!**

Name _____

Choose the correct answer.

1. About how many paper clips long is this key?

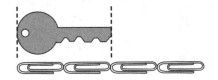

Ⓐ about 2   Ⓑ about 3
Ⓒ about 4   Ⓓ about 5

2. How long is this worm?

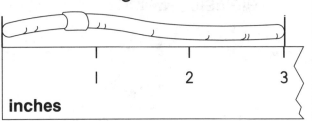

inches

Ⓐ 1 inch   Ⓑ 2 inches
Ⓒ 3 inches   Ⓓ 4 inches

3. Which object is more than 1 foot long?

Ⓐ

Ⓑ

Ⓒ

Ⓓ

4. How long is this piece of chalk?

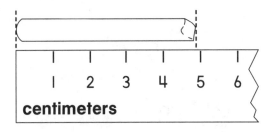

centimeters

Ⓐ about 4 centimeters
Ⓑ about 5 centimeters
Ⓒ about 6 centimeters
Ⓓ about 7 centimeters

5. How many centimeters is it around the figure?

3 cm
1 cm [   ] 1 cm
3 cm

Ⓐ 6   Ⓑ 8
Ⓒ 10   Ⓓ 12

6. How many squares will fit in the figure?

Ⓐ 1 square   Ⓑ 2 squares
Ⓒ 3 squares   Ⓓ 4 squares

7. About how much does this television weigh?

Ⓐ less than 1 pound
Ⓑ more than 1 pound

8. What is the temperature?

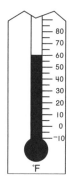

Ⓐ 60° F
Ⓑ 50° F
Ⓒ 45° F
Ⓓ 30° F

9. Which tool should Lucy use to find out how much water is in the pitcher?

Ⓐ cup
Ⓑ ruler
Ⓒ thermometer

10. What part is shaded?

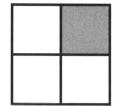

Ⓐ $\frac{1}{6}$ Ⓑ $\frac{1}{4}$

Ⓒ $\frac{1}{3}$ Ⓓ $\frac{1}{2}$

11. What fraction of the group of dogs is spotted?

Ⓐ $\frac{3}{4}$ Ⓑ $\frac{1}{2}$

Ⓒ $\frac{1}{4}$ Ⓓ $\frac{1}{6}$

12. Lee cut a pizza in sixths. Then he ate two pieces. What part did Lee eat?

Ⓐ $\frac{1}{4}$ Ⓑ $\frac{1}{6}$

Ⓒ $\frac{2}{6}$ Ⓓ $\frac{1}{2}$

Choose the correct answer.

1. $15 - 8 = 7$
$7 + 8 =$ ___

    (A) 7   (B) 10
    (C) 15   (D) 12

2. Which number is between?

    86, ___, 88

    (A) 84   (B) 89
    (C) 93   (D) not here

3. Mia saved 1 half-dollar, 1 quarter, and 3 pennies. How much money did she save in all?

    (A) 65¢   (B) 78¢
    (C) 80¢   (D) 83¢

4.
$$\begin{array}{r} 72 \\ -57 \\ \hline \end{array}$$

    (A) 15   (B) 19
    (C) 21   (D) 25

5. About how many paper clips long is this eraser?

    (A) about 1 paper clip
    (B) about 3 paper clips
    (C) about 4 paper clips
    (D) about 5 paper clips

6. About how long is this pencil?

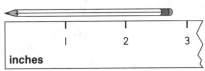

    (A) about 1 inch
    (B) about 2 inches
    (C) about 3 inches
    (D) about 4 inches

7. How long is this ribbon?

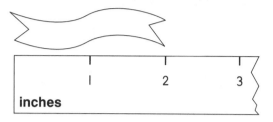

Ⓐ I inch   Ⓑ 2 inches
Ⓒ 3 inches   Ⓓ 4 inches

8. How long is this path?

Ⓐ 3 inches   Ⓑ 4 inches
Ⓒ 5 inches   Ⓓ 6 inches

9. How long is this ticket?

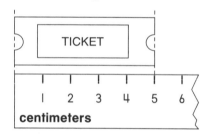

Ⓐ 3 centimeter
Ⓑ 4 centimeters
Ⓒ 5 centimeters
Ⓓ 6 centimeters

10. How many centimeters is it around the figure?

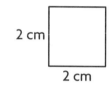

Ⓐ 6 centimeters
Ⓑ 8 centimeters
Ⓒ 10 centimeters
Ⓓ 12 centimeters

For questions 11 and 12, use a centimeter ruler.

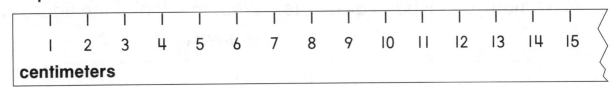

| | | | | | | | | | | | | | | |
1   2   3   4   5   6   7   8   9   10   11   12   13   14   15
centimeters

---

11. Which object is less than a decimeter long?

Ⓐ a stamp   Ⓑ a car
Ⓒ a door   Ⓓ a train

12. Which object is more than a decimeter long?

Ⓐ an ant   Ⓑ an eraser
Ⓒ a sofa   Ⓓ a peanut

---

13. How many squares will fit in the figure?

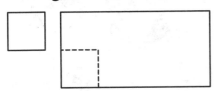

Ⓐ 2 squares   Ⓑ 4 squares
Ⓒ 8 squares   Ⓓ 12 squares

14. How many cups fill 2 pints?

Ⓐ 2 cups   Ⓑ 4 cups
Ⓒ 6 cups   Ⓓ 8 cups

---

15. About how much does this bed weigh?

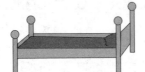

Ⓐ less than 1 pound
Ⓑ more than 1 pound

16. Which tool should Dave use to find out how much milk is in a bottle?

Ⓐ cup
Ⓑ ruler
Ⓒ thermometer

---

17. How many equal parts are there?

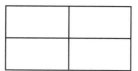

(A) 1

(B) 2

(C) 3

(D) 4

18. What fraction of the figure is shaded?

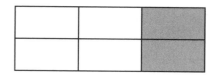

(A) $\frac{3}{4}$

(B) $\frac{2}{3}$

(C) $\frac{1}{2}$

(D) $\frac{2}{6}$

19. Which fraction tells what part is colored?

(A) $\frac{1}{6}$

(B) $\frac{1}{4}$

(C) $\frac{1}{3}$

(D) $\frac{1}{2}$

20. What fraction of the group of triangles is black?

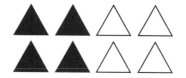

(A) $\frac{3}{4}$

(B) $\frac{1}{2}$

(C) $\frac{1}{4}$

(D) $\frac{1}{6}$

21. Rita cut a pizza in sixths. Then she ate one piece. What part did Rita eat?

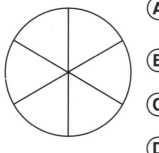

(A) $\frac{1}{2}$

(B) $\frac{1}{3}$

(C) $\frac{1}{4}$

(D) $\frac{1}{6}$

22. Three children share 9 apples. Each child gets an equal part of the group. What part does one child get?

(A) $\frac{1}{6}$

(B) $\frac{1}{4}$

(C) $\frac{1}{3}$

(D) $\frac{1}{2}$

Name _____

Choose the correct answer.

1. How many hundreds are there?

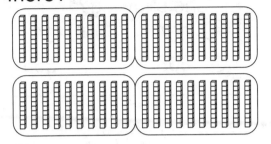

- (A) 4 hundreds
- (B) 40 hundreds
- (C) 400 hundreds

2. How many ones are there?

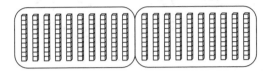

- (A) 2 ones
- (B) 20 ones
- (C) 200 ones

3. How many hundreds, tens, and ones are there?

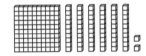

- (A) 1 hundred, 2 tens, 6 ones
- (B) 1 hundred, 6 tens, 2 ones
- (C) 2 hundreds, 6 tens, 2 ones
- (D) 6 hundreds, 1 ten, 2 ones

4. Which number does the model show?

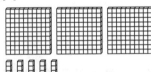

- (A) 345
- (B) 354
- (C) 435
- (D) 634

5. Which number does the model show?

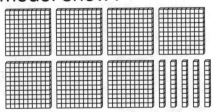

- (A) 75
- (B) 705
- (C) 750
- (D) 570

6. Which is the number?

5 ones + 9 hundreds + 6 tens

- (A) 659
- (B) 695
- (C) 956
- (D) 965

Form A • Multiple-Choice   A105   **Go on.**

7. Jarrad has 9 hundreds, 7 tens, and 3 ones. What number is he showing?
   (A) 397
   (B) 739
   (C) 793
   (D) 973

8. Pilar has 6 tens, 5 hundreds, and 0 ones. What number is she showing?
   (A) 506
   (B) 560
   (C) 605
   (D) 650

9. Which number does the model show?

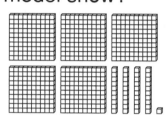

   (A) 415
   (B) 451
   (C) 514
   (D) 541

10. Which number does the model show?

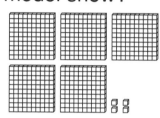

   (A) 54
   (B) 405
   (C) 504
   (D) 450

11. How many equal $1.00?

   (A) 2 dimes
   (B) 4 dimes
   (C) 10 dimes
   (D) 20 dimes

12. Which coins equal $1.00?

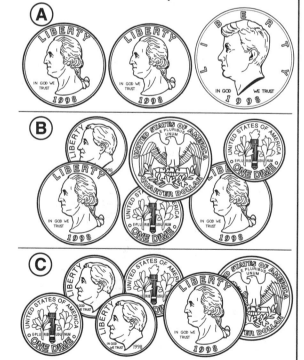

Name _____

Choose the correct answer.

1. Compare the two models. Which model shows the greater number?

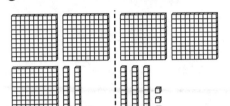

Ⓐ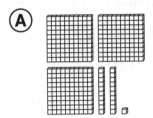

Ⓑ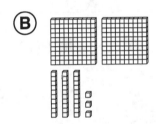

2. Compare the two models. Which model shows the number that is less?

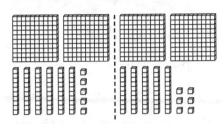

Ⓐ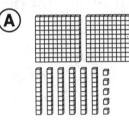

Ⓑ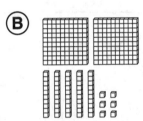

3. Which number is greater?
   Ⓐ 678   Ⓑ 706

4. Which number is greater?
   Ⓐ 441   Ⓑ 428

5. Which number is less?
   Ⓐ 490   Ⓑ 531

6. Which number is less?
   Ⓐ 782   Ⓑ 728

7. Lois has 105 baseball cards. Fred has 150 baseball cards. Who has the greater number of cards?
   Ⓐ Lois   Ⓑ Fred

8. Patrick has 610 pennies. Jocelyn has 599 pennies. Who has the number of pennies that is less?
   Ⓐ Patrick   Ⓑ Jocelyn

Harcourt Brace School Publishers

Form A • Multiple-Choice   A107   **Go on.**

9. Complete this sentence.

480 is ___ 48.

(A) greater than
(B) less than

10. Choose > or < to fill the circle.

699 ◯ 700

(A) >
(B) <

11. What number is just after 659?

(A) 606   (B) 658
(C) 660   (D) 700

12. What number is just before 110?

(A) 99   (B) 109
(C) 112   (D) 120

13. Which number belongs in the blank?

339, ___, 341

(A) 304   (B) 340
(C) 342   (D) 350

14. Which number belongs in the blank?

___, 900

(A) 899   (B) 901
(C) 910   (D) 950

15. Which shows the numbers 700, 780, 709, and 720 written in order from least to greatest?

(A) 700, 720, 780, 709
(B) 700, 780, 720, 709
(C) 780, 720, 709, 700
(D) 700, 709, 720, 780

16. Which shows the numbers 201, 120, 210, and 102 written in order from least to greatest?

(A) 201, 102, 210, 120
(B) 102, 201, 120, 210
(C) 102, 120, 201, 210
(D) 210, 201, 120, 102

Harcourt Brace School Publishers

Choose the correct answer.

1.

hundreds	tens □	ones
3	2	7
+ 1	3	3

   Ⓐ 450   Ⓑ 454
   Ⓒ 460   Ⓓ 550

2.

hundreds □	tens □	ones
2	9	3
+ 2	2	4

   Ⓐ 473   Ⓑ 517
   Ⓒ 531   Ⓓ 567

3.

$$\begin{array}{r} 2\;0\;6 \\ +3\;4\;7 \\ \hline \end{array}$$

   Ⓐ 541   Ⓑ 543
   Ⓒ 553   Ⓓ 643

4.

$$\begin{array}{r} 4\;5\;2 \\ +1\;5\;6 \\ \hline \end{array}$$

   Ⓐ 508   Ⓑ 518
   Ⓒ 604   Ⓓ 608

5.

hundreds	tens □	ones □
3	9	5
− 1	7	9

   Ⓐ 126   Ⓑ 214
   Ⓒ 216   Ⓓ 226

6.

hundreds □	tens □	ones
7	2	9
− 5	4	6

   Ⓐ 133   Ⓑ 183
   Ⓒ 213   Ⓓ 263

7.
```
  3 6 2
− 1 3 9
```

Ⓐ 133   Ⓑ 223
Ⓒ 233   Ⓓ 237

8.
```
  8 1 8
− 4 3 5
```

Ⓐ 383   Ⓑ 423
Ⓒ 453   Ⓓ 483

9. Add.

```
  $1. 0 4
+  2. 5 5
```

Ⓐ $3.59   Ⓑ $4.04
Ⓒ $4.09   Ⓓ $4.59

10. Subtract.

```
  $5. 2 5
−  3. 5 0
```

Ⓐ $1.25   Ⓑ $1.75
Ⓒ $2.25   Ⓓ $2.75

11. Daniel had $6.85. He spent $2.19 on a toy. How much money does he have left?

Ⓐ $4.66   Ⓑ $4.76
Ⓒ $8.94   Ⓓ $9.04

12. Celeste earned $1.65 on Monday and $1.60 on Tuesday. How much money in all did she earn?

Ⓐ $2.25   Ⓑ $2.35
Ⓒ $3.25   Ⓓ $3.35

Harcourt Brace School Publishers

Name _____

Choose the correct answer.

1. How many hundreds, tens, and ones are there?

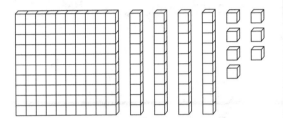

ⓐ 1 hundred, 4 tens, 7 ones

ⓑ 1 hundred, 7 tens, 4 ones

ⓒ 2 hundreds, 7 tens, 4 ones

ⓓ 7 hundreds, 4 tens, 1 one

2. Which number does the model show?

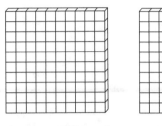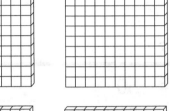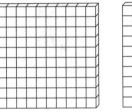

ⓐ 41   ⓑ 140

ⓒ 410   ⓓ 411

3. Ben has 9 tens, 3 hundreds, and 0 ones. What number is he showing?

ⓐ 390   ⓑ 903

ⓒ 939   ⓓ 933

4. How many equal $1.00?

ⓐ 1   ⓑ 2

ⓒ 3   ⓓ 4

5. Which number is greater?

ⓐ 829   ⓑ 892

6. Which number is less?

ⓐ 338   ⓑ 383

Form A • Multiple-Choice   **A111**   **Go on.**

7. Which number is between 569 and 571?

   (A) 470
   (B) 507
   (C) 568
   (D) 570

8. Which shows the numbers 200, 240, 205, and 280 written in order from least to greatest?

   (A) 280, 205, 200, 240
   (B) 240, 280, 200, 205
   (C) 200, 205, 240, 280
   (D) 280, 240, 205, 200

9.
$$\begin{array}{r} 109 \\ +473 \\ \hline \end{array}$$

   (A) 376   (B) 582
   (C) 586   (D) 682

10.
$$\begin{array}{r} 455 \\ -228 \\ \hline \end{array}$$

   (A) 227   (B) 233
   (C) 237   (D) 247

11. Kim had $7.84. She spent $3.49 on a book. How much money does she have left?

   (A) $4.25
   (B) $4.34
   (C) $4.35
   (D) $4.45

12. Tracy earned $2.70 on Wednesday and $2.75 on Thursday. How much money did he earn in all?

   (A) $4.45
   (B) $4.55
   (C) $5.35
   (D) $5.45

Harcourt Brace School Publishers

Name _____

Choose the correct answer.

1.
$$\begin{array}{r} 6 \\ +6 \\ \hline \end{array}$$

Ⓐ 10 　　Ⓑ 11
Ⓒ 12 　　Ⓓ not here

2. Which is the missing addend?

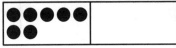

$7 + \underline{\quad} = 12$

Ⓐ 3 　　Ⓑ 5
Ⓒ 7 　　Ⓓ not here

3. Which number is just before?

_____, 68

Ⓐ 61 　　Ⓑ 66
Ⓒ 67 　　Ⓓ not here

4. Tina saved 1 half-dollar, 2 dimes, and 1 penny. How much money did she save in all?

Ⓐ 37¢ 　　Ⓑ 52¢
Ⓒ 62¢ 　　Ⓓ 71¢

5.

tens	ones
□	
3	9
+	5

Ⓐ 44
Ⓑ 57
Ⓒ 61
Ⓓ not here

6.

tens	ones
□	
6	1
− 2	3

Ⓐ 27 　　Ⓑ 38
Ⓒ 43 　　Ⓓ 45

Name _____

Use the picture to answer questions 7 and 8.

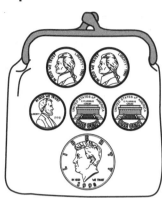

7. Which group of coins are you certain to find in the purse?

Ⓐ

Ⓑ

Ⓒ

8. Which group of coins is impossible to find in the purse?

Ⓐ

Ⓑ

Ⓒ

9. Which is the number?

5 ones + 8 hundreds + 4 tens

Ⓐ 548   Ⓑ 584
Ⓒ 854   Ⓓ 845

10. How many equal $1.00?

Ⓐ 2 nickels   Ⓑ 5 nickels
Ⓒ 10 nickels Ⓓ 20 nickels

Name _____

11. Katy has 5 hundreds, 1 ten, and 6 ones. What number is she showing?

- (A) 156
- (B) 165
- (C) 516
- (D) 561

12. Felix has 8 tens, 7 hundreds, and 0 ones. What number is he showing?

- (A) 708
- (B) 780
- (C) 807
- (D) 870

13. Which number is greater?

- (A) 436
- (B) 463

14. Which number is less?

- (A) 602
- (B) 620

15. Complete this sentence.
250 is ___ 25.

- (A) greater than
- (B) less than

16. Which number belongs in the blank?

529, ___, 531

- (A) 503
- (B) 530
- (C) 540
- (D) 545

Harcourt Brace School Publishers

Name _____

17.

hundreds	tens	ones
	☐	
5	2	8
+ 4	1	2

Ⓐ 914   Ⓑ 930
Ⓒ 936   Ⓓ 940

18.

hundreds	tens	ones
☐	☐	☐
2	8	4
− 1	7	7

Ⓐ 107   Ⓑ 113
Ⓒ 117   Ⓓ 351

19.
```
  6 3 1
+ 2 7 6
```

Ⓐ 805   Ⓑ 807
Ⓒ 905   Ⓓ 907

20.
```
  4 8 6
- 2 5 7
```

Ⓐ 229   Ⓑ 239
Ⓒ 633   Ⓓ 743

21. David had $4.75. He spent $1.29 on a snack. How much money does he have left?

Ⓐ $3.46   Ⓑ $3.56
Ⓒ $5.94   Ⓓ $6.04

22. Francis earned $1.75 on Friday and $1.50 on Saturday. How much money in all did she earn?

Ⓐ $1.25   Ⓑ $2.25
Ⓒ $3.25   Ⓓ $3.45

Harcourt Brace School Publishers

Form A • Multiple-Choice   A116   **Chapters 1–26**   **Stop!**

Choose the correct answer.

1. How many in all?

3 groups of 4

$4 + 4 + 4 =$ ___

(A) 8   (B) 10
(C) 12   (D) 16

2. How many in all?

4 groups of 2

$2 + 2 + 2 + 2 =$ ___

(A) 2   (B) 4
(C) 8   (D) 10

Which number sentence goes with the picture?

3.

$5 + 5 = 10$

(A) $10 - 5 = 5$
(B) $5 \times 5 = 25$
(C) $6 + 4 = 10$
(D) $2 \times 5 = 10$

4.

$3 + 3 + 3 + 3 = 12$

(A) $3 + 3 = 6$
(B) $4 \times 3 = 12$
(C) $9 + 3 = 12$
(D) $4 + 3 = 7$

5.

$2 \times 3 =$ ___

(A) 5   (B) 6
(C) 8   (D) 9

6.

$5 \times 5 =$ ___

(A) 10   (B) 15
(C) 20   (D) 25

Which multiplication sentence goes with the picture?

7.

(A) 3 × 3 = 9
(B) 3 × 4 = 12
(C) 5 × 3 = 15
(D) 4 × 4 = 16

8.

(A) 5 + 4 = 9
(B) 5 × 3 = 15
(C) 5 × 4 = 20
(D) 5 × 5 = 25

9. Which number completes the multiplication sentence?

4 × 4 = ___

(A) 8
(B) 10
(C) 12
(D) 16

10. Which number completes the multiplication sentence?

5 × 3 = ___

(A) 8
(B) 15
(C) 16
(D) 20

11. There are 3 woodpeckers on a tree. Each woodpecker has 2 wings. Which number sentence tells how many wings they have in all?

(A) 3 + 2 = 5
(B) 3 × 2 = 6
(C) 3 × 3 = 9
(D) 3 × 4 = 12

12. There are 2 boys buying cookies. Each boy buys 2 cookies. How many cookies are they buying in all?

(A) 4 cookies
(B) 5 cookies
(C) 6 cookies
(D) 8 cookies

Form A • Multiple-Choice

Stop!

Choose the correct answer.

1. 2 equal groups

How many are in each group?
- (A) 2
- (B) 3
- (C) 4
- (D) 6

2. 3 equal groups

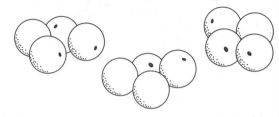

How many are in each group?
- (A) 2
- (B) 3
- (C) 4
- (D) 6

3. 4 equal groups

How many are in each group?
- (A) 1
- (B) 2
- (C) 4
- (D) 8

4. 2 equal groups

How many are in each group?
- (A) 2
- (B) 3
- (C) 4
- (D) 5

5. How many equal groups are there?

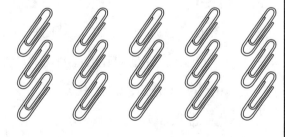

- (A) 1 group
- (B) 2 groups
- (C) 4 groups
- (D) 5 groups

6. How many equal groups are there?

- (A) 3 groups
- (B) 4 groups
- (C) 5 groups
- (D) 6 groups

7. Groups of 2

How many equal groups are there?
- (A) 2 groups
- (B) 4 groups
- (C) 7 groups
- (D) 14 groups

8. Groups of 4

How many equal groups are there?
- (A) 2 groups
- (B) 3 groups
- (C) 4 groups
- (D) 12 groups

Solve.

9. There are 8 markers. There are 4 children. Each child has the same number of markers. How many markers does each child have?
- (A) 2 markers
- (B) 4 markers
- (C) 8 markers
- (D) 12 markers

10. Noah gave 12 cupcakes to 4 friends. He gave each an equal number. How many cupcakes did each friend get?
- (A) 2 cupcakes
- (B) 3 cupcakes
- (C) 4 cupcakes
- (D) 8 cupcakes

11. Susan had 20 stickers. She gave away 5 stickers. How many stickers does she have left?
- (A) 4 stickers
- (B) 10 stickers
- (C) 15 stickers
- (D) 25 stickers

12. There are 5 children. Each child buys a book that costs $3.00. How much money in all do they spend?
- (A) $2.00
- (B) $8.00
- (C) $13.00
- (D) $15.00

Harcourt Brace School Publishers

Choose the correct answer.

1. How many in all?

3 groups of 2

$2 + 2 + 2 =$ _____

(A) 4   (B) 6
(C) 8   (D) 10

2. How many in all?

4 groups of 3

$3 + 3 + 3 + 3 =$ _____

(A) 6   (B) 9
(C) 12   (D) 15

3. Which multiplication sentence goes with the picture?

(A) $2 \times 4 = 8$
(B) $2 \times 5 = 10$
(C) $3 \times 4 = 12$
(D) $5 \times 3 = 15$

4. Which multiplication sentence goes with the picture?

(A) $4 + 4 = 8$
(B) $4 \times 3 = 12$
(C) $4 \times 4 = 16$
(D) $4 \times 5 = 20$

5. There are 2 children coloring. Each child has 4 crayons. Which number sentence tells how many crayons they have in all?

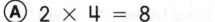

(A) $2 \times 4 = 8$
(B) $2 + 2 = 4$
(C) $3 \times 4 = 12$
(D) $4 \times 4 = 16$

6. There are 5 plants. Each plant has 2 flowers. How many flowers are there in all?

(A) 2 flowers
(B) 3 flowers
(C) 7 flowers
(D) 10 flowers

7. 3 equal groups

How many are in each group?

Ⓐ 2   Ⓑ 3
Ⓒ 4   Ⓓ 6

8. 2 equal groups

How many are in each group?

Ⓐ 2   Ⓑ 5
Ⓒ 7   Ⓓ 14

9. Groups of 4

How many equal groups are there?

Ⓐ 2 groups   Ⓑ 3 groups
Ⓒ 4 groups   Ⓓ 5 groups

10. Groups of 2

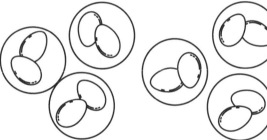

How many equal groups are there?

Ⓐ 4 groups   Ⓑ 5 groups
Ⓒ 6 groups   Ⓓ 7 groups

11. There are 6 pencils. There are 3 children. Each child has the same number of pencils. How many pencils does each child have?

Ⓐ 2 pencils   Ⓑ 3 pencils
Ⓒ 4 pencils   Ⓓ 5 pencils

12. Janet gave 20 books to 5 friends. She gave each an equal number. How many books did each friend get?

Ⓐ 2 books   Ⓑ 4 books
Ⓒ 5 books   Ⓓ 6 books

Harcourt Brace School Publishers

Name _____

Choose the correct answer.
Use base-ten blocks to answer questions 1 and 2.

1.
$$55 + 37$$

   (A) 22   (B) 72
   (C) 82   (D) 92

2.
$$18 + 25$$

   (A) 13   (B) 33
   (C) 43   (D) not here

Use base-ten blocks.
Choose the operation and solve. Write + or − .

3. There are 17 dodge balls and 14 basketballs in the gym. How many balls are in the gym?

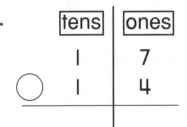

tens	ones
1	7
1	4

   (A) 13 balls   (B) 21 balls
   (C) 23 balls   (D) 31 balls

4. Nancy has 75¢. She buys a

59¢

How much money does Nancy have left?

tens	ones
7	5
5	9

   (A) 14¢   (B) 16¢
   (C) 24¢   (D) 26¢

Harcourt Brace School Publishers

Name _____

5. 72
 -53

Ⓐ 19 Ⓑ 21
Ⓒ 25 Ⓓ 29

6. 44
 -28

Ⓐ 16 Ⓑ 24
Ⓒ 26 Ⓓ 64

Use the graph to answer questions 7 to 10.

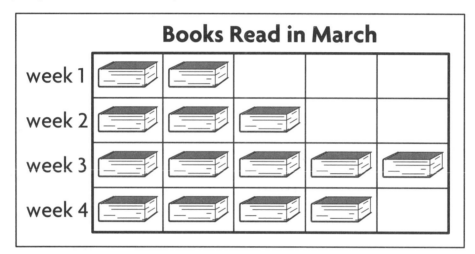

Each ⬛ stands for 5 books read.

7. In which week were 15 books read?
Ⓐ week 1 Ⓑ week 2
Ⓒ week 3 Ⓓ week 4

8. In which week were the fewest books read?
Ⓐ week 1 Ⓑ week 2
Ⓒ week 3 Ⓓ week 4

9. In which week were the most books read?
Ⓐ week 1 Ⓑ week 2
Ⓒ week 3 Ⓓ week 4

10. How many books were read in week 4?
Ⓐ 10 books Ⓑ 15 books
Ⓒ 20 books Ⓓ 25 books

Harcourt Brace School Publishers

11. How many in all?

3 + 3 + 3 = ___?___

Ⓐ 6 Ⓑ 9
Ⓒ 12 Ⓓ 15

12.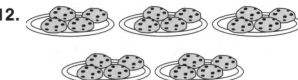

5 × 4 = ___?___

Ⓐ 10 Ⓑ 15
Ⓒ 20 Ⓓ 25

13. Which number completes the multiplication sentence?

3 × 4 = ___?___

Ⓐ 7 Ⓑ 8
Ⓒ 10 Ⓓ 12

14. Which number completes the multiplication sentence?

7 × 3 = ___?___

Ⓐ 4 Ⓑ 14
Ⓒ 21 Ⓓ 28

15. There are 4 dogs. Each dog has 2 ears. How many ears do they have in all?

Ⓐ 2 Ⓑ 6
Ⓒ 8 Ⓓ 16

16. There are 3 girls buying rings. Each girl buys 5 rings. How many rings are they buying in all?

Ⓐ 6 Ⓑ 9
Ⓒ 10 Ⓓ 15

17. 3 equal groups

How many are in each group?

Ⓐ 1   Ⓑ 2

Ⓒ 3   Ⓓ 9

18. Groups of 4

How many equal groups are there?

Ⓐ 2 groups   Ⓑ 4 groups

Ⓒ 12 groups   Ⓓ 16 groups

19. There are 6 cookies. There are 3 children. Each child has the same number of cookies. How many cookies does each child have?

Ⓐ 2   Ⓑ 3

Ⓒ 4   Ⓓ 6

20. Peter gave 20 marbles to 5 friends. He gave each an equal number. How many marbles did each friend get?

Ⓐ 2   Ⓑ 3

Ⓒ 4   Ⓓ 5

21. Kemp had 15 tickets. He gave away 5 tickets. How many tickets does he have left?

Ⓐ 5 tickets   Ⓑ 10 tickets

Ⓒ 15 tickets   Ⓓ 20 tickets

22. There are 2 children. Each child buys a shirt that costs $4.00. How much money in all do they spend?

Ⓐ $2.00   Ⓑ $4.00

Ⓒ $8.00   Ⓓ $10.00

Tested learning goals are indicated in red. The Inventory Test learning goals are from Grade 1.

Name _____

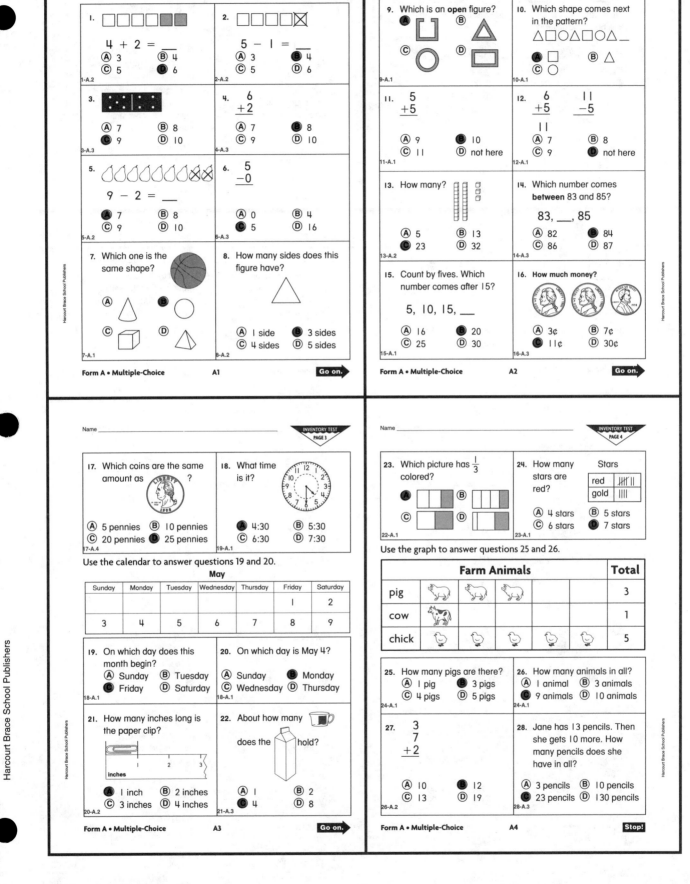

Choose the correct answer.

1. ▢▢▢▢▨▨

$4 + 2 =$ ___
Ⓐ 3   Ⓑ 4
Ⓒ 5   ● 6

1-A.2

2. ▢▢▢▢⊠

$5 - 1 =$ ___
Ⓐ 3   ● 4
Ⓒ 5   Ⓓ 6

2-A.2

3.
Ⓐ 7   Ⓑ 8
● 9   Ⓓ 10

3-A.3

4.
6
$+2$
Ⓐ 7   ● 8
Ⓒ 9   Ⓓ 10

4-A.3

5.
$9 - 2 =$ ___
● 7   Ⓑ 8
Ⓒ 9   Ⓓ 10

5-A.2

6.
5
-0
Ⓐ 0   Ⓑ 4
● 5   Ⓓ 16

6-A.3

7. Which one is the same shape?
Ⓐ
●
Ⓒ
Ⓓ

7-A.1

8. How many sides does this figure have?
Ⓐ 1 side   ● 3 sides
Ⓒ 4 sides   Ⓓ 5 sides

8-A.2

Form A • Multiple-Choice   A1   **Go on.**

---

9. Which is an **open** figure?
Ⓐ   Ⓑ
Ⓒ   Ⓓ

9-A.1

10. Which shape comes next in the pattern?
△▢○△▢○△ ___
● ▢   Ⓑ △
Ⓒ ○

10-A.1

11.
5
$+5$
Ⓐ 9   ● 10
Ⓒ 11   Ⓓ not here

11-A.1

12.
6 11
$+5$ -5
11
Ⓐ 7   Ⓑ 8
Ⓒ 9   ● not here

12-A.1

13. How many?
Ⓐ 5   Ⓑ 13
Ⓒ 23   Ⓓ 32

13-A.2

14. Which number comes **between** 83 and 85?
$83,$ ___$, 85$
Ⓐ 82   ● 84
Ⓒ 86   Ⓓ 87

14-A.3

15. Count by fives. Which number comes after 15?
$5, 10, 15,$ ___
Ⓐ 16   ● 20
Ⓒ 25   Ⓓ 30

15-A.1

16. How much money?
Ⓐ 3¢   Ⓑ 7¢
● 11¢   Ⓓ 30¢

16-A.3

Form A • Multiple-Choice   A2   **Go on.**

---

17. Which coins are the same amount as ___?
Ⓐ 5 pennies   Ⓑ 10 pennies
Ⓒ 20 pennies   ● 25 pennies

17-A.4

18. What time is it?
● 4:30   Ⓑ 5:30
Ⓒ 6:30   Ⓓ 7:30

19-A.1

Use the calendar to answer questions 19 and 20.

May

Sunday	Monday	Tuesday	Wednesday	Thursday	Friday	Saturday
					1	2
3	4	5	6	7	8	9

19. On which day does this month begin?
Ⓐ Sunday   Ⓑ Tuesday
● Friday   Ⓓ Saturday

18-A.1

20. On which day is May 4?
Ⓐ Sunday   ● Monday
Ⓒ Wednesday   Ⓓ Thursday

18-A.1

21. How many inches long is the paper clip?
● 1 inch   Ⓑ 2 inches
Ⓒ 3 inches   Ⓓ 4 inches

20-A.2

22. About how many ☕ does the 🥛 hold?
Ⓐ 1   Ⓑ 2
● 4   Ⓓ 8

21-A.3

Form A • Multiple-Choice   A3   **Go on.**

---

23. Which picture has $\frac{1}{3}$ colored?
● Ⓐ   Ⓑ
Ⓒ   Ⓓ

22-A.1

24. How many stars are red?

red	||||| ||
gold	||||

Ⓐ 4 stars   Ⓑ 5 stars
Ⓒ 6 stars   ● 7 stars

23-A.1

Use the graph to answer questions 25 and 26.

Farm Animals						**Total**
pig	🐷	🐷	🐷			3
cow	🐄					1
chick	🐥	🐥	🐥	🐥	🐥	5

25. How many pigs are there?
Ⓐ 1 pig   ● 3 pigs
Ⓒ 4 pigs   Ⓓ 5 pigs

24-A.1

26. How many animals in all?
Ⓐ 1 animal   Ⓑ 3 animals
● 9 animals   Ⓓ 10 animals

24-A.1

27.
3
7
$+2$
Ⓐ 10   Ⓑ 12
Ⓒ 13   Ⓓ 19

26-A.2

28. Jane has 13 pencils. Then she gets 10 more. How many pencils does she have in all?
Ⓐ 3 pencils   Ⓑ 10 pencils
● 23 pencils   Ⓓ 130 pencils

28-A.3

Form A • Multiple-Choice   A4   **Stop!**

Multiple Choice

Choose the correct answer.

1. Which addition sentence tells about the picture?

ⓐ 6 + 4 = 10
● 6 + 6 = 12
ⓒ 6 + 7 = 13
ⓓ 6 + 6 = 66

2. Which addition sentence tells about the picture?

ⓐ 8 + 8 = 88
ⓑ 8 + 8 = 15
● 8 + 8 = 16
ⓓ 8 + 8 = 17

3. 7
  +8
  ___
ⓐ 13   ⓑ 14
● 15   ⓓ not here

4. 7
  +6
  ___
● 13   ⓑ 14
ⓒ 15   ⓓ not here

5. 9
  +2
  ___
ⓐ 10   ● 11
ⓒ 12   ⓓ 13

6. 9
  +8
  ___
ⓐ 14   ⓑ 15
ⓒ 16   ● 17

7. 5
  +9
  ___
● 14   ⓑ 15
ⓒ 16   ⓓ not here

8. 3
  +9
  ___
ⓐ 9   ⓑ 10
ⓒ 11   ● not here

---

9. 7
  +3
  ___
ⓐ 8   ⓑ 9
ⓒ 10   ⓓ not here

10. 8
   +4
   ___
ⓐ 11   ● 12
ⓒ 13   ⓓ not here

11. Carl has 6 red stars and 6 gold stars. How many stars does he have?

ⓐ 9 stars   ⓑ 10 stars
ⓒ 11 stars   ⓓ 12 stars

12. Sara spent 9¢ for a pen and 5¢ for paper. How much money did she spend?

● 14¢   ⓑ 55¢
ⓒ 16¢   ⓓ 17¢

13. 3
   7
  +6
  ___
ⓐ 13   ⓑ 14
ⓒ 15   ● 16

14. 4
   9
  +4
  ___
ⓐ 15   ⓑ 16
● 17   ⓓ 18

15. Nan has 6 red pens, 6 blue pens, and 2 black pens. How many pens does she have?

ⓐ 13 pens   ● 14 pens
ⓒ 15 pens   ⓓ 16 pens

16. Cody has 8 red cars, 9 green cars, and 1 yellow car. How many cars does he have?

ⓐ 15 cars   ⓑ 16 cars
ⓒ 17 cars   ● 18 cars

Choose the correct answer.

1. 8   13
  +5   −8
  ___   ___
  13
ⓐ 4   ● 5
ⓒ 6   ⓓ 7

2. 15 − 6 = 9
   9 + 6 = ___
ⓐ 12   ⓑ 13
ⓒ 14   ● 15

3. 7   15
  +8   −8
  ___   ___
  15
ⓐ 4   ⓑ 5
ⓒ 6   ● 7

4. 17 − 9 = 8
   8 + 9 = ___
ⓐ 15   ⓑ 16
● 17   ⓓ 18

Use the number line to answer questions 5 and 6.

5. 14 − 7 = ___
● 7   ⓑ 8
ⓒ 9   ⓓ 10

6. 16 − 8 = ___
ⓐ 6   ⓑ 7
● 8   ⓓ 9

---

7. Which number sentence belongs in this fact family?
   7 + 9 = 16
   9 + 7 = 16
   16 − 9 = 7

ⓐ 19 − 6 = 13
● 16 − 7 = 9
ⓒ 7 + 6 = 13
ⓓ 9 + 9 = 18

8. Which number sentence belongs in this fact family?
   8 + 6 = 14
   6 + 8 = 14
   14 − 6 = 8

ⓐ 14 − 7 = 7
ⓑ 14 − 5 = 9
● 14 − 8 = 6
ⓓ 7 + 7 = 14

Which is the missing addend?

9. 9 + ___ = 15
ⓐ 4   ⓑ 5
● 6   ⓓ not here

10. 8 + ___ = 11
ⓐ 1   ⓑ 2
● 3   ⓓ not here

11. There were 9 boys and 5 girls playing ball. How many children were playing ball?

ⓐ 4 children
● 14 children
ⓒ 16 children
ⓓ 18 children

12. There were 15 birds in a tree. Then 7 birds flew away. How many birds were left?

● 8 birds   ⓑ 9 birds
ⓒ 12 birds   ⓓ 22 birds

Multiple Choice

Choose the correct answer.

1.
$$\begin{array}{r} 9 \\ +6 \\ \hline \end{array}$$

Ⓐ 14   Ⓑ 15
Ⓒ 16   Ⓓ 17

1-A.1

2.
$$\begin{array}{r} 5 \\ +5 \\ \hline \end{array}$$

Ⓐ 10   Ⓑ 11
Ⓒ 12   Ⓓ not here

1-A.1

3. Bill has 8 red fish and 8 gold fish. How many fish does he have?

Ⓐ 15 fish   Ⓑ 16 fish
Ⓒ 17 fish   Ⓓ 18 fish

1-A.1

4. Cora spent 7¢ for an orange and 6¢ for grapes. How much money did she spend?

Ⓐ 11¢   Ⓑ 12¢
Ⓒ 13¢   Ⓓ 14¢

1-A.1

5.
$$\begin{array}{r} 6 \\ 2 \\ +4 \\ \hline \end{array}$$

Ⓐ 9   Ⓑ 10
Ⓒ 11   Ⓓ 12

1-A.2

6.
$$\begin{array}{r} 3 \\ 8 \\ +3 \\ \hline \end{array}$$

Ⓐ 14   Ⓑ 15
Ⓒ 16   Ⓓ 17

1-A.2

Form A • Multiple-Choice   A9   Go on.

7.
$$\begin{array}{r} 8 \\ +7 \\ \hline 15 \end{array} \qquad \begin{array}{r} 15 \\ -8 \\ \hline \end{array}$$

Ⓐ 4   Ⓑ 5
Ⓒ 6   Ⓓ 7

2-A.1

8. $11 - 4 = 7$
$7 + 4 = \underline{}$

Ⓐ 9   Ⓑ 10
Ⓒ 11   Ⓓ 12

2-A.1

Use the number line to answer questions 9 and 10.

9. $16 - 7 = \underline{}$

Ⓐ 7   Ⓑ 9
Ⓒ 11   Ⓓ 12

2-A.2

10. $14 - 9 = \underline{}$

Ⓐ 5   Ⓑ 6
Ⓒ 7   Ⓓ 8

2-A.2

11. Which is the missing addend?

$6 + \underline{} = 11$

Ⓐ 3   Ⓑ 4
Ⓒ 5   Ⓓ not here

2-A.1

12. There were 7 boys and 5 girls in the contest. How many children were in the contest?

Ⓐ 12 children
Ⓑ 13 children
Ⓒ 14 children
Ⓓ 15 children

2-A.3

Form A • Multiple-Choice   A10   Stop!

Choose the correct answer.

1. Which addition sentence tells about the picture?

Ⓐ $4 + 4 = 8$
Ⓑ $4 + 5 = 9$
Ⓒ $4 + 8 = 12$

1-A.1

2. Which addition sentence tells about the picture?

Ⓐ $7 + 7 = 77$
Ⓑ $7 + 9 = 16$
Ⓒ $7 + 7 = 14$

1-A.1

3.
$$\begin{array}{r} 8 \\ +9 \\ \hline \end{array}$$

Ⓐ 16   Ⓑ 17
Ⓒ 18   Ⓓ not here

1-A.1

4.
$$\begin{array}{r} 6 \\ +5 \\ \hline \end{array}$$

Ⓐ 9   Ⓑ 10
Ⓒ 11   Ⓓ not here

1-A.1

5.
$$\begin{array}{r} 7 \\ +8 \\ \hline \end{array}$$

Ⓐ 14   Ⓑ 15
Ⓒ 16   Ⓓ not here

1-A.1

6.
$$\begin{array}{r} 3 \\ +2 \\ \hline \end{array}$$

Ⓐ 6   Ⓑ 7
Ⓒ 8   Ⓓ not here

1-A.1

7.
$$\begin{array}{r} 9 \\ +3 \\ \hline \end{array}$$

Ⓐ 10   Ⓑ 11
Ⓒ 12   Ⓓ 13

1-A.1

8.
$$\begin{array}{r} 2 \\ +9 \\ \hline \end{array}$$

Ⓐ 10   Ⓑ 11
Ⓒ 12   Ⓓ 13

1-A.1

Form A • Multiple-Choice   A11   Chapters 1–2   Go on.

---

9. Use the picture to find the sum.
$$\begin{array}{r} 8 \\ +5 \\ \hline \end{array}$$

Ⓐ 13   Ⓑ 14
Ⓒ 15   Ⓓ not here

1-A.1

10. Use the picture to find the sum.
$$\begin{array}{r} 5 \\ +7 \\ \hline \end{array}$$

Ⓐ 11   Ⓑ 12
Ⓒ 13   Ⓓ not here

1-A.1

11. Davey has 7 blue cars and 9 red cars. How many cars does he have?

Ⓐ 9 cars   Ⓑ 10 cars
Ⓒ 16 cars   Ⓓ 18 cars

1-A.1

12. Kris has 6 pink bows, 5 green bows, and 6 red bows. How many bows does she have?

Ⓐ 17 bows   Ⓑ 18 bows
Ⓒ 19 bows   Ⓓ 20 bows

1-A.2

13.
$$\begin{array}{r} 5 \\ 8 \\ +5 \\ \hline \end{array}$$

Ⓐ 17   Ⓑ 18
Ⓒ 19   Ⓓ 20

1-A.2

14.
$$\begin{array}{r} 7 \\ 3 \\ +5 \\ \hline \end{array}$$

Ⓐ 15   Ⓑ 16
Ⓒ 17   Ⓓ 18

1-A.2

Form A • Multiple-Choice   A12   Chapters 1–2   Go on.

Name _____

15.
$$3 \qquad 10$$
$$+7 \qquad -3$$
$$\overline{10}$$

Ⓐ 4   Ⓑ 5
Ⓒ 6   ● 7
2-A.1

16. $18 - 9 = 9$
$9 + 9 = $ ___

Ⓐ 19   ● 18
Ⓒ 17   Ⓓ 16
2-A.1

17.
$$9 \qquad 15$$
$$+6 \qquad -9$$
$$\overline{15}$$

● 6   Ⓑ 7
Ⓒ 8   Ⓓ 9
2-A.1

18. $12 - 8 = 4$
$8 + 4 = $ ___

Ⓐ 10   Ⓑ 11
● 12   Ⓓ 13
2-A.1

19. Which number sentence belongs in this fact family?

$$9 + 5 = 14$$
$$5 + 9 = 14$$
$$14 - 9 = 5$$

Ⓐ $9 - 5 = 4$
Ⓑ $4 + 5 = 9$
● $14 - 5 = 9$
Ⓓ $9 + 9 = 18$
2-A.1

20. Which number sentence belongs in this fact family?

$$7 + 4 = 11$$
$$4 + 7 = 11$$
$$11 - 7 = 4$$

Ⓐ $7 + 7 = 14$
● $11 - 4 = 7$
Ⓒ $4 + 3 = 7$
Ⓓ $7 - 4 = 3$
2-A.1

Form A • Multiple-Choice   A13   Chapters 1–2   Go on.

Name _____

21. Which is the missing addend?

$$\begin{array}{r} 6 \\ +\square \\ \hline 13 \end{array}$$

Ⓐ 6   ● 7
Ⓒ 8   Ⓓ not here
2-A.1

22. Which is the missing addend?

$$\begin{array}{r} 3 \\ +\square \\ \hline 10 \end{array}$$

Ⓐ 4   Ⓑ 3
● 2   Ⓓ not here
2-A.1

Use the number line to answer questions 25 and 26.

0 1 2 3 4 5 6 7 8 9 10 11 12 13 14 15 16 17 18

23. $14 - 6 = $ ___

Ⓐ 7   ● 8
Ⓒ 9   Ⓓ 10
2-A.2

24. $16 - 7 = $ ___

● 9   Ⓑ 10
Ⓒ 11   Ⓓ 12
2-A.2

27. There were 4 boys and 9 girls eating popcorn. How many children were eating?

Ⓐ 5   Ⓑ 12
● 13   Ⓓ 14
2-A.3

28. There were 11 pigs in the field. Then 8 pigs left. How many pigs were still in the field?

Ⓐ 7 pigs   Ⓑ 5 pigs
Ⓒ 4 pigs   ● 3 pigs
2-A.3

Form A • Multiple-Choice   A14   Chapters 1–2   Stop!

Name _____

Choose the correct answer.

1. How many ones are there?

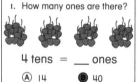

4 tens $= $ ___ ones

Ⓐ 14   ● 40
Ⓒ 44   Ⓓ 140

2. How many ones are there?

2 tens $= $ ___ ones

Ⓐ 2   Ⓑ 12
● 20   Ⓓ 22

3. How many tens and ones are there?

Ⓐ 2 tens 3 ones $= 23$
● 3 tens 2 ones $= 32$
Ⓒ 4 tens 3 ones $= 43$
Ⓓ 4 tens 4 ones $= 44$

4. How many tens and ones are there?

Ⓐ 7 tens 4 ones $= 74$
Ⓑ 7 tens 7 ones $= 77$
Ⓒ 10 tens 4 ones $= 104$
● 4 tens 7 ones $= 47$

5. Which is the number?

9 tens 6 ones $= $ ___

Ⓐ 3   Ⓑ 69
● 96   Ⓓ 906

6. Which is the number?

8 tens 0 ones $= $ ___

Ⓐ 8   Ⓑ 18
● 80   Ⓓ 88

Form A • Multiple-Choice   A15   Go on.

Name _____

7. Which is the number?

7 tens 9 ones $= $ ___

Ⓐ 19   ● 79
Ⓒ 97   Ⓓ not here

8. Which is the number?

5 tens 1 one $= $ ___

Ⓐ 6   Ⓑ 15
● 51   Ⓓ not here

9. Which number is shown?

Ⓐ 8   ● 18
Ⓒ 81   Ⓓ 88

10. Which number is shown?

Ⓐ 6   Ⓑ 16
● 60   Ⓓ 66

Use these groups to help you answer questions 11 and 12.

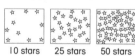

10 stars   25 stars   50 stars

11. Which is the best estimate?

Ⓐ about 10 stars
● about 25 stars
Ⓒ about 50 stars

12. Which is the best estimate?

● about 10 stars
Ⓑ about 25 stars
Ⓒ about 50 stars

Form A • Multiple-Choice   A16   Stop!

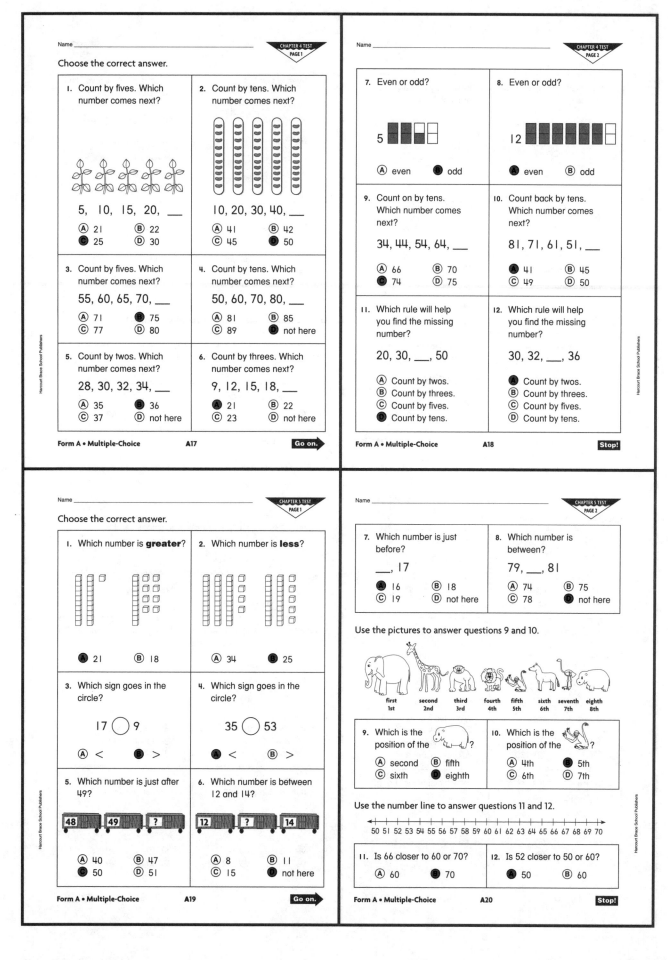

Name _____

Choose the correct answer.

1. Count by fives. Which number comes next?

5, 10, 15, 20, ___

(A) 21   (B) 22
● 25   (D) 30

2. Count by tens. Which number comes next?

10, 20, 30, 40, ___

(A) 41   (B) 42
(C) 45   ● 50

3. Count by fives. Which number comes next?

55, 60, 65, 70, ___

(A) 71   ● 75
(C) 77   (D) 80

4. Count by tens. Which number comes next?

50, 60, 70, 80, ___

(A) 81   (B) 85
(C) 89   ● not here

5. Count by twos. Which number comes next?

28, 30, 32, 34, ___

(A) 35   ● 36
(C) 37   (D) not here

6. Count by threes. Which number comes next?

9, 12, 15, 18, ___

● 21   (B) 22
(C) 23   (D) not here

Form A • Multiple-Choice   A17   Go on.

Name _____

7. Even or odd?

5 ▦

(A) even   ● odd

8. Even or odd?

12 ▦

● even   (B) odd

9. Count on by tens. Which number comes next?

34, 44, 54, 64, ___

(A) 66   (B) 70
● 74   (D) 75

10. Count back by tens. Which number comes next?

81, 71, 61, 51, ___

● 41   (B) 45
(C) 49   (D) 50

11. Which rule will help you find the missing number?

20, 30, ___, 50

(A) Count by twos.
(B) Count by threes.
(C) Count by fives.
● Count by tens.

12. Which rule will help you find the missing number?

30, 32, ___, 36

● Count by twos.
(B) Count by threes.
(C) Count by fives.
(D) Count by tens.

Form A • Multiple-Choice   A18   Stop!

Name _____

Choose the correct answer.

1. Which number is **greater**?

● 21   (B) 18

2. Which number is **less**?

(A) 34   ● 25

3. Which sign goes in the circle?

17 ◯ 9

(A) <   ● >

4. Which sign goes in the circle?

35 ◯ 53

● <   (B) >

5. Which number is just after 49?

| 48 | 49 | ? |

(A) 40   (B) 47
● 50   (D) 51

6. Which number is between 12 and 14?

| 12 | ? | 14 |

(A) 8   (B) 11
(C) 15   ● not here

Form A • Multiple-Choice   A19   Go on.

Name _____

7. Which number is just before?

___, 17

● 16   (B) 18
(C) 19   (D) not here

8. Which number is between?

79, ___, 81

(A) 74   (B) 75
(C) 78   ● not here

Use the pictures to answer questions 9 and 10.

first   second   third   fourth   fifth   sixth   seventh   eighth
1st   2nd   3rd   4th   5th   6th   7th   8th

9. Which is the position of the 🐻?

(A) second   (B) fifth
(C) sixth   ● eighth

10. Which is the position of the 🦢?

(A) 4th   ● 5th
(C) 6th   (D) 7th

Use the number line to answer questions 11 and 12.

50 51 52 53 54 55 56 57 58 59 60 61 62 63 64 65 66 67 68 69 70

11. Is 66 closer to 60 or 70?

(A) 60   ● 70

12. Is 52 closer to 50 or 60?

● 50   (B) 60

Form A • Multiple-Choice   A20   Stop!

Multiple Choice

131

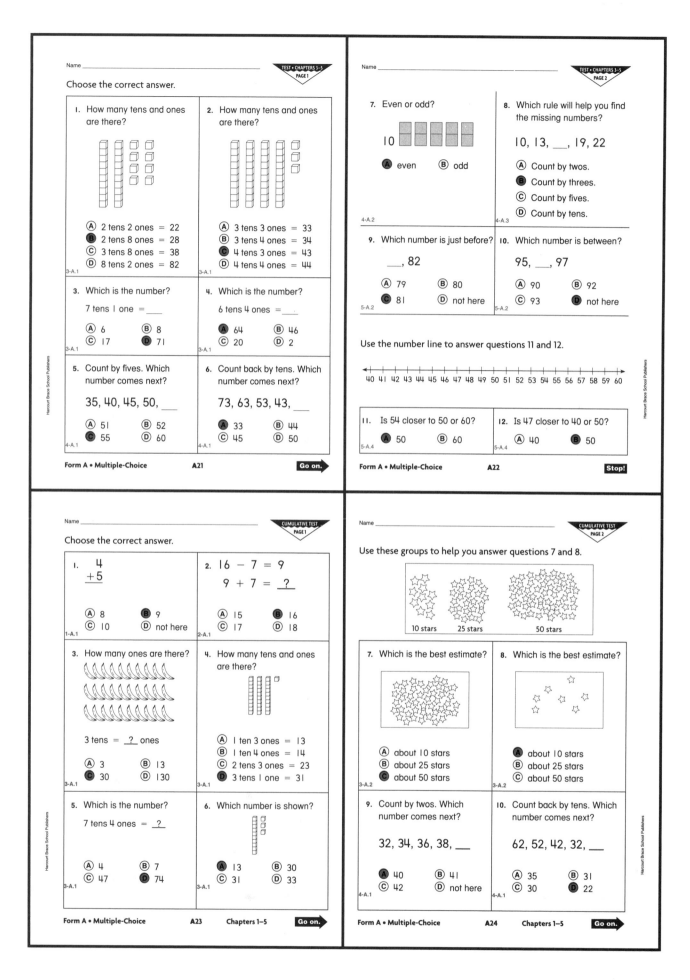

Name _____

Choose the correct answer.

1. How many tens and ones are there?

- (A) 2 tens 2 ones = 22
- (B) 2 tens 8 ones = 28
- (C) 3 tens 8 ones = 38
- (D) 8 tens 2 ones = 82

3-A.1

2. How many tens and ones are there?

- (A) 3 tens 3 ones = 33
- (B) 3 tens 4 ones = 34
- (C) 4 tens 3 ones = 43
- (D) 4 tens 4 ones = 44

3-A.1

3. Which is the number?

7 tens 1 one = ___

- (A) 6
- (B) 8
- (C) 17
- (D) 71

3-A.1

4. Which is the number?

6 tens 4 ones = ___

- (A) 64
- (B) 46
- (C) 20
- (D) 2

3-A.1

5. Count by fives. Which number comes next?

35, 40, 45, 50, ___

- (A) 51
- (B) 52
- (C) 55
- (D) 60

4-A.1

6. Count back by tens. Which number comes next?

73, 63, 53, 43, ___

- (A) 33
- (B) 44
- (C) 45
- (D) 50

4-A.1

Form A • Multiple-Choice   A21   **Go on.**

Name _____

7. Even or odd?

10

- (A) even
- (B) odd

4-A.2

8. Which rule will help you find the missing numbers?

10, 13, ___, 19, 22

- (A) Count by twos.
- (B) Count by threes.
- (C) Count by fives.
- (D) Count by tens.

4-A.3

9. Which number is just before?

___, 82

- (A) 79
- (B) 80
- (C) 81
- (D) not here

5-A.2

10. Which number is between?

95, ___, 97

- (A) 90
- (B) 92
- (C) 93
- (D) not here

5-A.2

Use the number line to answer questions 11 and 12.

40 41 42 43 44 45 46 47 48 49 50 51 52 53 54 55 56 57 58 59 60

11. Is 54 closer to 50 or 60?

- (A) 50
- (B) 60

5-A.4

12. Is 47 closer to 40 or 50?

- (A) 40
- (B) 50

5-A.4

Form A • Multiple-Choice   A22   **Stop!**

Name _____

Choose the correct answer.

1.
  4
 +5
 ___

- (A) 8
- (B) 9
- (C) 10
- (D) not here

1-A.1

2. 16 − 7 = 9

9 + 7 = ___?

- (A) 15
- (B) 16
- (C) 17
- (D) 18

2-A.1

3. How many ones are there?

3 tens = ___? ones

- (A) 3
- (B) 13
- (C) 30
- (D) 130

3-A.1

4. How many tens and ones are there?

- (A) 1 ten 3 ones = 13
- (B) 1 ten 4 ones = 14
- (C) 2 tens 3 ones = 23
- (D) 3 tens 1 one = 31

3-A.1

5. Which is the number?

7 tens 4 ones = ___?

- (A) 4
- (B) 7
- (C) 47
- (D) 74

3-A.1

6. Which number is shown?

- (A) 13
- (B) 30
- (C) 31
- (D) 33

3-A.1

Form A • Multiple-Choice   A23   Chapters 1–5   **Go on.**

Name _____

Use these groups to help you answer questions 7 and 8.

10 stars   25 stars   50 stars

7. Which is the best estimate?

- (A) about 10 stars
- (B) about 25 stars
- (C) about 50 stars

3-A.2

8. Which is the best estimate?

- (A) about 10 stars
- (B) about 25 stars
- (C) about 50 stars

3-A.2

9. Count by twos. Which number comes next?

32, 34, 36, 38, ___

- (A) 40
- (B) 41
- (C) 42
- (D) not here

4-A.1

10. Count back by tens. Which number comes next?

62, 52, 42, 32, ___

- (A) 35
- (B) 31
- (C) 30
- (D) 22

4-A.1

Form A • Multiple-Choice   A24   Chapters 1–5   **Go on.**

Multiple Choice

11. Even or odd?

6

(A) even (B) odd

4-A.2

12. Which rule will help you find the missing numbers?

15, 20, 25, 30, ___

(A) Count by twos.
(B) Count by threes.
(C) Count by fives.
(D) Count by tens.

4-A.3

13. Which number is **greater**?

(A) 16 (B) 22

5-A.1

14. Which number is **less**?

(A) 49 (B) 54

5-A.1

15. Which sign goes in the circle?

6 ◯ 11

(A) < (B) >

5-A.1

16. Which number is between?

59, ___, 61

(A) 58 (B) 65
(C) 71 (D) not here

5-A.2

Form A • Multiple-Choice   A25   Chapters 1–5   [Go on.]

Use the pictures below to answer questions 17 and 18.

first 1st second 2nd third 3rd fourth 4th fifth 5th sixth 6th seventh 7th eighth 8th

17. Which is the position of the

(A) third (B) fifth
(C) sixth (D) seventh

5-A.3

18. Which is the position of the

(A) 1st (B) 3rd
(C) 4th (D) 6th

5-A.3

Use the number line to answer questions 19 and 20.

50 51 52 53 54 55 56 57 58 59 60 61 62 63 64 65 66 67 68 69 70

19. Is 37 closer to 30 or 40?

(A) 30 (B) 40

5-A.4

20. Is 41 closer to 40 or 50?

(A) 40 (B) 50

5-A.4

Form A • Multiple-Choice   A26   Chapters 1–5   [Stop!]

Choose the correct answer.

1. Count on. Which is the total amount?

(A) 27¢ (B) 31¢
(C) 8¢   (D) 13¢

2. Count on. Which is the total amount?

(A) 8¢   (B) 16¢
(C) 31¢ (D) 35¢

3. Count on. Which is the total amount?

(A) 5¢   (B) 12¢
(C) 22¢ (D) 25¢

4. Count on. Which is the total amount?

(A) 26¢ (B) 40¢
(C) 42¢ (D) 45¢

5. Count on. Which is the total amount?

(A) 27¢ (B) 31¢
(C) 35¢ (D) 36¢

6. Count on. Which is the total amount?

(A) 25¢ (B) 30¢
(C) 35¢ (D) 40¢

Form A • Multiple-Choice   A27   [Go on.]

---

7. Which answer shows the coins in order from greatest to least value?

(A)

(B)

(C)

8. Which answer shows the coins in order from greatest to least value?

(A)

(B)

(C)

9. Which is the total amount?

(A) 30¢ (B) 31¢
(C) 32¢ (D) not here

10. Which is the total amount?

(A) 37¢ (B) 45¢
(C) 50¢ (D) not here

Form A • Multiple-Choice   A28   [Go on.]

Harcourt Brace School Publishers

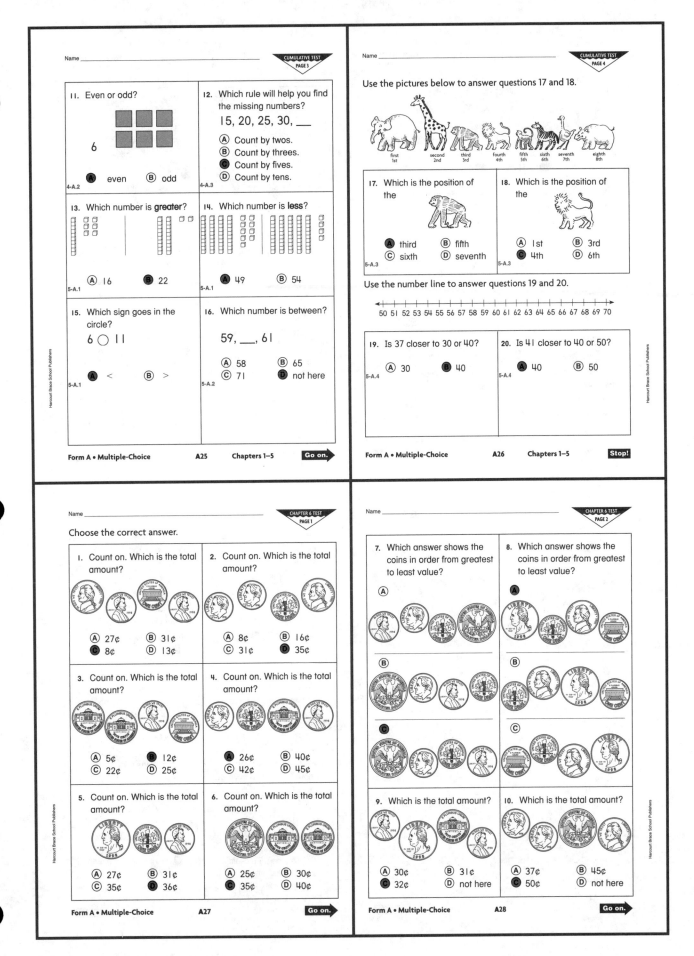

11. Which is the total amount?

Ⓐ 55¢ Ⓑ 62¢
Ⓒ 67¢ **Ⓓ** not here

12. Which is the total amount?

Ⓐ 40¢ Ⓑ 78¢
Ⓒ 80¢ Ⓓ not here

13. Which group of coins will buy 70¢ ?

Ⓐ
Ⓑ
Ⓒ
Ⓓ

14. Which group of coins will buy 85¢ ?

Ⓐ
Ⓑ
Ⓒ
Ⓓ

1. Which group of coins has the same value as ?

Ⓐ
Ⓑ

2. Which group of coins has the same value as ?

Ⓐ
Ⓑ

Which group uses fewer coins to show the same amount?

3.

Ⓐ
Ⓑ

4.

Ⓐ
Ⓑ

5. Which toy could you buy with this group of coins?

Ⓐ 79¢
Ⓑ 95¢
Ⓒ 88¢
Ⓓ 85¢

6. Which toy could you buy with this group of coins?

Ⓐ 75¢
Ⓑ 91¢
Ⓒ 83¢
Ⓓ 68¢

7. You have 50¢.
You buy 47¢.

48¢ ___¢ ___¢
Your change is ___.

Ⓐ 2¢ **Ⓑ** 3¢
Ⓒ 4¢ Ⓓ 6¢

8. You have 35¢.
You buy 31¢.

32¢ ___¢ ___¢ ___¢
Your change is ___.

Ⓐ 2¢ Ⓑ 3¢
Ⓒ 4¢ Ⓓ 5¢

9. Adam saved 1 half-dollar, 2 dimes, and 5 pennies. How much money did he save in all?

Ⓐ 50¢ Ⓑ 57¢
Ⓒ 70¢ **Ⓓ** 75¢

10. Kari saved 1 half-dollar, 1 quarter, 1 nickel, and 1 penny. How much money did she save in all?

Ⓐ 71¢ Ⓑ 76¢
Ⓒ 81¢ Ⓓ 86¢

11. Which coins give you enough money to buy 50¢ ?

Ⓐ 4 dimes, 1 nickel
Ⓑ 2 quarters
Ⓒ 1 quarter, 3 nickels
Ⓓ 3 dimes, 3 nickels, 3 pennies

12. Which coins give you enough money to buy 65¢ ?

Ⓐ 1 quarter, 5 nickels
Ⓑ 2 quarters, 5 pennies
Ⓒ 1 half-dollar, 1 dime, 1 nickel
Ⓓ 6 nickels, 5 pennies

Multiple Choice

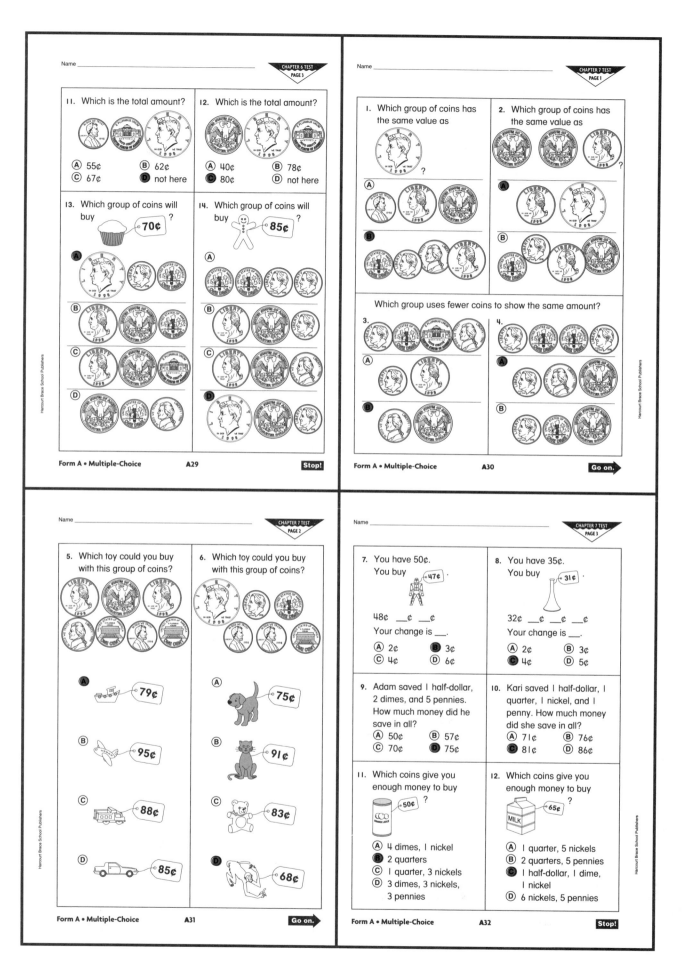

Choose the correct answer.

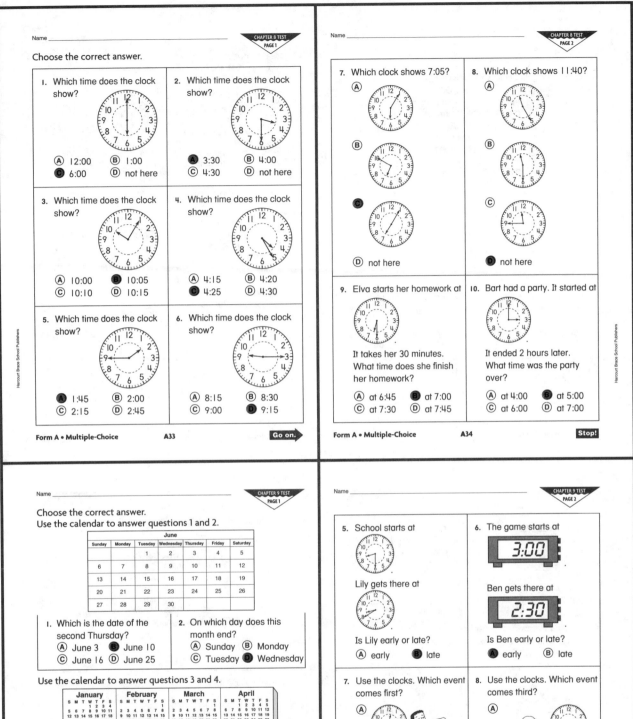

1. Which time does the clock show?
   Ⓐ 12:00   Ⓑ 1:00
   ● 6:00   Ⓓ not here

2. Which time does the clock show?
   ● 3:30   Ⓑ 4:00
   Ⓒ 4:30   Ⓓ not here

3. Which time does the clock show?
   Ⓐ 10:00   ● 10:05
   Ⓒ 10:10   Ⓓ 10:15

4. Which time does the clock show?
   ● 4:15   Ⓑ 4:20
   Ⓒ 4:25   Ⓓ 4:30

5. Which time does the clock show?
   ● 1:45   Ⓑ 2:00
   Ⓒ 2:15   Ⓓ 2:45

6. Which time does the clock show?
   Ⓐ 8:15   Ⓑ 8:30
   Ⓒ 9:00   ● 9:15

Form A • Multiple-Choice   A33   Go on.

7. Which clock shows 7:05?
   Ⓐ
   Ⓑ
   ●
   Ⓓ not here

8. Which clock shows 11:40?
   Ⓐ
   Ⓑ
   Ⓒ
   ● not here

9. Elva starts her homework at

   It takes her 30 minutes. What time does she finish her homework?
   Ⓐ at 6:45   ● at 7:00
   Ⓒ at 7:30   Ⓓ at 7:45

10. Bart had a party. It started at

   It ended 2 hours later. What time was the party over?
   Ⓐ at 4:00   ● at 5:00
   Ⓒ at 6:00   Ⓓ at 7:00

Form A • Multiple-Choice   A34   Stop!

Choose the correct answer.
Use the calendar to answer questions 1 and 2.

June						
Sunday	Monday	Tuesday	Wednesday	Thursday	Friday	Saturday
		1	2	3	4	5
6	7	8	9	10	11	12
13	14	15	16	17	18	19
20	21	22	23	24	25	26
27	28	29	30			

1. Which is the date of the second Thursday?
   Ⓐ June 3   ● June 10
   Ⓒ June 16   Ⓓ June 25

2. On which day does this month end?
   Ⓐ Sunday   Ⓑ Monday
   Ⓒ Tuesday   ● Wednesday

Use the calendar to answer questions 3 and 4.

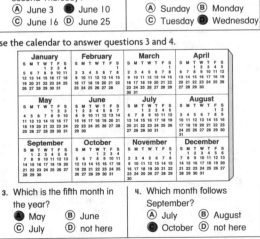

3. Which is the fifth month in the year?
   ● May   Ⓑ June
   Ⓒ July   Ⓓ not here

4. Which month follows September?
   Ⓐ July   Ⓑ August
   ● October   Ⓓ not here

Form A • Multiple-Choice   A35   Go on.

5. School starts at

   Lily gets there at

   Is Lily early or late?
   Ⓐ early   ● late

6. The game starts at
   3:00

   Ben gets there at
   2:30

   Is Ben early or late?
   ● early   Ⓑ late

7. Use the clocks. Which event comes first?

   Ⓐ
   ●
   Ⓒ

8. Use the clocks. Which event comes third?
   Ⓐ
   ●
   Ⓒ

Form A • Multiple-Choice   A36   Go on.

Use the schedule to answer questions 9 to 12.

Camp Schedule

9:00 – 10:00	Team Games
10:00 – 11:30	Swimming
11:30 – 12:00	Camp Meeting
12:00 – 1:00	Lunch
1:00 – 1:30	Hiking
1:30 – 2:30	Art
2:30 – 3:00	Song Time
3:00	Bus Time

9. What time does swimming end?

Ⓐ 11:30   Ⓑ 12:00
Ⓒ 1:00   Ⓓ not here

10. How long is the camp meeting?

Ⓐ 45 minutes   Ⓑ 1 hour
Ⓒ 2 hours   Ⓓ not here

11. How long is lunch?

Ⓐ 30 minutes   Ⓑ 1 hour
Ⓒ 2 hours   Ⓓ not here

12. What time does art begin?

Ⓐ 1:00   Ⓑ 1:30
Ⓒ 2:00   Ⓓ 2:30

Form A • Multiple-Choice   A37   **Stop!**

Choose the correct answer.

1. Count on. Which is the total amount?

Ⓐ 4¢   Ⓑ 20¢
Ⓒ 25¢   Ⓓ 40¢

6-A.1

2. Count on. Which is the total amount?

Ⓐ 55¢   Ⓑ 30¢
Ⓒ 25¢   Ⓓ 15¢

6-A.1

3. Which is the total amount?

Ⓐ 40¢   Ⓑ 50¢
Ⓒ 65¢   Ⓓ not here

6-A.1

4. Which group uses fewer coins to show the same amount?

Ⓐ

Ⓑ

7-A.1

Form A • Multiple-Choice   A38   **Go on.**

---

5. You have 25¢.
You buy

[22¢]

23¢ ___ ¢ ___ ¢
Your change is ___.

Ⓐ 3¢   Ⓑ 4¢
Ⓒ 5¢   Ⓓ 6¢

7-A.3

6. Tina saved 1 half-dollar, 1 dime, and 2 pennies. How much money did she save in all?

Ⓐ 37¢   Ⓑ 52¢
Ⓒ 62¢   Ⓓ 77¢

7-A.1

7. Which time does the clock show?

Ⓐ 6:10   Ⓑ 6:15
Ⓒ 6:20   Ⓓ 6:25

8-A.1

8. Which time does the clock show?

Ⓐ 3:45   Ⓑ 4:45
Ⓒ 5:00   Ⓓ 5:15

8-A.1

9. Lil went to a picnic. It started at

It ended 3 hours later.
What time was the picnic over?

Ⓐ at 3:00   Ⓑ at 4:00
Ⓒ at 5:00   Ⓓ at 6:00

8-A.2

10. The class starts at

[2:00]

Dave gets there at

[1:30]

Is Dave early or late?

Ⓐ early   Ⓑ late

9-A.2

Form A • Multiple-Choice   A39   **Go on.**

Use the schedule to answer questions 11 and 12.

Team Sports Day

8:30 – 10:00	Soccer
10:30 – 12:00	Kickball
12:00 – 1:00	Lunch
1:30 – 2:00	Rest
2:30 – 3:30	Baseball

11. What time does kickball start?

Ⓐ 8:30
Ⓑ 10:00
Ⓒ 10:30
Ⓓ not here

9-A.4

12. How long is the baseball game?

Ⓐ 30 minutes
Ⓑ 1 hour
Ⓒ 2 hours
Ⓓ not here

9-A.4

13. How long is the rest period?

Ⓐ 30 minutes
Ⓑ 1 hour
Ⓒ 2 hours
Ⓓ not here

9-A.4

14. What time does baseball end?

Ⓐ 8:30
Ⓑ 10:00
Ⓒ 1:30
Ⓓ 3:30

9-A.4

Form A • Multiple-Choice   A40   **Stop!**

Multiple Choice

Name _____

Choose the correct answer.

1.
```
   5
   7
 + 5
```
Ⓐ 16   Ⓑ 17
Ⓒ 18   Ⓓ 19
1-A.2

2.
```
   6
   4
 + 5
```
Ⓐ 15   Ⓑ 16
Ⓒ 17   Ⓓ 18
1-A.2

3. 14 − 6 = ___
Ⓐ 7   Ⓑ 8
Ⓒ 9   Ⓓ 10
2-A.2

4. 18 − 9 = ___
Ⓐ 8   Ⓑ 9
Ⓒ 10   Ⓓ 11
2-A.2

5. There were 3 big cats and 9 little cats in a barn. How many cats were in the barn?
Ⓐ 6 cats   Ⓑ 11 cats
Ⓒ 12 cats   Ⓓ 13 cats
2-A.3

6. There were 11 birds in a tree. Then 7 birds left. How many birds were still in the tree?
Ⓐ 7 birds   Ⓑ 6 birds
Ⓒ 5 birds   Ⓓ 4 birds
2-A.3

7. Count by fives. Which number comes next?
25, 30, 35, 40, ___
Ⓐ 41   Ⓑ 45
Ⓒ 46   Ⓓ 50
4-A.1

8. Which rule will help you find the missing numbers?
33, 36, ___, 42, 45
Ⓐ Count by twos.
Ⓑ Count by threes.
Ⓒ Count by fives.
Ⓓ Count by tens.
4-A.3

Form A • Multiple-Choice   A41   **Chapters 1–9**   Go on.

Name _____

9. Count back by tens. Which number comes next?
64, 54, 44, 34, ___
Ⓐ 35   Ⓑ 32
Ⓒ 30   Ⓓ 24
4-A.1

10. Even or odd?
7
Ⓐ even   Ⓑ odd
4-A.2

11. Which sign goes in the circle?
12 ◯ 9
Ⓐ <   Ⓑ >
5-A.1

12. Which number is between?
69, ___, 71
Ⓐ 68   Ⓑ 72
Ⓒ 81   Ⓓ not here
5-A.2

Use the pictures below to answer questions 13 and 14.

first 1st   second 2nd   third 3rd   fourth 4th   fifth 5th   sixth 6th   seventh 7th   eighth 8th

13. Which is the position of the ?
Ⓐ first   Ⓑ third
Ⓒ fifth   Ⓓ seventh
5-A.3

14. Which is the position of the ?
Ⓐ 1st   Ⓑ 2nd
Ⓒ 4th   Ⓓ not here
5-A.3

Form A • Multiple-Choice   A42   **Chapters 1–9**   Go on.

Name _____

15. Count on. Which is the total amount?
Ⓐ 7¢   Ⓑ 12¢
Ⓒ 25¢   Ⓓ 27¢
6-A.1

16. You have 50¢. You buy 47¢.
Your change is __?__.
Ⓐ 1¢   Ⓑ 2¢
Ⓒ 3¢   Ⓓ 4¢
7-A.3

17. Which group of coins will buy 55¢ ?
Ⓐ
Ⓑ
Ⓒ
6-A.2

18. Which toy could you buy with this group of coins?
Ⓐ 90¢
Ⓑ 89¢
Ⓒ 85¢
7-A.2

Form A • Multiple-Choice   A43   **Chapters 1–9**   Go on.

Name _____

19. Which time does the clock show
Ⓐ 11:00   Ⓑ 11:05
Ⓒ 11:10   Ⓓ 11:15
8-A.1

20. Which time does the clock show
Ⓐ 5:15   Ⓑ 5:30
Ⓒ 6:10   Ⓓ 6:15
8-A.1

Use the calendar to answer questions 21 and 22.

May						
Sunday	Monday	Tuesday	Wednesday	Thursday	Friday	Saturday
				1	2	3
4	5	6	7	8	9	10
11	12	13	14	15	16	17
18	19	20	21	22	23	24
25	26	27	28	29	30	31

21. On which day does this month begin?
Ⓐ Sunday   Ⓑ Monday
Ⓒ Tuesday   Ⓓ Thursday
9-A.1

22. Which is the date of the third Friday?
Ⓐ May 9   Ⓑ May 16
Ⓒ May 23   Ⓓ May 30
9-A.1

Use the schedule to answer questions 23 and 24.

Camp Schedule

23. What time does the hike end?
Ⓐ 9:30   Ⓑ 10:30
Ⓒ 11:30   Ⓓ not here
9-A.4

24. How long is lunch?
Ⓐ 30 minutes
Ⓑ 45 minutes
Ⓒ 1 hour
Ⓓ 2 hours
9-A.4

Form A • Multiple-Choice   A44   **Chapters 1–9**   Go on.

Multiple Choice

Name _____

Choose the correct answer.
Use base-ten blocks to answer questions 1 and 2.

1. $9 + 4 = 13$ ones

How many tens and ones?
- (A) 1 ten   3 ones ●
- (B) 1 ten   4 ones
- (C) 3 tens   4 ones
- (D) 3 tens   9 ones

2. $5 + 3 = 8$ ones

How many tens and ones?
- (A) 0 tens   5 ones
- (B) 0 tens   8 ones ●
- (C) 8 tens   3 ones
- (D) 8 tens   5 ones

3. $15 + 6$

How many in all?
- (A) 11   (B) 19
- (C) 21 ●   (D) 29

4. $13 + 7$

How many in all?
- (A) 10   (B) 20 ●
- (C) 23   (D) 30

5. $12 + 14$

How many in all?
- (A) 26 ●   (B) 28
- (C) 30   (D) 36

6. $17 + 18$

How many in all?
- (A) 11   (B) 25
- (C) 29   (D) 35 ●

Form A • Multiple-Choice   A45   Go on.

Name _____

7.

tens	ones
2	2
+ 1	9

- (A) 31   (B) 37
- (C) 41 ●   (D) 47

8.

tens	ones
2	5
+ 1	3

- (A) 38 ●   (B) 42
- (C) 48   (D) 52

Make a model to answer questions 9 and 10.

9. The library has 18 books on trains and 14 books on airplanes. How many books does the library have about trains and airplanes?

tens	ones
1	8
+ 1	4

- (A) 22 books   (B) 31 books
- (C) 32 books ●   (D) 42 books

10. There are 16 boys and 13 girls in Ms. Wong's class. How many children are in Ms. Wong's class?

tens	ones
1	6
+ 1	3

- (A) 3 children   (B) 19 children
- (C) 23 children   (D) not here ●

Form A • Multiple-Choice   A46   Stop!

Name _____

Choose the correct answer.
Use base-ten blocks to answer questions 1 and 2.
Add. Regroup if you need to.

1.

tens	ones
2	5
+	6

- (A) 29   (B) 30
- (C) 31 ●   (D) 32

2.

tens	ones
1	4
+ 1	6

- (A) 20   (B) 28
- (C) 29   (D) 30 ●

3.

tens	ones
1	9
+	3

- (A) 22 ●   (B) 23
- (C) 32   (D) not here

4.

tens	ones
3	6
+	8

- (A) 34   (B) 36
- (C) 44 ●   (D) not here

5.

tens	ones
5	3
+ 1	5

- (A) 62   (B) 68 ●
- (C) 72   (D) not here

6.

tens	ones
4	7
+ 1	9

- (A) 56   (B) 59
- (C) 62   (D) not here ●

7. $45 + 28$
- (A) 53   (B) 63
- (C) 68   (D) 73 ●

8. $22 + 39$
- (A) 51   (B) 61 ●
- (C) 71   (D) not here

Form A • Multiple-Choice   A47   Go on.

Name _____

9. $66 + 9$
- (A) 75 ●   (B) 77
- (C) 85   (D) not here

10. $59 + 24$
- (A) 73   (B) 75
- (C) 83 ●   (D) not here

11. The children in two classes collected cans. One class collected 27 cans. The other class collected 38 cans. How many cans did the two classes collect?
- (A) 11 cans
- (B) 55 cans
- (C) 65 cans ●
- (D) 515 cans

12. On Saturday, Fred made 28 cookies. On Sunday, he made 21 cookies. How many cookies did he make in all?
- (A) 49 cookies ●
- (B) 51 cookies
- (C) 59 cookies
- (D) 61 cookies

13. Rosie planted 16 flowers in her garden. It took her 10 minutes on Monday and 25 minutes on Tuesday. How many minutes did she work?
- (A) 26 minutes
- (B) 35 minutes ●
- (C) 41 minutes
- (D) 51 minutes

14. Mr. Allen's class planted 31 corn seeds and 39 bean seeds. They raked for 20 minutes. How many seeds did they plant?
- (A) 59 seeds
- (B) 60 seeds
- (C) 70 seeds ●
- (D) 90 seeds

Form A • Multiple-Choice   A48   Stop!

Harcourt Brace School Publishers

Multiple Choice

Choose the correct answer.

1. $17 + 11$

How many in all?
- (A) 18
- (B) 28
- (C) 37
- (D) 38

10-A.1

2. $16 + 15$

How many in all?
- (A) 21
- (B) 26
- (C) 31
- (D) 41

10-A.1

Make a model to answer questions 3 and 4.

3. Troy saw one train with 19 boxcars and another train with 16 boxcars. How many boxcars did Troy see?

tens	ones
1	9
+ 1	6

- (A) 35 boxcars
- (B) 36 boxcars
- (C) 45 boxcars
- (D) 96 boxcars

10-A.2

4. There are 17 blue marbles and 12 green marbles in Julie's bag. How many marbles are in Julie's bag?

tens	ones
1	7
+ 1	2

- (A) 5 marbles
- (B) 19 marbles
- (C) 29 marbles
- (D) not here

10-A.2

5.

tens	ones
□	
3	8
+	3

- (A) 41
- (B) 57
- (C) 61
- (D) not here

11-A.1

6.

tens	ones
□	
5	8
+ 2	6

- (A) 74
- (B) 76
- (C) 84
- (D) not here

11-A.1

7. $43 + 8$
- (A) 45
- (B) 48
- (C) 61
- (D) not here

11-A.1

8. $68 + 27$
- (A) 85
- (B) 95
- (C) 96
- (D) not here

11-A.1

9. Luis played with his new game 25 minutes on Friday and 17 minutes on Monday. He did not play on Saturday. How many minutes did Luis play the game?
- (A) 30 minutes
- (B) 32 minutes
- (C) 40 minutes
- (D) 42 minutes

11-A.2

10. Lynn baked 49 chocolate cookies and 29 sugar cookies. It took her 3 hours. Lynn ate 2 of the cookies. How many cookies did she bake?
- (A) 20 cookies
- (B) 60 cookies
- (C) 78 cookies
- (D) 88 cookies

11-A.2

Choose the correct answer.

1.
$$\begin{array}{r} 3 \\ 6 \\ +3 \\ \hline \end{array}$$
- (A) 9
- (B) 10
- (C) 11
- (D) 12

1-A.2

2. Which is the missing addend?

$5 + \_\_ = 12$
- (A) 5
- (B) 6
- (C) 7
- (D) not here

2-A.1

3. How many tens and ones are there?
- (A) 2 tens 6 ones = 26
- (B) 4 tens 8 ones = 48
- (C) 6 tens 8 ones = 68
- (D) 8 tens 4 ones = 84

3-A.1

4. Count back by tens. Which number comes next?

$95, 85, 75, 65, \_\_$
- (A) 55
- (B) 56
- (C) 64
- (D) 66

4-A.1

5. Which number is between?

$34, \_\_, 36$
- (A) 33
- (B) 37
- (C) 45
- (D) not here

5-A.2

6. Count on. Which is the total amount?
- (A) 3¢
- (B) 20¢
- (C) 25¢
- (D) 30¢

6-A.1

---

7. Dave saved 1 half-dollar, 1 nickel, and 4 pennies. How much money did he save in all?
- (A) 55¢
- (B) 57¢
- (C) 59¢
- (D) 90¢

7-A.1

8. Suzi went to a party. It started at

It ended 2 hours later. What time was the party over?
- (A) at 3:00
- (B) at 4:00
- (C) at 5:00
- (D) at 6:00

8-A.2

9. The movie starts at

Lucy gets there at

Is Lucy early or late?
- (A) early
- (B) late

9-A.2

10. Lunch starts at

12:30

Billy gets there at

11:45

Is Billy early or late?
- (A) early
- (B) late

9-A.2

Multiple Choice

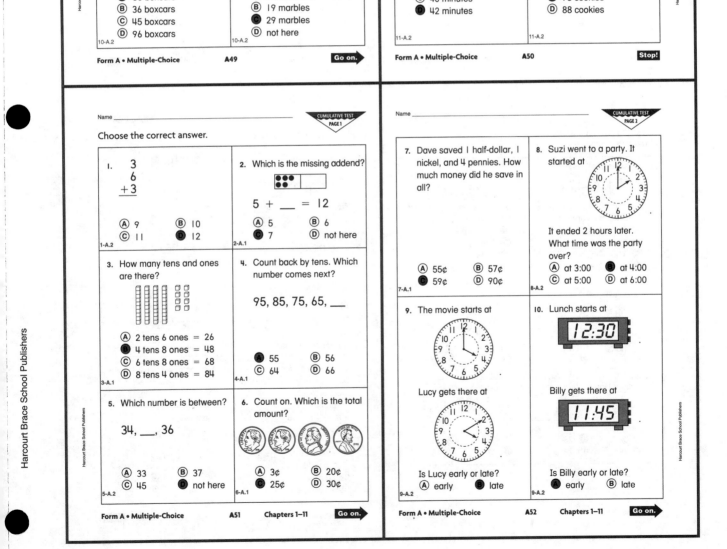

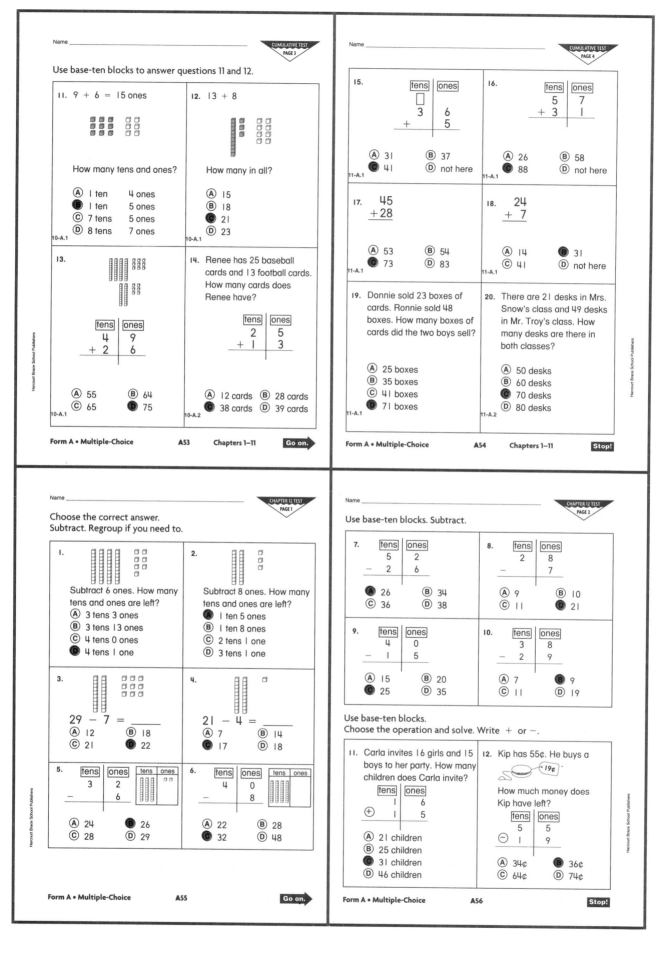

Use base-ten blocks to answer questions 11 and 12.

11. 9 + 6 = 15 ones

How many tens and ones?

Ⓐ 1 ten   4 ones
● 1 ten   5 ones
Ⓒ 7 tens   5 ones
Ⓓ 8 tens   7 ones

10-A.1

12. 13 + 8

How many in all?

Ⓐ 15
Ⓑ 18
● 21
Ⓓ 23

10-A.1

13.

tens	ones
4	9
+ 2	6

Ⓐ 55   Ⓑ 64
● 65   ● 75

10-A.1

14. Renee has 25 baseball cards and 13 football cards. How many cards does Renee have?

tens	ones
2	5
+ 1	3

Ⓐ 12 cards   Ⓑ 28 cards
● 38 cards   Ⓓ 39 cards

10-A.2

Form A • Multiple-Choice   A53   Chapters 1–11   **Go on.**

15.

tens	ones
☐ 3	6
+	5

Ⓐ 31   Ⓑ 37
● 41   Ⓓ not here

11-A.1

16.

tens	ones
5	7
+ 3	1

Ⓐ 26   Ⓑ 58
● 88   Ⓓ not here

11-A.1

17. 45
+ 28

Ⓐ 53   Ⓑ 54
● 73   Ⓓ 83

11-A.1

18. 24
+ 7

Ⓐ 14   ● 31
Ⓒ 41   Ⓓ not here

11-A.1

19. Donnie sold 23 boxes of cards. Ronnie sold 48 boxes. How many boxes of cards did the two boys sell?

Ⓐ 25 boxes
Ⓑ 35 boxes
Ⓒ 41 boxes
● 71 boxes

11-A.1

20. There are 21 desks in Mrs. Snow's class and 49 desks in Mr. Troy's class. How many desks are there in both classes?

Ⓐ 50 desks
Ⓑ 60 desks
● 70 desks
Ⓓ 80 desks

11-A.2

Form A • Multiple-Choice   A54   Chapters 1–11   **Stop!**

Choose the correct answer.
Subtract. Regroup if you need to.

1. Subtract 6 ones. How many tens and ones are left?
Ⓐ 3 tens 3 ones
Ⓑ 3 tens 13 ones
Ⓒ 4 tens 0 ones
● 4 tens 1 one

2. Subtract 8 ones. How many tens and ones are left?
● 1 ten 5 ones
Ⓑ 1 ten 8 ones
Ⓒ 2 tens 1 one
Ⓓ 3 tens 1 one

3. 29 − 7 = _____
Ⓐ 12   Ⓑ 18
Ⓒ 21   ● 22

4. 21 − 4 = _____
Ⓐ 7   Ⓑ 14
● 17   Ⓓ 18

5.

tens	ones
3	2
−	6

Ⓐ 24   ● 26
Ⓒ 28   Ⓓ 29

6.

tens	ones
4	0
−	8

Ⓐ 22   Ⓑ 28
● 32   Ⓓ 48

Form A • Multiple-Choice   A55   **Go on.**

Use base-ten blocks. Subtract.

7.

tens	ones
5	2
− 2	6

● 26   Ⓑ 34
Ⓒ 36   Ⓓ 38

8.

tens	ones
2	8
−	7

Ⓐ 9   Ⓑ 10
Ⓒ 11   ● 21

9.

tens	ones
4	0
−	15

Ⓐ 15   Ⓑ 20
● 25   Ⓓ 35

10.

tens	ones
3	8
− 2	9

Ⓐ 7   ● 9
Ⓒ 11   Ⓓ 19

Use base-ten blocks.
Choose the operation and solve. Write + or −.

11. Carla invites 16 girls and 15 boys to her party. How many children does Carla invite?

tens	ones
1	6
⊕ 1	5

Ⓐ 21 children
Ⓑ 25 children
● 31 children
Ⓓ 46 children

12. Kip has 55¢. He buys a ⬡ 19¢

How much money does Kip have left?

tens	ones
5	5
⊖ 1	9

Ⓐ 34¢   ● 36¢
Ⓒ 64¢   Ⓓ 74¢

Form A • Multiple-Choice   A56   **Stop!**

Multiple Choice

Harcourt Brace School Publishers

Name _____

Choose the correct answer.
Subtract. Regroup if you need to.

1.
tens	ones
3	2
−	7

(A) 19 (B) 23
(C) 25 (D) 29

2.
tens	ones
8	1
−	9

(A) 70 (B) 72
(C) 75 (D) 78

3.
tens	ones
7	7
− 2	7

(A) 40 (B) 45
(C) 47 (D) 50

4.
tens	ones
5	3
− 2	5

(A) 22 (B) 28
(C) 32 (D) 38

5.
82
−43

(A) 31 (B) 39
(C) 41 (D) 49

6.
56
−48

(A) 8 (B) 12
(C) 14 (D) 18

Form A • Multiple-Choice   A57   Go on.

Name _____

7.
41
−18

(A) 23 (B) 27
(C) 37 (D) 59

8.
79
−37

(A) 32 (B) 36
(C) 38 (D) 42

9. Which numbers should you add to check this subtraction problem?
73
−57
16

(A) 16
+57
(B) 16
+73
(C) 73
+57
(D) 57
+57

10. Which numbers should you add to check this subtraction problem?
42
−18
24

(A) 24
+42
(B) 42
+18
(C) 24
+18
(D) 24
+24

Choose the operation and solve. Write + or −.

11. You have 65¢. You buy [whistle 29¢]. How much do you have left?
65¢
⊖29¢

(A) 36¢ (B) 46¢
(C) 84¢ (D) 94¢

12. How much money would you need to buy [car 58¢] and [balloon 12¢]?
58¢
⊕12¢

(A) 46¢ (B) 60¢
(C) 70¢ (D) 76¢

Form A • Multiple-Choice   A58   Stop!

Name _____

Choose the correct answer.

1.
tens	ones
4	3
−	7

(A) 34 (B) 35
(C) 36 (D) 46
12-A.1

2.
tens	ones
2	0
−	6

(A) 14 (B) 16
(C) 24 (D) 26
12-A.1

3.
tens	ones
5	5
− 3	8

(A) 16 (B) 17
(C) 23 (D) 27
12-A.1

4.
tens	ones
3	9
−	4

(A) 5 (B) 25
(C) 33 (D) 35
12-A.1

Choose the operation and solve. Write + or −.

5. Dan sees 15 blue birds and 17 red birds in a tree. How many birds does Dan see?
tens	ones
1	5
⊕ 1	7

(A) 22 birds (B) 32 birds
(C) 33 birds (D) 42 birds
12-A.2

6. Lily has 41¢. She buys a [star 18¢]. How much money does Lily have left?
tens	ones
4	1
⊖ 1	8

(A) 3¢ (B) 13¢
(C) 23¢ (D) 49¢
12-A.2

Form A • Multiple-Choice   A59   Go on.

Name _____

7.
tens	ones
6	6
− 3	6

(A) 20 (B) 30
(C) 31 (D) 36
13-A.1

8.
tens	ones
5	2
− 2	3

(A) 21 (B) 25
(C) 26 (D) 29
13-A.1

9.
75
−67

(A) 8 (B) 12
(C) 17 (D) 22
13-A.1

10.
77
−32

(A) 35 (B) 39
(C) 44 (D) 45
13-A.1

Choose the operation and solve. Write + or −.

11. You have 97¢. You buy a [rocking horse 49¢]. How much do you have left?
97¢
⊖49¢

(A) 25¢ (B) 48¢
(C) 49¢ (D) 52¢
13-A.2

12. How much money would you need to buy [notebook 46¢] and [coloring fun 14¢]?
46¢
⊕14¢

(A) 32¢ (B) 50¢
(C) 59¢ (D) 60¢
13-A.2

Form A • Multiple-Choice   A60   Stop!

Harcourt Brace School Publishers

Multiple Choice   141

Choose the correct answer.

1. Which group uses fewer coins to show the same amount?

Ⓐ

Ⓑ

7-A.1

2. Which group uses fewer coins to show the same amount?

Ⓐ

Ⓑ

7-A.1

3. Which coins give you enough money to buy CRACKERS 75¢ ?

Ⓐ 2 quarters, 1 dime
Ⓑ 5 dimes, 3 nickels
Ⓒ 3 quarters
Ⓓ 2 quarters, 4 nickels, 3 pennies

7-A.1

4. Which coins give you enough money to buy 🍎 40¢ ?

Ⓐ 1 quarter, 5 pennies
Ⓑ 3 dimes, 1 nickel
Ⓒ 4 nickels, 10 pennies
Ⓓ 1 quarter, 1 dime, 1 nickel

7-A.1

---

5. Which time does the clock show?

Ⓐ 4:30   Ⓑ 5:00
Ⓒ 5:30   Ⓓ not here

8-A.1

6. Subtract 4 ones. How many tens and ones are left?

Ⓐ 3 tens 12 ones
Ⓑ 3 tens 4 ones
Ⓒ 4 tens 3 ones
Ⓓ 4 tens 4 ones

12-A.1

7.

$45 - 3 =$ ___

Ⓐ 15   Ⓑ 23
Ⓒ 41   Ⓓ 42

12-A.1

8.

tens	ones
2	0
−	6

Ⓐ 4   Ⓑ 8
Ⓒ 14   Ⓓ 26

12-A.1

9.

tens	ones
4	1
−1	4

Ⓐ 27   Ⓑ 35
Ⓒ 37   Ⓓ 55

12-A.1

10.

tens	ones
6	0
−2	5

Ⓐ 25   Ⓑ 35
Ⓒ 45   Ⓓ 85

12-A.1

Choose the operation and solve. Write $+$ or $-$.

11. There are 18 girls and 13 boys in Mara's class. How many children are in Mara's class?

tens	ones
1	8
⊕ 1	3

Ⓐ 15 children
Ⓑ 25 children
Ⓒ 31 children
Ⓓ 35 children

12-A.2

12. Alice has 75¢. She buys a 🥪 59¢.

How much money does Alice have left?

tens	ones
7	5
⊖ 5	9

Ⓐ 16¢   Ⓑ 24¢
Ⓒ 34¢   Ⓓ 54¢

12-A.2

Subtract. Regroup if you need to.

13.

tens	ones
3	4
−	5

Ⓐ 21   Ⓑ 29
Ⓒ 31   Ⓓ 39

13-A.1

14.

tens	ones
7	1
− 5	3

Ⓐ 18   Ⓑ 22
Ⓒ 24   Ⓓ 28

13-A.1

15.

$62 - 25$

Ⓐ 47   Ⓑ 43
Ⓒ 37   Ⓓ 33

13-A.1

16.

$87 - 43$

Ⓐ 44   Ⓑ 43
Ⓒ 40   Ⓓ 34

13-A.1

17. Which numbers should you add to check this subtraction problem?

$91 - 65 = 26$

Ⓐ 26 + 91   Ⓑ 26 + 65
Ⓒ 65 + 91   Ⓓ 26 + 26

13-A.1

18. Which numbers should you add to check this subtraction problem?

$62 - 26 = 36$

Ⓐ 62 + 36   Ⓑ 26 + 26
Ⓒ 62 + 26   Ⓓ 26 + 36

13-A.1

Choose the operation. Write $+$ or $-$.

19. You have 75¢. You buy 🚚 59¢.

How much do you have left?

75¢
⊖59¢

Ⓐ 14¢   Ⓑ 16¢
Ⓒ 24¢   Ⓓ 26¢

13-A.2

20. How much money would you need to buy 24¢ ✏️ and 📓 ?

36¢
⊕24¢

Ⓐ 12¢   Ⓑ 60¢
Ⓒ 62¢   Ⓓ 70¢

13-A.2

Multiple Choice

Choose the correct answer.
Use the picture to answer questions 1 and 2.

1. Which tally marks show how many dogs there are?
   (A) ‖
   (B) ‖‖
   (C) ‖‖‖
   (D) ‖‖‖ ‖

2. Which tally marks show how many bears there are?
   (A) ‖
   (B) ‖‖
   (C) ‖‖‖
   (D) ‖‖‖ ‖

Max asked classmates about their pets.
The tally table shows what he found.
Use the table to answer questions 3 and 4.

Kinds of Pets	Tally Marks	Totals
dogs	‖	2
cats	‖‖‖	5
fish	‖	2
birds	‖	1

3. How many children have fish for pets?
   (A) 2   (B) 7
   (C) 9   (D) 10

4. Which animal do most children have as a pet?
   (A) cats   (B) dogs
   (C) fish   (D) birds

Use the table to answer questions 5 to 8.

Number of Children Absent on Monday	Tally Marks	Totals
Ms. Wilson's Class	‖‖	4
Mr. Wang's Class	‖	2
Ms. Johnson's Class	‖‖‖	5
Ms. King's Class	‖‖	4

5. In which two classes were the same number of children absent?
   (A) Ms. Wilson's and Mr. Wang's
   (B) Mr. Wang's and Ms. Johnson's
   (C) Ms. Johnson's and Ms. King's
   (D) Ms. Wilson's and Ms. King's

6. How many more children were absent from Ms. Johnson's class than from Mr. Wang's?
   (A) 1 more child
   (B) 2 more children
   (C) 3 more children
   (D) 5 more children

7. How many children in all were absent?
   (A) 12 children
   (B) 13 children
   (C) 14 children
   (D) 15 children

8. In which class were the most children absent?
   (A) Ms. King's class
   (B) Ms. Johnson's class
   (C) Mr. Wang's class
   (D) Ms. Wilson's class

Use the tables to answer questions 9 to 12.

Favorite Seasons in Room 21	Tally Marks	Totals
fall	‖‖‖ ‖	7
winter	‖‖‖ ‖‖	8
spring	‖‖‖ ‖	6
summer	‖‖‖ ‖‖‖	10

Favorite Seasons in Room 22	Tally Marks	Totals
fall	‖‖‖ ‖	7
winter	‖‖‖ ‖‖	9
spring	‖‖‖	5
summer	‖‖‖ ‖‖‖	10

9. In which room do more children like spring best?
   (A) Room 21
   (B) Room 22
   (C) Both rooms are the same.

10. In which room do more children like fall best?
    (A) Room 21
    (B) Room 22
    (C) Both rooms are the same.

11. Which season got the most votes in both rooms?
    (A) summer
    (B) fall
    (C) winter
    (D) spring

12. Which season got more votes in Room 22 than in Room 21?
    (A) fall
    (B) winter
    (C) spring
    (D) summer

Choose the correct answer.
Use the graph to answer questions 1 to 4.

Our Favorite Dinner Foods

pizza
tacos
chicken
spaghetti

0   1   2   3   4   5

1. Which is the favorite dinner food of the most people?
   (A) pizza
   (B) tacos
   (C) chicken
   (D) spaghetti

2. Which is the favorite dinner food of the fewest people?
   (A) pizza
   (B) tacos
   (C) chicken
   (D) spaghetti

3. How many more people like spaghetti than like pizza?
   (A) 1 more   (B) 2 more
   (C) 3 more   (D) 4 more

4. How many fewer people like chicken than like tacos?
   (A) 1 fewer   (B) 2 fewer
   (C) 3 fewer   (D) 4 fewer

Multiple Choice

Name _____

Use the graph to answer questions 5 to 8.

Inches of Snow in February

week 1	✳ ✳ ✳
week 2	✳ ✳
week 3	✳ ✳ ✳ ✳ ✳ ✳
week 4	✳ ✳ ✳

0 1 2 3 4 5 6

Each ✳ stands for 2 inches of snow.

5. Which week had 6 inches of snow?
 Ⓐ week 1
 Ⓑ week 2
 Ⓒ week 3
 Ⓓ week 4

6. Which week had the fewest inches of snow?
 Ⓐ week 1
 Ⓑ week 2
 Ⓒ week 3
 Ⓓ week 4

7. Which week had the most inches of snow?
 Ⓐ week 1
 Ⓑ week 2
 Ⓒ week 3
 Ⓓ week 4

8. How many inches of snow were there in week 4?
 Ⓐ 4 inches
 Ⓑ 6 inches
 Ⓒ 7 inches
 Ⓓ 8 inches

Name _____

Use the graph to answer questions 9 to 14.

Favorite Art Materials

crayons										
paints										
markers										
colored pencils										

0 1 2 3 4 5 6 7 8 9 10

9. How many people like colored pencils the best?
 Ⓐ 2 people Ⓑ 3 people
 Ⓒ 4 people **Ⓓ** 5 people

10. How many people like crayons the best?
 Ⓐ 5 people **Ⓑ** 6 people
 Ⓒ 7 people Ⓓ 8 people

11. Which art materials do the most people like the best?
 Ⓐ crayons
 Ⓑ paints
 Ⓒ markers
 Ⓓ colored pencils

12. Which art materials do the fewest people like the best?
 Ⓐ crayons
 Ⓑ paints
 Ⓒ markers
 Ⓓ colored pencils

13. How many more people like crayons than like paints the best?
 Ⓐ 1 more Ⓑ 2 more
 Ⓒ 3 more **Ⓓ** 4 more

14. How many fewer people like colored pencils than like markers the best?
 Ⓐ 1 fewer **Ⓑ** 2 fewer
 Ⓒ 3 fewer Ⓓ 4 fewer

Name _____

Choose the correct answer.
Use the picture to answer questions 1 to 4.

1. Which group of coins are you certain to find on the tray?
 Ⓐ
 Ⓑ
 Ⓒ

2. Which group of coins is impossible to find on the tray?
 Ⓐ
 Ⓑ
 Ⓒ

3. Which group of coins are you certain to find on the tray?
 Ⓐ
 Ⓑ
 Ⓒ

4. Which group of coins is impossible to find on the tray?
 Ⓐ
 Ⓑ
 Ⓒ

Name _____

Use the table to answer questions 5 and 6.
This table shows the outcomes of 10 pulls from the bag.

Shape	Tally Marks	Totals
triangle	ⅢⅡ II	7
circle	III	3

5. Which shape was pulled out more often?
 Ⓐ triangle
 Ⓑ circle

6. How many times was a circle pulled out?
 Ⓐ 2 times **Ⓑ** 3 times
 Ⓒ 5 times Ⓓ 10 times

7. In a bag there are 5 yellow tiles, 5 blue tiles, and 15 red tiles. Which color do you think will be pulled out most often?
 Ⓐ yellow
 Ⓑ blue
 Ⓒ red

8. This spinner can stop on stripes, dots, or zigzags. Which do you think it will stop on most often?
 Ⓐ stripes
 Ⓑ dots
 Ⓒ zigzags

9. From which bag do you think a cube will be pulled least often?
 Ⓐ Ⓑ
 Ⓒ Ⓓ

10. This spinner can stop on stripes, dots, or zigzags. Which do you think it will stop on least often?
 Ⓐ stripes
 Ⓑ dots
 Ⓒ zigzags

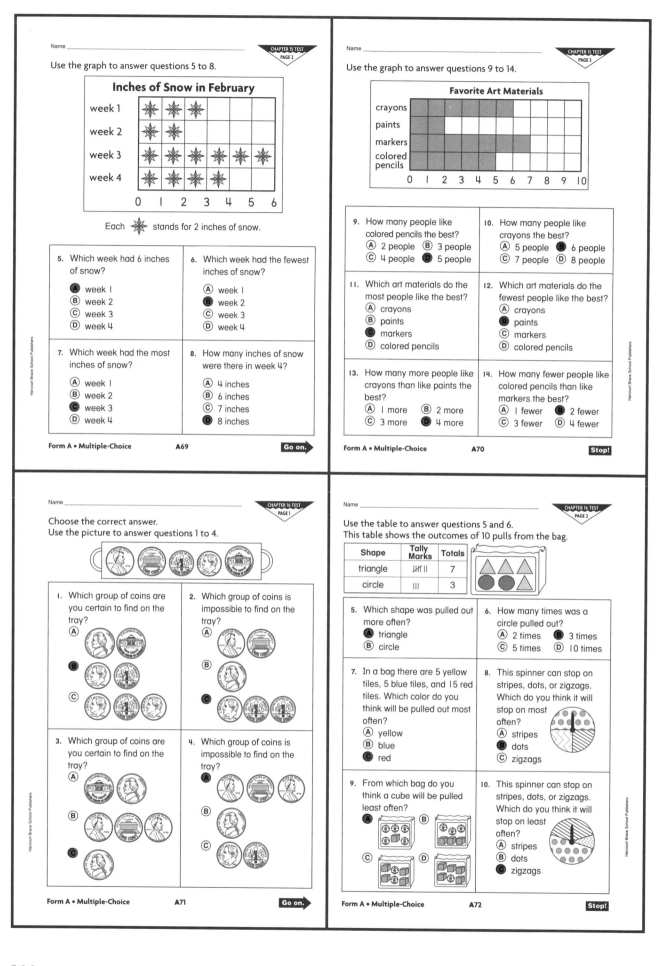

Multiple Choice

Harcourt Brace School Publishers

Choose the correct answer.
Use the tables to answer questions 1 to 4.

Favorite Story in Room 28	Tally Marks	Totals
Snow White	JHT IIII	
Bambi	JHT JHT	
Three Little Pigs	JHT	
Peter Rabbit	IIII	

Favorite Story in Room 29	Tally Marks	Totals
Snow White	JHT II	
Bambi	JHT JHT	
Three Little Pigs	JHT I	
Peter Rabbit	IIII	

1. In which room do more children like Snow White best?

  (A) Room 29
  (B) Room 28
  (C) Both rooms are the same.

14-A.1

2. In which room do more children like Peter Rabbit best?

  (A) Room 29
  (B) Room 28
  (C) Both rooms are the same.

14-A.1

3. Which story got the most votes in both rooms?

  (A) Snow White
  (B) Bambi
  (C) Three Little Pigs
  (D) Peter Rabbit

14-A.1

4. Which story got more votes in Room 29 than in Room 28?

  (A) Snow White
  (B) Bambi
  (C) Three Little Pigs
  (D) Peter Rabbit

14-A.1

Use the graph to answer questions 5 to 8.

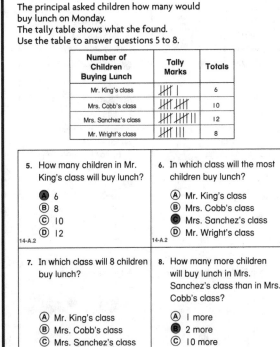

Favorite Juice

Orange / Apple / Grape / Prune

5. Which is the favorite juice of the most people?
  (A) orange (B) apple
  (C) grape (D) prune

15-A.1

6. How many more like apple than orange juice best?
  (A) 1 more (B) 2 more
  (C) 3 more (D) 4 more

15-A.1

Use the picture to answer questions 7 and 8.

7. Which group of coins are you certain to find on the tray?
  (A)
  (B)

16-A.1

8. Which group of coins is impossible to find on the tray?
  (A)
  (B)

16-A.1

Choose the correct answer.

1.
$$\begin{array}{r} 8 \\ +7 \\ \hline \end{array}$$
  (A) 8   (B) 10
  (C) 15   (D) 17

1-A.1

2. Which rule will help you find the missing numbers?

10, 20, ___, 40, 50

  (A) Count by twos.
  (B) Count by threes.
  (C) Count by fives.
  (D) Count by tens.

4-A.3

3. Jill went to a play. It started at

It ended 2 hours later. What time was the play over?
  (A) at 3:00 (B) at 4:00
  (C) at 5:00 (D) at 6:00

8-A.2

4. Mia found 16 cans on Monday and 27 cans on Friday. Mia read 2 books on Tuesday. How many cans did Mia find?

  (A) 39 cans
  (B) 43 cans
  (C) 48 cans
  (D) 52 cans

11-A.2

The principal asked children how many would buy lunch on Monday.
The tally table shows what she found.
Use the table to answer questions 5 to 8.

Number of Children Buying Lunch	Tally Marks	Totals
Mr. King's class	JHT I	6
Mrs. Cobb's class	JHT JHT	10
Mrs. Sanchez's class	JHT JHT II	12
Mr. Wright's class	JHT III	8

5. How many children in Mr. King's class will buy lunch?
  (A) 6
  (B) 8
  (C) 10
  (D) 12

14-A.2

6. In which class will the most children buy lunch?
  (A) Mr. King's class
  (B) Mrs. Cobb's class
  (C) Mrs. Sanchez's class
  (D) Mr. Wright's class

14-A.2

7. In which class will 8 children buy lunch?
  (A) Mr. King's class
  (B) Mrs. Cobb's class
  (C) Mrs. Sanchez's class
  (D) Mr. Wright's class

14-A.1

8. How many more children will buy lunch in Mrs. Sanchez's class than in Mrs. Cobb's class?
  (A) 1 more
  (B) 2 more
  (C) 10 more
  (D) 12 more

14-A.1

Multiple Choice

Use the graph to answer questions 9 and 10.

Favorite Musical Instruments

	0	1	2	3	4	5	6	7	8	9	10
piano											
drums											
guitar											
trumpet											

9. How many fewer people like drums than like guitar?

(A) 1 fewer (B) 2 fewer
(C) 3 fewer (D) 5 fewer

15-A.1

10. How many people like the trumpet the best?

(A) 3 people (B) 5 people
(C) 6 people (D) 8 people

15-A.1

Use the graph to answer questions 11 and 12.

Our Favorite Pets

bird						
cat						
dog						
hamster						

11. How many fewer people like hamsters than like cats?

(A) 1 fewer (B) 2 fewer
(C) 3 fewer (D) 4 fewer

15-A.1

12. Which is the favorite pet of the most people?

(A) bird (B) cat
(C) dog (D) hamster

15-A.2

Form A • Multiple-Choice   A77   Chapters 1–16   Go on.

Use the table to answer questions 13 and 14.
This table shows the outcomes of 10 pulls from the bag.

Shape	Tally Marks
squares	IIII I
triangles	IIII

13. Which shape was pulled out more often?

(A) square
(B) triangle

16-A.2

14. How many times was a triangle pulled out?

(A) 2 times (B) 3 times
(C) 4 times (D) 6 times

16-A.2

15. In a bag there are 2 dimes, 2 pennies, and 10 nickels. Which coin do you think will be pulled out most often?

(A) dime
(B) penny
(C) nickel

16-A.1

16. This spinner can stop on stripes, dots, or zigzags. Which do you think it will stop on most often?

(A) dots
(B) stripes
(C) zigzags

16-A.1

17. From which bag do you think a ball will be pulled most often?

(A) (B)
(C) (D)

16-A.1

18. This spinner can stop on stripes, dots, or zigzags. Which do you think it will stop on least often?

(A) stripes
(B) dots
(C) zigzags

16-A.1

Form A • Multiple-Choice   A78   Chapters 1–16   Stop!

Choose the correct answer.

1. Which object is shaped like this solid figure?

(A) (B)
(C) (D)

2. Which object is shaped like this solid figure?

(A) (B)
(C) (D)

3. Which object is shaped like this solid figure?

(A) (B)
(C) (D)

4. Which solid figure is the same shape as this solid figure?

(A) (B)
(C) (D)

5. Which solid figure has only two flat faces and can be stacked?

(A) (B)
(C) (D)

6. Which solid figure has six flat faces and can be stacked?

(A) (B)
(C) (D)

Form A • Multiple-Choice   A79   Go on.

---

7. Which solid figure has no flat faces and can roll?

(A) (B)
(C) (D)

8. Which solid figure can stack and roll?

(A) (B)
(C) (D)

9. Which solid figure is missing in the pattern?

(A) (B)

10. Which solid figure is missing in the pattern?

(A) (B)
(C)

11. Which plane figure could you trace from the solid figure?

(A) △ (B) ○
(C) ☐ (D) ▭

12. Which plane figure could you trace from the solid figure?

(A) △ (B) ○
(C) ☐ (D) ▭

Form A • Multiple-Choice   A80   Stop!

Multiple Choice

Choose the correct answer.

1. Which figure is a circle?

Ⓐ ▭ Ⓑ ▱
● Ⓒ ○ Ⓓ △

2. Which figure is a square?

Ⓐ ⬡ ● Ⓑ ▢
Ⓒ △ Ⓓ ▭

3. How many sides does this figure have?

Ⓐ 3 sides Ⓑ 4 sides
● 5 sides Ⓓ 6 sides

4. How many corners does this figure have?

Ⓐ 0 corners ● 3 corners
Ⓒ 4 corners Ⓓ 5 corners

5. Which figure has 4 sides and 4 corners?

Ⓐ △ Ⓑ ⬡
Ⓒ ⬠ ● Ⓓ ▱

6. Which figure has 6 sides and 6 corners?

Ⓐ ▭ Ⓑ ▭
● Ⓒ ⬡ Ⓓ ⬠

Form A • Multiple-Choice   A81   **Go on.**

Harcourt Brace School Publishers

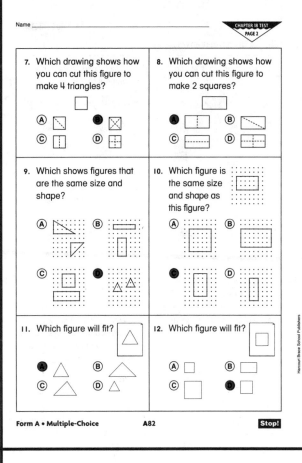

7. Which drawing shows how you can cut this figure to make 4 triangles?

8. Which drawing shows how you can cut this figure to make 2 squares?

9. Which shows figures that are the same size and shape?

10. Which figure is the same size and shape as this figure?

11. Which figure will fit?

12. Which figure will fit?

Form A • Multiple-Choice   A82   **Stop!**

Harcourt Brace School Publishers

Choose the correct answer.

1. Which picture has symmetry?

Ⓐ 🏠 Ⓑ 🚂
● Ⓒ 🧸 Ⓓ 🍂

2. Which picture does NOT have symmetry?

Ⓐ ♥ ● Ⓑ ✋
Ⓒ ◇ Ⓓ 🌲

3. Which picture has symmetry?

Ⓐ 🎩 Ⓑ
● Ⓒ 🐕 Ⓓ

4. Which picture does NOT have symmetry?

Ⓐ ♥ ● Ⓑ 🌼
Ⓒ 🦋 Ⓓ 🌳

Harcourt Brace School Publishers

Form A • Multiple-Choice   A83   **Go on.**

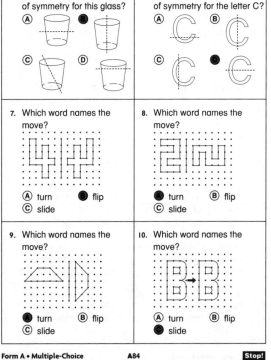

5. Which picture shows the line of symmetry for this glass?

6. Which picture shows the line of symmetry for the letter C?

7. Which word names the move?

Ⓐ turn ● Ⓑ flip
Ⓒ slide

8. Which word names the move?

● Ⓐ turn Ⓑ flip
Ⓒ slide

9. Which word names the move?

● Ⓐ turn Ⓑ flip
Ⓒ slide

10. Which word names the move?

Ⓐ turn Ⓑ flip
● Ⓒ slide

Form A • Multiple-Choice   A84   **Stop!**

Harcourt Brace School Publishers

Multiple Choice

Harcourt Brace School Publishers

Choose the correct answer.

1. Which object is shaped like this solid figure?

(A) CEREAL

(B) Tissues

(C) [basketball]

(D) DOG food

17-A.1

2. Which solid figure can slide and roll?

(A) [sphere, cube, cone, rectangular prism, triangle]

(B) [rectangular prism]

(C) [cylinder]

(D) [pyramid]

17-A.1

3. Which solid figure is missing in the pattern?

[sphere, cylinder, cone, sphere, cone, sphere ?]

(A) [sphere]

(B) [cylinder]

(C) [cone]

(D) [rectangular prism]

17-A.2

4. Which plane figure could you trace from the solid figure?

[cylinder]

(A) [square]

(B) [triangle]

(C) [rectangle]

(D) [circle]

17-A.3

5. Which figure has 5 sides and 5 corners?

(A) [pentagon]

(B) [trapezoid]

(C) [square]

(D) [hexagon]

18-A.2

6. Which drawing shows how you can cut this figure to make 4 triangles?

(A) [square divided]

(B) [square divided in grid]

(C) [square with diagonal]

(D) [square with X]

18-A.3

7. Which figure will fit?

[large square outline]

(A) [square]

(B) [smaller square]

(C) [rectangle]

(D) [small square]

18.A.4

8. Which picture shows the line of symmetry for the letter M?

(A) M [vertical line]

(B) M

(C) M [horizontal line]

(D) M [diagonal line]

19.A.1

9. Which word names the move?

[L shape figures]

(A) turn   (B) flip   (C) slide

19.A.2

10. Which word names the move?

[two triangles]

(A) turn   (B) flip   (C) slide

19.A.2

Choose the correct answer.

1. Which is the total amount?

[coins]

(A) 28¢   (B) 40¢
(C) 45¢   (D) not here

6-A.1

2. Which is the total amount?

[coins]

(A) 53¢   (B) 57¢
(C) 75¢   (D) not here

6-A.1

Use the tables to answer questions 3 and 4.

Favorite Colors in Room 24	Tally Marks	Totals
red	卌 卌	
blue	卌 I	
yellow	卌 III	
green	卌 II	

Favorite Colors in Room 25	Tally Marks	Totals
red	卌 III	
blue	卌 IIII	
yellow	卌 I	
green	卌 II	

3. In which room do more children like red best?

(A) Room 24
(B) Room 25
(C) Both rooms are the same.

14-A.1

4. In which room do more children like green best?

(A) Room 24
(B) Room 25
(C) Both rooms are the same.

14-A.1

5. Which clock shows 9:05?

(A) [clock]

(B) [clock]

(C) [clock]

(D) not here

8-A.1

6. Which clock shows 2:40?

(A) [clock]

(B) [clock]

(C) [clock]

(D) not here

8-A.1

7. Which solid figure has only two flat faces and can be rolled?

(A) [cylinder]

(B) [cube]

(C) [rectangular prism]

(D) [pyramid]

17-A.1

8. Which solid figure has no flat faces and can be rolled?

(A) [rectangular prism]

(B) [sphere]

(C) [pyramid]

(D) [cube]

17-A.1

Multiple Choice

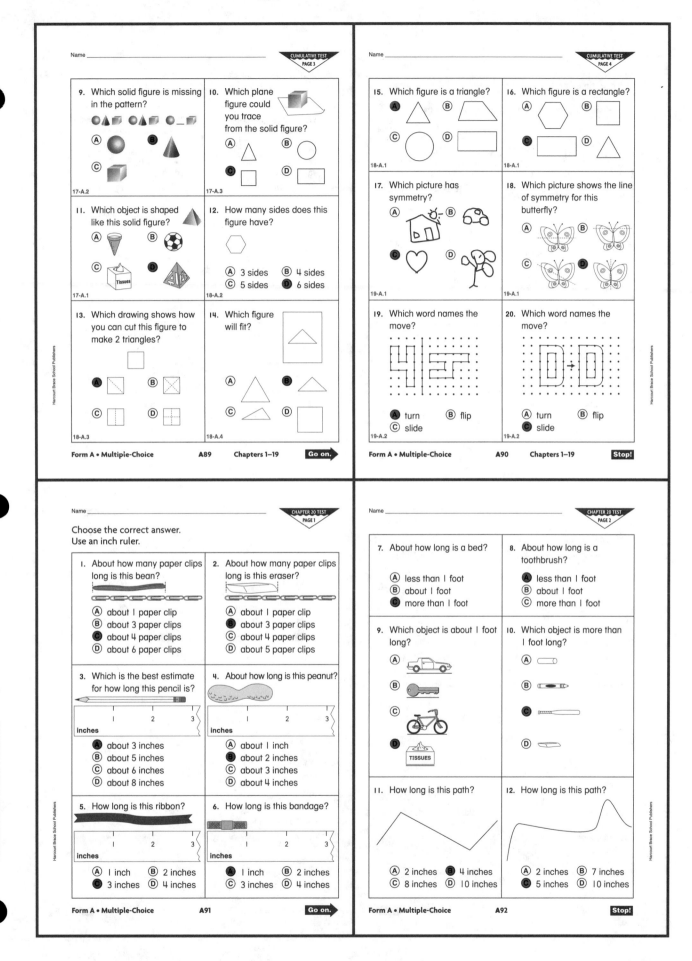

9. Which solid figure is missing in the pattern?

Ⓐ Ⓑ Ⓒ

17-A.2

10. Which plane figure could you trace from the solid figure?

Ⓐ Ⓑ Ⓒ Ⓓ

17-A.3

11. Which object is shaped like this solid figure?

Ⓐ Ⓑ Ⓒ Ⓓ

17-A.1

12. How many sides does this figure have?

Ⓐ 3 sides   Ⓑ 4 sides
Ⓒ 5 sides   Ⓓ 6 sides

18-A.2

13. Which drawing shows how you can cut this figure to make 2 triangles?

Ⓐ Ⓑ Ⓒ Ⓓ

18-A.3

14. Which figure will fit?

Ⓐ Ⓑ Ⓒ Ⓓ

18-A.4

Form A • Multiple-Choice   A89   Chapters 1–19   Go on. ▶

15. Which figure is a triangle?

Ⓐ Ⓑ Ⓒ Ⓓ

18-A.1

16. Which figure is a rectangle?

Ⓐ Ⓑ Ⓒ Ⓓ

18-A.1

17. Which picture has symmetry?

Ⓐ Ⓑ Ⓒ Ⓓ

19-A.1

18. Which picture shows the line of symmetry for this butterfly?

Ⓐ Ⓑ Ⓒ Ⓓ

19-A.1

19. Which word names the move?

Ⓐ turn   Ⓑ flip
Ⓒ slide

19-A.2

20. Which word names the move?

Ⓐ turn   Ⓑ flip
Ⓒ slide

19-A.2

Form A • Multiple-Choice   A90   Chapters 1–19   Stop!

Choose the correct answer.
Use an inch ruler.

1. About how many paper clips long is this bean?

Ⓐ about 1 paper clip
Ⓑ about 3 paper clips
Ⓒ about 4 paper clips
Ⓓ about 6 paper clips

2. About how many paper clips long is this eraser?

Ⓐ about 1 paper clip
Ⓑ about 3 paper clips
Ⓒ about 4 paper clips
Ⓓ about 5 paper clips

3. Which is the best estimate for how long this pencil is?

inches

Ⓐ about 3 inches
Ⓑ about 5 inches
Ⓒ about 6 inches
Ⓓ about 8 inches

4. About how long is this peanut?

inches

Ⓐ about 1 inch
Ⓑ about 2 inches
Ⓒ about 3 inches
Ⓓ about 4 inches

5. How long is this ribbon?

inches

Ⓐ 1 inch   Ⓑ 2 inches
Ⓒ 3 inches   Ⓓ 4 inches

6. How long is this bandage?

inches

Ⓐ 1 inch   Ⓑ 2 inches
Ⓒ 3 inches   Ⓓ 4 inches

Form A • Multiple-Choice   A91   Go on. ▶

7. About how long is a bed?

Ⓐ less than 1 foot
Ⓑ about 1 foot
Ⓒ more than 1 foot

8. About how long is a toothbrush?

Ⓐ less than 1 foot
Ⓑ about 1 foot
Ⓒ more than 1 foot

9. Which object is about 1 foot long?

Ⓐ Ⓑ Ⓒ Ⓓ

10. Which object is more than 1 foot long?

Ⓐ Ⓑ Ⓒ Ⓓ

11. How long is this path?

Ⓐ 2 inches   Ⓑ 4 inches
Ⓒ 8 inches   Ⓓ 10 inches

12. How long is this path?

Ⓐ 2 inches   Ⓑ 7 inches
Ⓒ 5 inches   Ⓓ 10 inches

Form A • Multiple-Choice   A92   Stop!

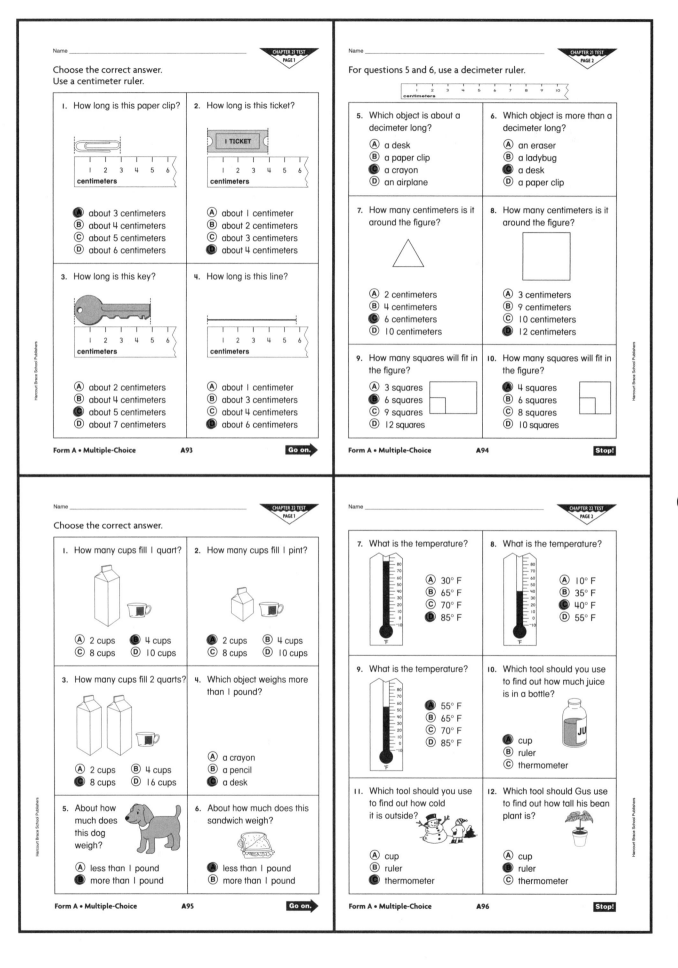

Name _____

Choose the correct answer.
Use a centimeter ruler.

1. How long is this paper clip?

centimeters

(A) about 3 centimeters
(B) about 4 centimeters
(C) about 5 centimeters
(D) about 6 centimeters

2. How long is this ticket?

I TICKET

centimeters

(A) about 1 centimeter
(B) about 2 centimeters
(C) about 3 centimeters
(D) about 4 centimeters

3. How long is this key?

centimeters

(A) about 2 centimeters
(B) about 4 centimeters
(C) about 5 centimeters
(D) about 7 centimeters

4. How long is this line?

centimeters

(A) about 1 centimeter
(B) about 3 centimeters
(C) about 4 centimeters
(D) about 6 centimeters

Form A • Multiple-Choice   A93   Go on.

Name _____

For questions 5 and 6, use a decimeter ruler.

centimeters

5. Which object is about a decimeter long?

(A) a desk
(B) a paper clip
(C) a crayon
(D) an airplane

6. Which object is more than a decimeter long?

(A) an eraser
(B) a ladybug
(C) a desk
(D) a paper clip

7. How many centimeters is it around the figure?

(A) 2 centimeters
(B) 4 centimeters
(C) 6 centimeters
(D) 10 centimeters

8. How many centimeters is it around the figure?

(A) 3 centimeters
(B) 9 centimeters
(C) 10 centimeters
(D) 12 centimeters

9. How many squares will fit in the figure?

(A) 3 squares
(B) 6 squares
(C) 9 squares
(D) 12 squares

10. How many squares will fit in the figure?

(A) 4 squares
(B) 6 squares
(C) 8 squares
(D) 10 squares

Form A • Multiple-Choice   A94   Stop!

Name _____

Choose the correct answer.

1. How many cups fill 1 quart?

(A) 2 cups   (B) 4 cups
(C) 8 cups   (D) 10 cups

2. How many cups fill 1 pint?

(A) 2 cups   (B) 4 cups
(C) 8 cups   (D) 10 cups

3. How many cups fill 2 quarts?

(A) 2 cups   (B) 4 cups
(C) 8 cups   (D) 16 cups

4. Which object weighs more than 1 pound?

(A) a crayon
(B) a pencil
(C) a desk

5. About how much does this dog weigh?

(A) less than 1 pound
(B) more than 1 pound

6. About how much does this sandwich weigh?

(A) less than 1 pound
(B) more than 1 pound

Form A • Multiple-Choice   A95   Go on.

Name _____

7. What is the temperature?

(A) 30° F
(B) 65° F
(C) 70° F
(D) 85° F

8. What is the temperature?

(A) 10° F
(B) 35° F
(C) 40° F
(D) 55° F

9. What is the temperature?

(A) 55° F
(B) 65° F
(C) 70° F
(D) 85° F

10. Which tool should you use to find out how much juice is in a bottle?

(A) cup
(B) ruler
(C) thermometer

11. Which tool should you use to find out how cold it is outside?

(A) cup
(B) ruler
(C) thermometer

12. Which tool should Gus use to find out how tall his bean plant is?

(A) cup
(B) ruler
(C) thermometer

Form A • Multiple-Choice   A96   Stop!

Multiple Choice

Harcourt Brace School Publishers

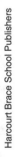

Choose the correct answer.

1. How many equal parts are there?

   Ⓐ 1 Ⓑ 2
   Ⓒ 3 ● 4

2. How many equal parts are there?

   Ⓐ 1 ● 2
   Ⓒ 3 Ⓓ 4

3. What part is colored?

   ● $\frac{1}{2}$ Ⓑ $\frac{1}{3}$
   Ⓒ $\frac{1}{4}$ Ⓓ $\frac{1}{6}$

4. Which picture shows $\frac{1}{4}$ colored?

   Ⓐ [ ] Ⓑ [ ]
   ● [ ] Ⓓ [ ]

5. Which fraction tells what part is colored?

   Ⓐ $\frac{1}{6}$ Ⓑ $\frac{1}{4}$
   ● $\frac{1}{3}$ Ⓓ $\frac{1}{2}$

6. Which fraction tells what part is colored?

   Ⓐ $\frac{1}{2}$ Ⓑ $\frac{1}{3}$
   Ⓒ $\frac{1}{4}$ ● $\frac{1}{6}$

Form A • Multiple-Choice   A97   Go on.

---

7. What fraction of the figure is colored?

   Ⓐ $\frac{3}{4}$ Ⓑ $\frac{2}{3}$
   Ⓒ $\frac{1}{2}$ Ⓓ $\frac{2}{6}$

8. Which figure shows $\frac{3}{6}$ colored?

   Ⓐ [ ] Ⓑ [ ]
   ● [ ] Ⓓ [ ]

9. What fraction of the group of circles is colored?

   Ⓐ $\frac{3}{4}$ ● $\frac{1}{2}$
   Ⓒ $\frac{1}{4}$ Ⓓ $\frac{1}{6}$

10. What fraction of the group of cupcakes is white?

    ● $\frac{2}{3}$ Ⓑ $\frac{1}{2}$
    Ⓒ $\frac{1}{3}$ Ⓓ $\frac{1}{6}$

11. Thea cut a pie in sixths. Then she ate one piece. What part did Thea eat?

    Ⓐ $\frac{1}{2}$
    Ⓑ $\frac{1}{3}$
    Ⓒ $\frac{1}{4}$
    ● $\frac{1}{6}$

12. Four children share 8 cookies. Each gets an equal part of the group. What part does one child get?

    Ⓐ $\frac{1}{6}$
    ● $\frac{1}{4}$
    Ⓒ $\frac{1}{3}$
    Ⓓ $\frac{1}{2}$

Form A • Multiple-Choice   A98   Stop!

Choose the correct answer.

1. About how many paper clips long is this key?

   ● about 2 Ⓑ about 3
   Ⓒ about 4 Ⓓ about 5
   20-A.1

2. How long is this worm?

   Ⓐ 1 inch Ⓑ 2 inches
   ● 3 inches Ⓓ 4 inches
   20-A.2

3. Which object is more than 1 foot long?

   Ⓐ
   Ⓑ
   Ⓒ
   ●
   20-A.3

4. How long is this piece of chalk?

   Ⓐ about 4 centimeters
   ● about 5 centimeters
   Ⓒ about 6 centimeters
   Ⓓ about 7 centimeters
   21-A.1

5. How many centimeters is it around the figure?

   3 cm
   1 cm [ ] 1 cm
   3 cm

   Ⓐ 6 ● 8
   Ⓒ 10 Ⓓ 12
   21-A.3

6. How many squares will fit in the figure?

   Ⓐ 1 square Ⓑ 2 squares
   Ⓒ 3 squares ● 4 squares
   21-A.4

Form A • Multiple-Choice   A99   Go on.

---

7. About how much does this television weigh?

   Ⓐ less than 1 pound
   ● more than 1 pound
   22-A.2

8. What is the temperature?

   Ⓐ 60° F
   Ⓑ 50° F
   Ⓒ 45° F
   Ⓓ 30° F
   22-A.3

9. Which tool should Lucy use to find out how much water is in the pitcher?

   ● cup
   Ⓑ ruler
   Ⓒ thermometer
   22-A.4

10. What part is shaded?

    Ⓐ $\frac{1}{6}$ ● $\frac{1}{4}$
    Ⓒ $\frac{1}{3}$ Ⓓ $\frac{1}{2}$
    23-A.1

11. What fraction of the group of dogs is spotted?

    Ⓐ $\frac{3}{4}$ ● $\frac{1}{2}$
    Ⓒ $\frac{1}{4}$ Ⓓ $\frac{1}{6}$
    23-A.2

12. Lee cut a pizza in sixths. Then he ate two pieces. What part did Lee eat?

    Ⓐ $\frac{1}{4}$ Ⓑ $\frac{1}{6}$
    ● $\frac{2}{6}$ Ⓓ $\frac{1}{2}$
    23-A.3

Form A • Multiple-Choice   A100   Stop!

Choose the correct answer.

1. $15 - 8 = 7$
$7 + 8 = \_\_$

Ⓐ 7   Ⓑ 10
Ⓒ 15   Ⓓ 12

2-A.1

2. Which number is between?
86, ___, 88

Ⓐ 84   Ⓑ 89
Ⓒ 93   Ⓓ not here

5-A.2

3. Mia saved 1 half-dollar, 1 quarter, and 3 pennies. How much money did she save in all?

Ⓐ 65¢   Ⓑ 78¢
Ⓒ 80¢   Ⓓ 83¢

7-A.1

4.
$$72 \\ -57$$

Ⓐ 15   Ⓑ 19
Ⓒ 21   Ⓓ 25

13-A.1

5. About how many paper clips long is this eraser?

Ⓐ about 1 paper clip
Ⓑ about 3 paper clips
Ⓒ about 4 paper clips
Ⓓ about 5 paper clips

20-A.1

6. About how long is this pencil?

Ⓐ about 1 inch
Ⓑ about 2 inches
Ⓒ about 3 inches
Ⓓ about 4 inches

20-A.2

Form A • Multiple-Choice   A101   Chapters 1–23   Go on.

---

7. How long is this ribbon?

Ⓐ 1 inch   Ⓑ 2 inches
Ⓒ 3 inches   Ⓓ 4 inches

20-A.2

8. How long is this path?

Ⓐ 3 inches   Ⓑ 4 inches
Ⓒ 5 inches   Ⓓ 6 inches

20-A.4

9. How long is this ticket?

TICKET

Ⓐ 3 centimeter
Ⓑ 4 centimeters
Ⓒ 5 centimeters
Ⓓ 6 centimeters

21-A.1

10. How many centimeters is it around the figure?

2 cm   2 cm

Ⓐ 6 centimeters
Ⓑ 8 centimeters
Ⓒ 10 centimeters
Ⓓ 12 centimeters

21-A.3

Form A • Multiple-Choice   A102   Chapters 1–23   Go on.

For questions 11 and 12, use a centimeter ruler.

11. Which object is less than a decimeter long?

Ⓐ a stamp   Ⓑ a car
Ⓒ a door   Ⓓ a train

21-A.2

12. Which object is more than a decimeter long?

Ⓐ an ant   Ⓑ an eraser
Ⓒ a sofa   Ⓓ a peanut

21-A.2

13. How many squares will fit in the figure?

Ⓐ 2 squares   Ⓑ 4 squares
Ⓒ 8 squares   Ⓓ 12 squares

21-A.4

14. How many cups fill 2 pints?

Ⓐ 2 cups   Ⓑ 4 cups
Ⓒ 6 cups   Ⓓ 8 cups

22-A.1

15. About how much does this bed weigh?

Ⓐ less than 1 pound
Ⓑ more than 1 pound

22-A.2

16. Which tool should Dave use to find out how much milk is in a bottle?

Ⓐ cup
Ⓑ ruler
Ⓒ thermometer

22-A.4

Form A • Multiple-Choice   A103   Chapters 1–23   Go on.

---

17. How many equal parts are there?

Ⓐ 1   Ⓑ 2
Ⓒ 3   Ⓓ 4

23-A.1

18. What fraction of the figure is shaded?

Ⓐ $\frac{3}{4}$ Ⓑ $\frac{2}{3}$
Ⓒ $\frac{1}{2}$ Ⓓ $\frac{2}{6}$

23-A.1

19. Which fraction tells what part is colored?

Ⓐ $\frac{1}{6}$ Ⓑ $\frac{1}{4}$
Ⓒ $\frac{1}{3}$ Ⓓ $\frac{1}{2}$

23-A.1

20. What fraction of the group of triangles is black?

Ⓐ $\frac{3}{4}$ Ⓑ $\frac{1}{2}$
Ⓒ $\frac{1}{4}$ Ⓓ $\frac{1}{6}$

23-A.2

21. Rita cut a pizza in sixths. Then she ate one piece. What part did Rita eat?

Ⓐ $\frac{1}{2}$
Ⓑ $\frac{1}{3}$
Ⓒ $\frac{1}{4}$
Ⓓ $\frac{1}{6}$

23-A.3

22. Three children share 9 apples. Each child gets an equal part of the group. What part does one child get?

Ⓐ $\frac{1}{6}$
Ⓑ $\frac{1}{4}$
Ⓒ $\frac{1}{3}$
Ⓓ $\frac{1}{2}$

23-A.3

Form A • Multiple-Choice   A104   Chapters 1–23   Stop!

Multiple Choice

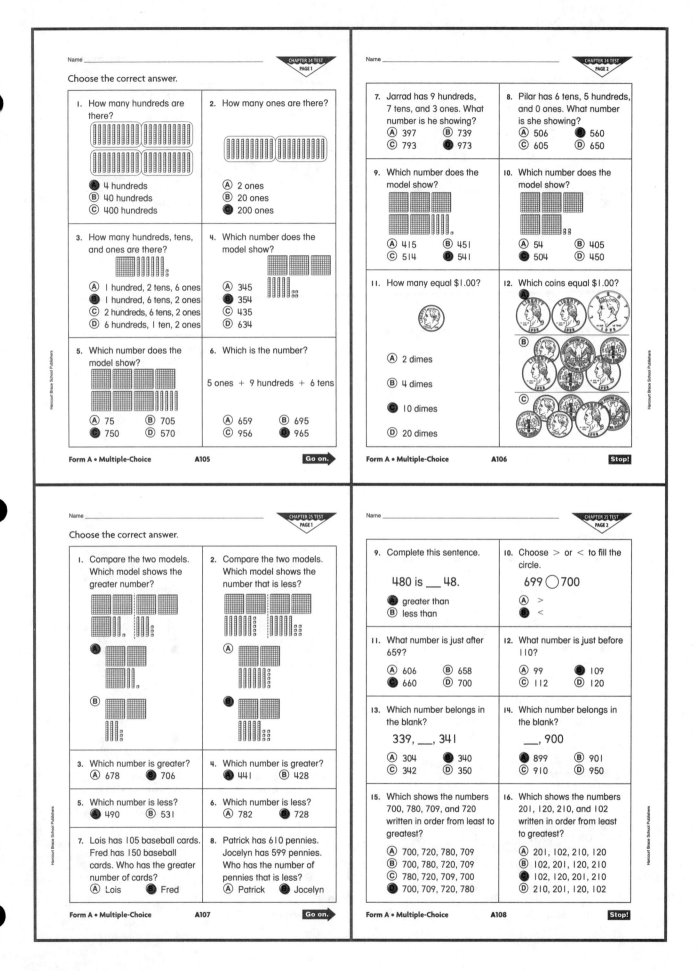

Name _____

Choose the correct answer.

1. How many hundreds are there?

- (A) 4 hundreds ●
- (B) 40 hundreds
- (C) 400 hundreds

2. How many ones are there?

- (A) 2 ones
- (B) 20 ones
- (C) 200 ones ●

3. How many hundreds, tens, and ones are there?

- (A) 1 hundred, 2 tens, 6 ones
- (B) 1 hundred, 6 tens, 2 ones ●
- (C) 2 hundreds, 6 tens, 2 ones
- (D) 6 hundreds, 1 ten, 2 ones

4. Which number does the model show?

- (A) 345
- (B) 354 ●
- (C) 435
- (D) 634

5. Which number does the model show?

- (A) 75
- (B) 705
- (C) 750 ●
- (D) 570

6. Which is the number?

5 ones + 9 hundreds + 6 tens

- (A) 659
- (B) 695
- (C) 956
- (D) 965 ●

Name _____

7. Jarrad has 9 hundreds, 7 tens, and 3 ones. What number is he showing?

- (A) 397
- (B) 739
- (C) 793
- (D) 973 ●

8. Pilar has 6 tens, 5 hundreds, and 0 ones. What number is she showing?

- (A) 506
- (B) 560 ●
- (C) 605
- (D) 650

9. Which number does the model show?

- (A) 415
- (B) 451
- (C) 514 ●
- (D) 541

10. Which number does the model show?

- (A) 54
- (B) 405
- (C) 504 ●
- (D) 450

11. How many equal $1.00?

- (A) 2 dimes
- (B) 4 dimes
- (C) 10 dimes ●
- (D) 20 dimes

12. Which coins equal $1.00?

- (A)
- (B)
- (C) ●

Name _____

Choose the correct answer.

1. Compare the two models. Which model shows the greater number?

- (A) ●
- (B)

2. Compare the two models. Which model shows the number that is less?

- (A)
- (B) ●

3. Which number is greater?

- (A) 678
- (B) 706 ●

4. Which number is greater?

- (A) 441 ●
- (B) 428

5. Which number is less?

- (A) 490 ●
- (B) 531

6. Which number is less?

- (A) 782
- (B) 728 ●

7. Lois has 105 baseball cards. Fred has 150 baseball cards. Who has the greater number of cards?

- (A) Lois
- (B) Fred ●

8. Patrick has 610 pennies. Jocelyn has 599 pennies. Who has the number of pennies that is less?

- (A) Patrick
- (B) Jocelyn ●

Name _____

9. Complete this sentence.

480 is ___ 48.

- (A) greater than ●
- (B) less than

10. Choose > or < to fill the circle.

699 ◯ 700

- (A) >
- (B) < ●

11. What number is just after 659?

- (A) 606
- (B) 658
- (C) 660 ●
- (D) 700

12. What number is just before 110?

- (A) 99
- (B) 109 ●
- (C) 112
- (D) 120

13. Which number belongs in the blank?

339, ___, 341

- (A) 304
- (B) 340 ●
- (C) 342
- (D) 350

14. Which number belongs in the blank?

___, 900

- (A) 899 ●
- (B) 901
- (C) 910
- (D) 950

15. Which shows the numbers 700, 780, 709, and 720 written in order from least to greatest?

- (A) 700, 720, 780, 709
- (B) 700, 780, 720, 709
- (C) 780, 720, 709, 700
- (D) 700, 709, 720, 780 ●

16. Which shows the numbers 201, 120, 210, and 102 written in order from least to greatest?

- (A) 201, 102, 210, 120
- (B) 102, 201, 120, 210
- (C) 102, 120, 201, 210 ●
- (D) 210, 201, 120, 102

Multiple Choice

Choose the correct answer.

1.

hundreds	tens	ones
	☐	☐
3	2	7
+ 1	3	3

- Ⓐ 450
- Ⓑ 454
- ⬤Ⓒ 460
- Ⓓ 550

2.

hundreds	tens	ones
	☐	☐
2	9	3
+ 2	2	4

- Ⓐ 473
- ⬤Ⓑ 517
- Ⓒ 531
- Ⓓ 567

3.
```
  2 0 6
+ 3 4 7
```
- Ⓐ 541
- Ⓑ 543
- ⬤Ⓒ 553
- Ⓓ 643

4.
```
  4 5 2
+ 1 5 6
```
- Ⓐ 508
- Ⓑ 518
- Ⓒ 604
- ⬤Ⓓ 608

5.

hundreds	tens	ones
	☐	☐
3	9	5
− 1	7	9

- Ⓐ 126
- Ⓑ 214
- ⬤Ⓒ 216
- Ⓓ 226

6.

hundreds	tens	ones
	☐	☐
7	2	9
− 5	4	6

- Ⓐ 133
- ⬤Ⓑ 183
- Ⓒ 213
- Ⓓ 263

7.
```
  3 6 2
− 1 3 9
```
- Ⓐ 133
- Ⓑ 223
- Ⓒ 233
- Ⓓ 237

8.
```
  8 1 8
− 4 3 5
```
- Ⓐ 383
- Ⓑ 423
- Ⓒ 453
- Ⓓ 483

9. Add.
```
  $1.0 4
+ 2.5 5
```
- ⬤Ⓐ $3.59
- Ⓑ $4.04
- Ⓒ $4.09
- Ⓓ $4.59

10. Subtract.
```
  $5.2 5
− 3.5 0
```
- Ⓐ $1.25
- ⬤Ⓑ $1.75
- Ⓒ $2.25
- Ⓓ $2.75

11. Daniel had $6.85. He spent $2.19 on a toy. How much money does he have left?

- ⬤Ⓐ $4.66
- Ⓑ $4.76
- Ⓒ $8.94
- Ⓓ $9.04

12. Celeste earned $1.65 on Monday and $1.60 on Tuesday. How much money in all did she earn?

- Ⓐ $2.25
- Ⓑ $2.35
- ⬤Ⓒ $3.25
- Ⓓ $3.35

Choose the correct answer.

1. How many hundreds, tens, and ones are there?

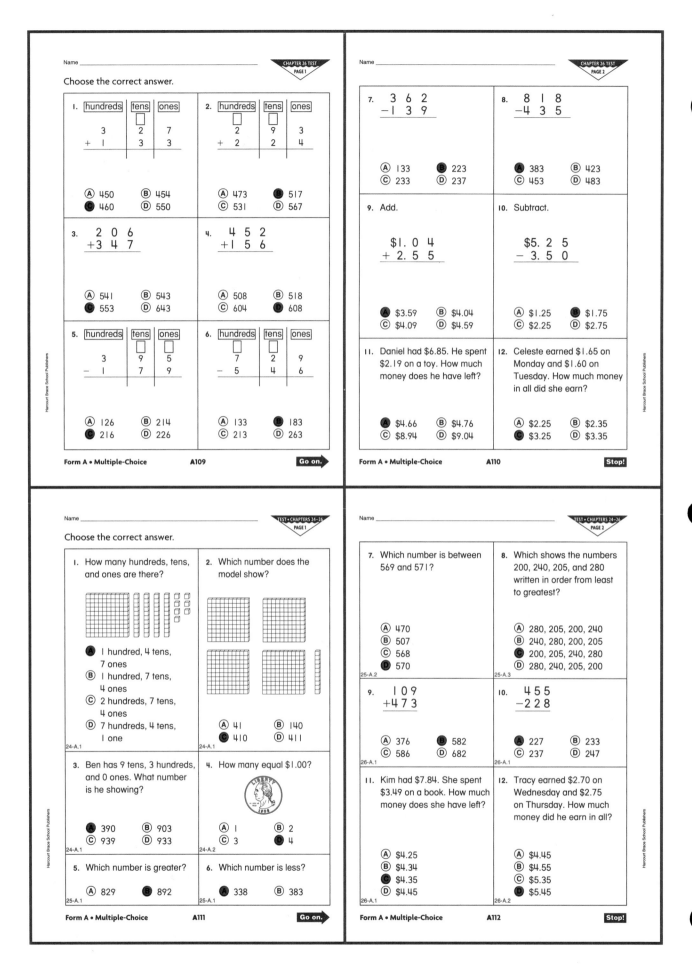

- ⬤Ⓐ 1 hundred, 4 tens, 7 ones
- Ⓑ 1 hundred, 7 tens, 4 ones
- Ⓒ 2 hundreds, 7 tens, 4 ones
- Ⓓ 7 hundreds, 4 tens, 1 one

24-A.1

2. Which number does the model show?

- Ⓐ 41
- Ⓑ 140
- Ⓒ 410
- Ⓓ 411

24-A.1

3. Ben has 9 tens, 3 hundreds, and 0 ones. What number is he showing?

- ⬤Ⓐ 390
- Ⓑ 903
- Ⓒ 939
- Ⓓ 933

24-A.1

4. How many equal $1.00?

- Ⓐ 1
- Ⓑ 2
- Ⓒ 3
- ⬤Ⓓ 4

24-A.2

5. Which number is greater?
- Ⓐ 829
- ⬤Ⓑ 892

25-A.1

6. Which number is less?
- ⬤Ⓐ 338
- Ⓑ 383

25-A.1

7. Which number is between 569 and 571?

- Ⓐ 470
- Ⓑ 507
- Ⓒ 568
- Ⓓ 570

25-A.2

8. Which shows the numbers 200, 240, 205, and 280 written in order from least to greatest?

- Ⓐ 280, 205, 200, 240
- Ⓑ 240, 280, 200, 205
- ⬤Ⓒ 200, 205, 240, 280
- Ⓓ 280, 240, 205, 200

25-A.3

9.
```
  1 0 9
+ 4 7 3
```
- Ⓐ 376
- ⬤Ⓑ 582
- Ⓒ 586
- Ⓓ 682

26-A.1

10.
```
  4 5 5
− 2 2 8
```
- ⬤Ⓐ 227
- Ⓑ 233
- Ⓒ 237
- Ⓓ 247

26-A.1

11. Kim had $7.84. She spent $3.49 on a book. How much money does she have left?

- Ⓐ $4.25
- Ⓑ $4.34
- ⬤Ⓒ $4.35
- Ⓓ $4.45

26-A.2

12. Tracy earned $2.70 on Wednesday and $2.75 on Thursday. How much money did he earn in all?

- Ⓐ $4.45
- Ⓑ $4.55
- Ⓒ $5.35
- ⬤Ⓓ $5.45

26-A.2

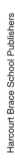

Name _____

Choose the correct answer.

1.
$$\begin{array}{r} 6 \\ +6 \\ \hline \end{array}$$

- (A) 10
- (B) 11
- (C) 12
- (D) not here

1-A.1

2. Which is the missing addend?

⬤⬤⬤⬤⬤ |

$$7 + \underline{} = 12$$

- (A) 3
- (B) 5
- (C) 7
- (D) not here

2-A.1

3. Which number is just before?

____, 68

- (A) 61
- (B) 66
- (C) 67
- (D) not here

5-A.2

4. Tina saved 1 half-dollar, 2 dimes, and 1 penny. How much money did she save in all?

- (A) 37¢
- (B) 52¢
- (C) 62¢
- (D) 71¢

7-A.1

5.

tens	ones
☐	
3	9
+	5

- (A) 44
- (B) 57
- (C) 61
- (D) not here

11-A.1

6.

tens	ones
☐	
6	1
− 2	3

- (A) 27
- (B) 38
- (C) 43
- (D) 45

13-A.1

Form A • Multiple-Choice A113 Chapters 1–26 Go on. ▶

Name _____

Use the picture to answer questions 7 and 8.

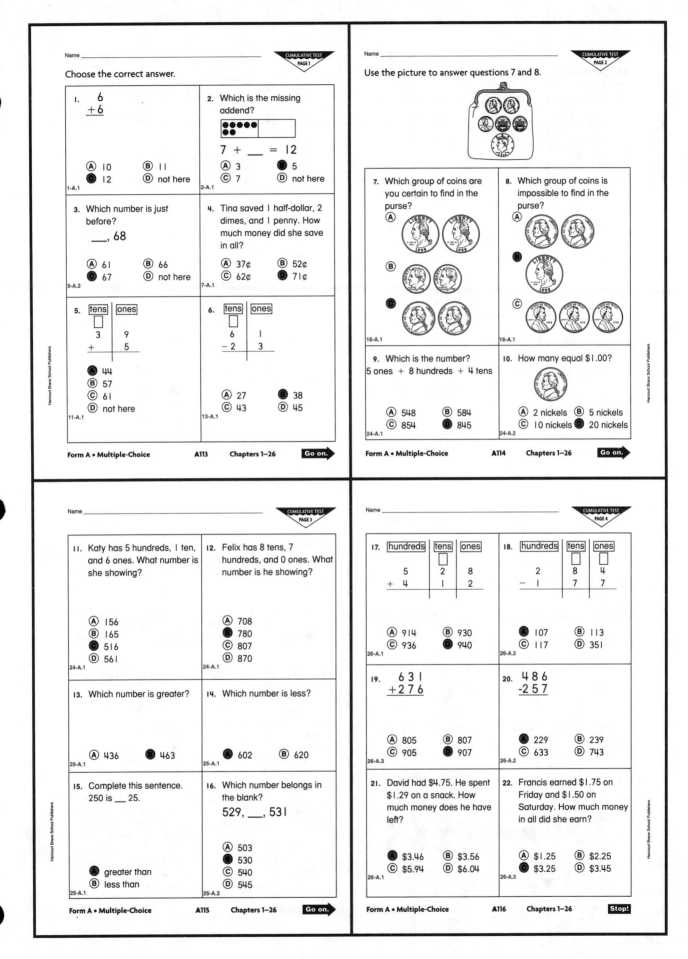

7. Which group of coins are you certain to find in the purse?

- (A)
- (B)
- (C)

16-A.1

8. Which group of coins is impossible to find in the purse?

- (A)
- (B)
- (C)

16-A.1

9. Which is the number?
5 ones + 8 hundreds + 4 tens

- (A) 548
- (B) 584
- (C) 854
- (D) 845

24-A.2

10. How many equal $1.00?

- (A) 2 nickels
- (B) 5 nickels
- (C) 10 nickels
- (D) 20 nickels

24-A.2

Form A • Multiple-Choice A114 Chapters 1–26 Go on. ▶

Name _____

11. Katy has 5 hundreds, 1 ten, and 6 ones. What number is she showing?

- (A) 156
- (B) 165
- (C) 516
- (D) 561

24-A.1

12. Felix has 8 tens, 7 hundreds, and 0 ones. What number is he showing?

- (A) 708
- (B) 780
- (C) 807
- (D) 870

24-A.1

13. Which number is greater?

- (A) 436
- (B) 463

25-A.1

14. Which number is less?

- (A) 602
- (B) 620

25-A.1

15. Complete this sentence.
250 is ___ 25.

- (A) greater than
- (B) less than

25-A.1

16. Which number belongs in the blank?

529, ___, 531

- (A) 503
- (B) 530
- (C) 540
- (D) 545

25-A.2

Form A • Multiple-Choice A115 Chapters 1–26 Go on. ▶

Name _____

17.

hundreds	tens	ones
	☐	
5	2	8
+ 4	1	2

- (A) 914
- (B) 930
- (C) 936
- (D) 940

26-A.1

18.

hundreds	tens	ones
	☐	
2	8	4
− 1	7	7

- (A) 107
- (B) 113
- (C) 117
- (D) 351

26-A.2

19.
$$\begin{array}{r} 631 \\ +276 \\ \hline \end{array}$$

- (A) 805
- (B) 807
- (C) 905
- (D) 907

26-A.3

20.
$$\begin{array}{r} 486 \\ -257 \\ \hline \end{array}$$

- (A) 229
- (B) 239
- (C) 633
- (D) 743

26-A.2

21. David had $4.75. He spent $1.29 on a snack. How much money does he have left?

- (A) $3.46
- (B) $3.56
- (C) $5.94
- (D) $6.04

26-A.1

22. Francis earned $1.75 on Friday and $1.50 on Saturday. How much money in all did she earn?

- (A) $1.25
- (B) $2.25
- (C) $3.25
- (D) $3.45

26-A.3

Form A • Multiple-Choice A116 Chapters 1–26 Stop!

Multiple Choice

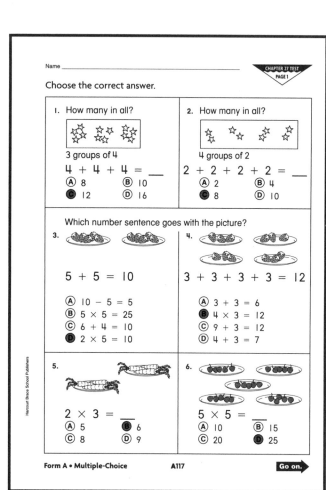

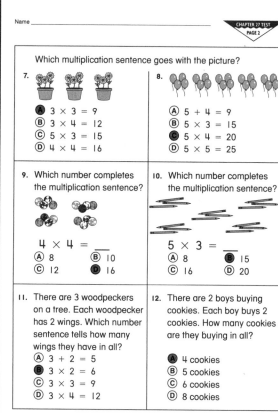

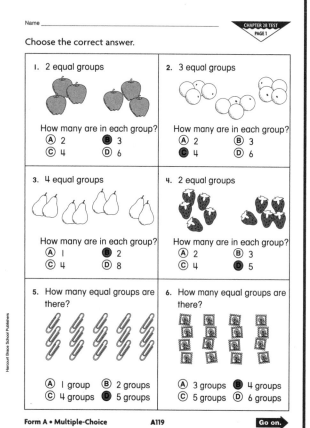

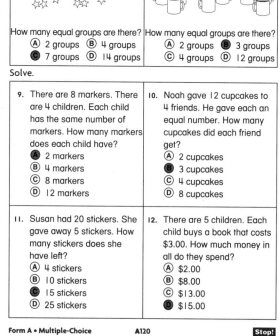

Choose the correct answer.

1. How many in all?

3 groups of 4

4 + 4 + 4 = ___
Ⓐ 8   Ⓑ 10
Ⓒ 12   Ⓓ 16

2. How many in all?

4 groups of 2

2 + 2 + 2 + 2 = ___
Ⓐ 2   Ⓑ 4
Ⓒ 8   Ⓓ 10

Which number sentence goes with the picture?

3.

5 + 5 = 10
Ⓐ 10 − 5 = 5
Ⓑ 5 × 5 = 25
Ⓒ 6 + 4 = 10
Ⓓ 2 × 5 = 10

4.

3 + 3 + 3 + 3 = 12
Ⓐ 3 + 3 = 6
Ⓑ 4 × 3 = 12
Ⓒ 9 + 3 = 12
Ⓓ 4 + 3 = 7

5.

2 × 3 = ___
Ⓐ 5   Ⓑ 6
Ⓒ 8   Ⓓ 9

6.

5 × 5 = ___
Ⓐ 10   Ⓑ 15
Ⓒ 20   Ⓓ 25

Go on. ▶

Which multiplication sentence goes with the picture?

7.

Ⓐ 3 × 3 = 9
Ⓑ 3 × 4 = 12
Ⓒ 5 × 3 = 15
Ⓓ 4 × 4 = 16

8.

Ⓐ 5 + 4 = 9
Ⓑ 5 × 3 = 15
Ⓒ 5 × 4 = 20
Ⓓ 5 × 5 = 25

9. Which number completes the multiplication sentence?

4 × 4 = ___
Ⓐ 8   Ⓑ 10
Ⓒ 12   Ⓓ 16

10. Which number completes the multiplication sentence?

5 × 3 = ___
Ⓐ 8   Ⓑ 15
Ⓒ 16   Ⓓ 20

11. There are 3 woodpeckers on a tree. Each woodpecker has 2 wings. Which number sentence tells how many wings they have in all?
Ⓐ 3 + 2 = 5
Ⓑ 3 × 2 = 6
Ⓒ 3 × 3 = 9
Ⓓ 3 × 4 = 12

12. There are 2 boys buying cookies. Each boy buys 2 cookies. How many cookies are they buying in all?
Ⓐ 4 cookies
Ⓑ 5 cookies
Ⓒ 6 cookies
Ⓓ 8 cookies

Stop!

Choose the correct answer.

1. 2 equal groups

How many are in each group?
Ⓐ 2   Ⓑ 3
Ⓒ 4   Ⓓ 6

2. 3 equal groups

How many are in each group?
Ⓐ 2   Ⓑ 3
Ⓒ 4   Ⓓ 6

3. 4 equal groups

How many are in each group?
Ⓐ 1   Ⓑ 2
Ⓒ 4   Ⓓ 8

4. 2 equal groups

How many are in each group?
Ⓐ 2   Ⓑ 3
Ⓒ 4   Ⓓ 5

5. How many equal groups are there?

Ⓐ 1 group   Ⓑ 2 groups
Ⓒ 4 groups   Ⓓ 5 groups

6. How many equal groups are there?

Ⓐ 3 groups   Ⓑ 4 groups
Ⓒ 5 groups   Ⓓ 6 groups

Go on. ▶

7. Groups of 2

How many equal groups are there?
Ⓐ 2 groups   Ⓑ 4 groups
Ⓒ 7 groups   Ⓓ 14 groups

8. Groups of 4

How many equal groups are there?
Ⓐ 2 groups   Ⓑ 3 groups
Ⓒ 4 groups   Ⓓ 12 groups

Solve.

9. There are 8 markers. There are 4 children. Each child has the same number of markers. How many markers does each child have?
Ⓐ 2 markers
Ⓑ 4 markers
Ⓒ 8 markers
Ⓓ 12 markers

10. Noah gave 12 cupcakes to 4 friends. He gave each an equal number. How many cupcakes did each friend get?
Ⓐ 2 cupcakes
Ⓑ 3 cupcakes
Ⓒ 4 cupcakes
Ⓓ 8 cupcakes

11. Susan had 20 stickers. She gave away 5 stickers. How many stickers does she have left?
Ⓐ 4 stickers
Ⓑ 10 stickers
Ⓒ 15 stickers
Ⓓ 25 stickers

12. There are 5 children. Each child buys a book that costs $3.00. How much money in all do they spend?
Ⓐ $2.00
Ⓑ $8.00
Ⓒ $13.00
Ⓓ $15.00

Stop!

Multiple Choice

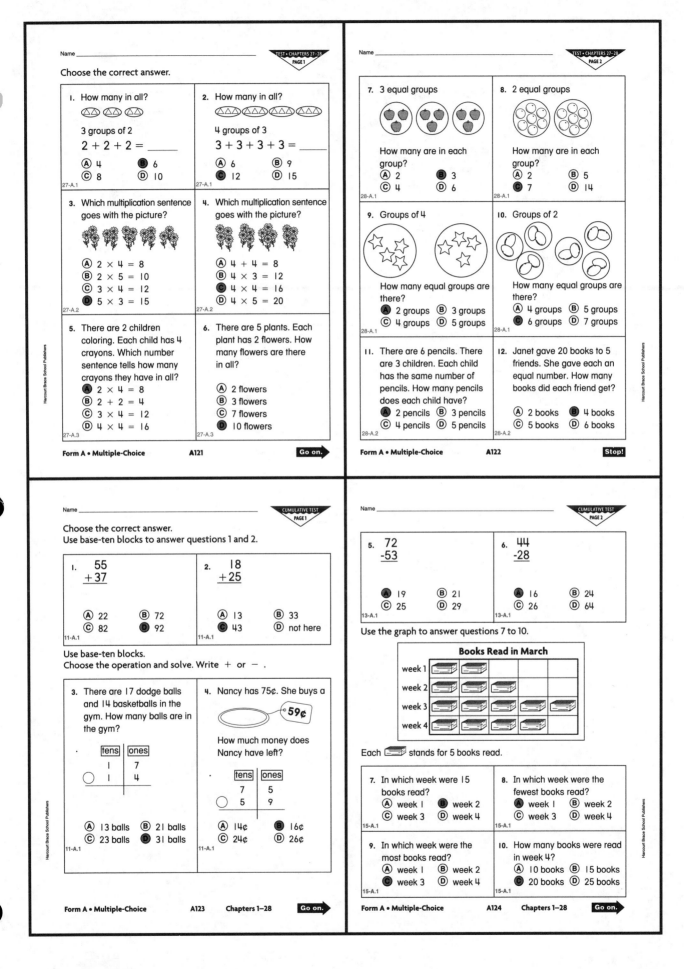

Choose the correct answer.

1. How many in all?

3 groups of 2

$2 + 2 + 2 =$ _____

Ⓐ 4   **Ⓑ 6**
Ⓒ 8   Ⓓ 10

27-A.1

2. How many in all?

4 groups of 3

$3 + 3 + 3 + 3 =$ _____

Ⓐ 6   Ⓑ 9
Ⓒ 12   Ⓓ 15

27-A.1

3. Which multiplication sentence goes with the picture?

Ⓐ $2 \times 4 = 8$
Ⓑ $2 \times 5 = 10$
Ⓒ $3 \times 4 = 12$
Ⓓ $5 \times 3 = 15$

27-A.2

4. Which multiplication sentence goes with the picture?

Ⓐ $4 + 4 = 8$
Ⓑ $4 \times 3 = 12$
Ⓒ $4 \times 4 = 16$
Ⓓ $4 \times 5 = 20$

27-A.2

5. There are 2 children coloring. Each child has 4 crayons. Which number sentence tells how many crayons they have in all?

Ⓐ $2 \times 4 = 8$
Ⓑ $2 + 2 = 4$
Ⓒ $3 \times 4 = 12$
Ⓓ $4 \times 4 = 16$

27-A.3

6. There are 5 plants. Each plant has 2 flowers. How many flowers are there in all?

Ⓐ 2 flowers
Ⓑ 3 flowers
Ⓒ 7 flowers
Ⓓ 10 flowers

27-A.3

Form A • Multiple-Choice   A121   Go on.

---

7. 3 equal groups

How many are in each group?

Ⓐ 2   **Ⓑ 3**
Ⓒ 4   Ⓓ 6

28-A.1

8. 2 equal groups

How many are in each group?

Ⓐ 2   Ⓑ 5
Ⓒ 7   Ⓓ 14

28-A.1

9. Groups of 4

How many equal groups are there?

Ⓐ 2 groups   Ⓑ 3 groups
Ⓒ 4 groups   Ⓓ 5 groups

28-A.1

10. Groups of 2

How many equal groups are there?

Ⓐ 4 groups   Ⓑ 5 groups
Ⓒ 6 groups   Ⓓ 7 groups

28-A.1

11. There are 6 pencils. There are 3 children. Each child has the same number of pencils. How many pencils does each child have?

Ⓐ 2 pencils   Ⓑ 3 pencils
Ⓒ 4 pencils   Ⓓ 5 pencils

28-A.2

12. Janet gave 20 books to 5 friends. She gave each an equal number. How many books did each friend get?

Ⓐ 2 books   **Ⓑ 4 books**
Ⓒ 5 books   Ⓓ 6 books

28-A.2

Form A • Multiple-Choice   A122   Stop!

Choose the correct answer.
Use base-ten blocks to answer questions 1 and 2.

1.
55
$+37$

Ⓐ 22   Ⓑ 72
Ⓒ 82   **Ⓓ 92**

11-A.1

2.
18
$+25$

Ⓐ 13   Ⓑ 33
Ⓒ 43   Ⓓ not here

11-A.1

Use base-ten blocks.
Choose the operation and solve. Write $+$ or $-$.

3. There are 17 dodge balls and 14 basketballs in the gym. How many balls are in the gym?

tens	ones
1	7
1	4

○

Ⓐ 13 balls   Ⓑ 21 balls
Ⓒ 23 balls   **Ⓓ 31 balls**

11-A.1

4. Nancy has 75¢. She buys a

59¢

How much money does Nancy have left?

tens	ones
7	5
5	9

○

Ⓐ 14¢   **Ⓑ 16¢**
Ⓒ 24¢   Ⓓ 26¢

11-A.1

Form A • Multiple-Choice   A123   Chapters 1–28   Go on.

5.
72
-53

Ⓐ 19   Ⓑ 21
Ⓒ 25   Ⓓ 29

13-A.1

6.
44
-28

Ⓐ 16   Ⓑ 24
Ⓒ 26   Ⓓ 64

13-A.1

Use the graph to answer questions 7 to 10.

Books Read in March

week 1	
week 2	
week 3	
week 4	

Each 🗆 stands for 5 books read.

7. In which week were 15 books read?

Ⓐ week 1   **Ⓑ week 2**
Ⓒ week 3   Ⓓ week 4

15-A.1

8. In which week were the fewest books read?

Ⓐ week 1   Ⓑ week 2
Ⓒ week 3   Ⓓ week 4

15-A.1

9. In which week were the most books read?

Ⓐ week 1   Ⓑ week 2
Ⓒ week 3   Ⓓ week 4

15-A.1

10. How many books were read in week 4?

Ⓐ 10 books   Ⓑ 15 books
Ⓒ 20 books   Ⓓ 25 books

15-A.1

Form A • Multiple-Choice   A124   Chapters 1–28   Go on.

Multiple Choice   157

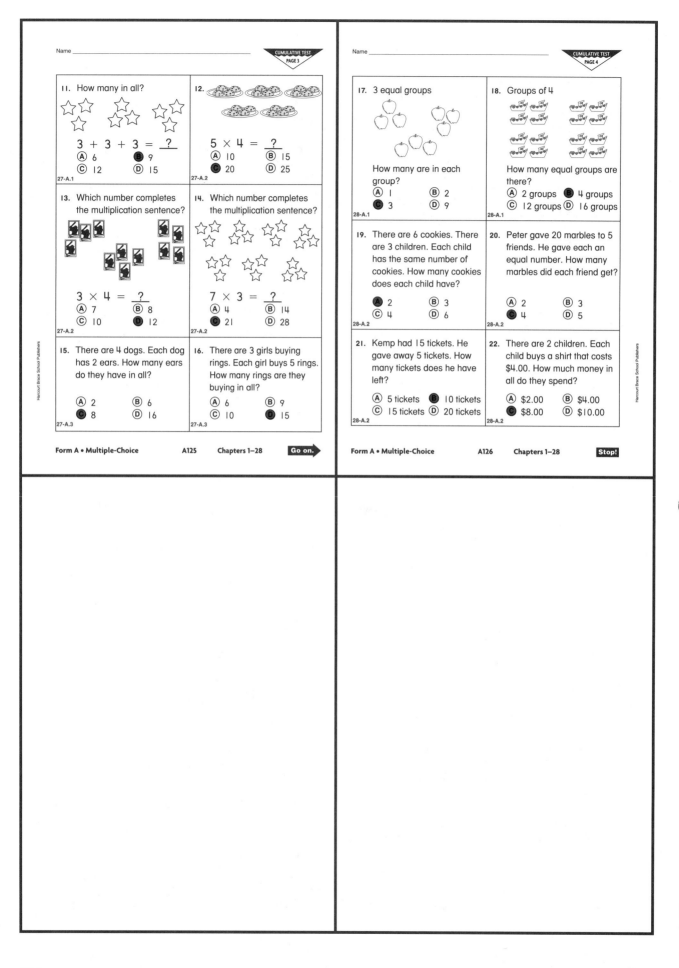

11. How many in all?

$$3 + 3 + 3 = \underline{?}$$
- (A) 6
- (B) 9
- (C) 12
- (D) 15

27-A.1

12.

$$5 \times 4 = \underline{?}$$
- (A) 10
- (B) 15
- (C) 20
- (D) 25

27-A.2

13. Which number completes the multiplication sentence?

$$3 \times 4 = \underline{?}$$
- (A) 7
- (B) 8
- (C) 10
- (D) 12

27-A.2

14. Which number completes the multiplication sentence?

$$7 \times 3 = \underline{?}$$
- (A) 4
- (B) 14
- (C) 21
- (D) 28

27-A.2

15. There are 4 dogs. Each dog has 2 ears. How many ears do they have in all?
- (A) 2
- (B) 6
- (C) 8
- (D) 16

27-A.3

16. There are 3 girls buying rings. Each girl buys 5 rings. How many rings are they buying in all?
- (A) 6
- (B) 9
- (C) 10
- (D) 15

27-A.3

Form A • Multiple-Choice   A125   **Chapters 1–28**   Go on.

17. 3 equal groups

How many are in each group?
- (A) 1
- (B) 2
- (C) 3
- (D) 9

28-A.1

18. Groups of 4

How many equal groups are there?
- (A) 2 groups
- (B) 4 groups
- (C) 12 groups
- (D) 16 groups

28-A.1

19. There are 6 cookies. There are 3 children. Each child has the same number of cookies. How many cookies does each child have?
- (A) 2
- (B) 3
- (C) 4
- (D) 6

28-A.2

20. Peter gave 20 marbles to 5 friends. He gave each an equal number. How many marbles did each friend get?
- (A) 2
- (B) 3
- (C) 4
- (D) 5

28-A.2

21. Kemp had 15 tickets. He gave away 5 tickets. How many tickets does he have left?
- (A) 5 tickets
- (B) 10 tickets
- (C) 15 tickets
- (D) 20 tickets

28-A.2

22. There are 2 children. Each child buys a shirt that costs $4.00. How much money in all do they spend?
- (A) $2.00
- (B) $4.00
- (C) $8.00
- (D) $10.00

28-A.2

Form A • Multiple-Choice   A126   **Chapters 1–28**   Stop!

Multiple Choice

Free-Response Format Tests

The free-response format tests are useful as diagnostic tools. The work the student performs provides information about what the student understands about the concepts and/or procedures so that appropriate reteaching can be chosen from the many options in the program.

There is an Inventory Test which tests the learning goals from the previous grade level. This can be used at the beginning of the year or as a placement test when a new student enters your class.

There is a Chapter Test for each chapter and a Multi-Chapter Test to be used as review after several chapters in a content cluster. Also, there are Cumulative Tests at the same point as the Multi-Chapter Tests. The Cumulative Test reviews content from Chapter 1 through the current chapter.

Math Advantage also provides multiple-choice format tests that parallel the free-response format tests. You may wish to use one form as a pretest and one form as a posttest.

Harcourt Brace School Publishers

Write the correct answer.

1.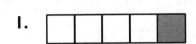

$$5 + 1 = \underline{}$$

2.

$$4 - 1 = \underline{}$$

3.
$$\begin{array}{r} 5 \\ +3 \\ \hline \end{array}$$

4.
$$\begin{array}{r} 7 \\ +2 \\ \hline \end{array}$$

5.

$$8 - 2 = \underline{}$$

6.
$$\begin{array}{r} 7 \\ -0 \\ \hline \end{array}$$

7. Circle the object that has the same shape.

8. Write how many sides this shape has.

_____ sides

9. Circle the **closed** figure.

10. Circle the shape that comes next in the pattern.

11.
$$\begin{array}{r} 6 \\ +6 \\ \hline \end{array}$$

12.
$$\begin{array}{r} 8 \\ +3 \\ \hline 11 \end{array} \qquad \begin{array}{r} 11 \\ -8 \\ \hline \end{array}$$

13. How many?

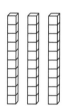

_____

14. Write the number that comes **between** 76 and 78.

76, _____, 78

15. Count by fives. Write the number that comes after 25.

15, 20, 25, _____

16. Write the amount.

_____ ¢

17. Write how many nickels equal a .

_____ nickels

18. Write the time.

_____

Use the calendar to answer questions 19 and 20.

July

Sunday	Monday	Tuesday	Wednesday	Thursday	Friday	Saturday
		1	2	3	4	5
6	7	8	9	10	11	12

19. On which day does this month begin?

_____

20. On which day is July 11?

_____

21. How many inches long?

_____ inches

22. About how many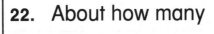

does the hold?

about _____

23. Circle the figure that has $\frac{1}{3}$ colored black.

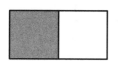 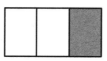

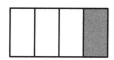 

24. Write how many flowers are pink.

Flowers

| pink | |||| |
| yellow | ЖНГ I |

_____ are pink.

Use the graph to answer questions 25 and 26.

Circus Acts

seals	🦭	🦭	🦭	🦭
tigers	🐯	🐯	🐯	
elephants	🐘			

25. Write how many tigers there are.

_____ tigers

26. Write how many animals there are in all.

_____ animals

27.
```
   4
   6
 + 4
```

28. Bill has 12 toys.
He gets 10 more.
How many toys does he have in all?

_____ toys

Harcourt Brace School Publishers

Name _____

Write the correct answer.

1. $\begin{array}{r} 7 \\ +4 \\ \hline 11 \end{array}$ $\qquad$ $\begin{array}{r} 11 \\ -4 \\ \hline \end{array}$	2. $16 - 7 = 9$ $9 + 7 =$ _____
3. $\begin{array}{r} 8 \\ +5 \\ \hline 13 \end{array}$ $\qquad$ $\begin{array}{r} 13 \\ -5 \\ \hline \end{array}$	4. $14 - 5 = 9$ $9 + 5 =$ _____

Use the number line to answer questions 5 and 6.

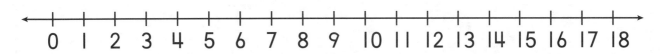

5. $15 - 9 =$ _____	6. $12 - 5 =$ _____
7. Write the number sentence that belongs in this fact family. $9 + 8 = 17$ $8 + 9 = 17$ $17 - 9 = 8$ _____ $-$ _____ $=$ _____	8. Write the number sentence that belongs in this fact family. $9 + 2 = 11$ $11 - 2 = 9$ $11 - 9 = 2$ _____ $+$ _____ $=$ _____

Form B • Free-Response

Go on.

Name _____

9. Write the missing addend.

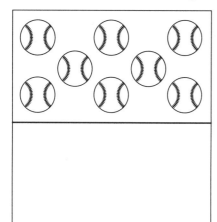

$$\begin{array}{r} 8 \\ +\square \\ \hline 15 \end{array}$$

10. Write the missing addend.

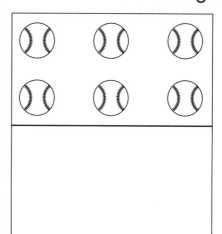

$$\begin{array}{r} 6 \\ +\square \\ \hline 14 \end{array}$$

11. There were 7 brown ducks and 6 white ducks at the pond. How many ducks were at the pond?

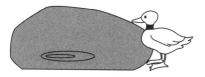

_____ducks

12. There were 11 bats at the store. Then 8 bats were sold. How many bats were still at the store?

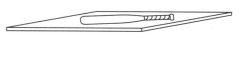

_____bats

Harcourt Brace School Publishers

Name _____

Write the correct answer.

1. Write the addition sentence that tells about the picture.

_____ + _____ = _____

2. Use the picture to find the sum.

$$\begin{array}{r} 9 \\ +3 \\ \hline \end{array}$$

3. Anna has 5 green bows and 9 blue bows. How many bows does she have?

_____ bows

4. Jake spent 9¢ for a pencil and 4¢ for paper. How much money did he spend?

_____ ¢

5.
$$\begin{array}{r} 8 \\ 6 \\ +4 \\ \hline \end{array}$$

6.
$$\begin{array}{r} 4 \\ 4 \\ +9 \\ \hline \end{array}$$

Form B • Free-Response

Go on.

7.
$$6 \quad\quad 14$$
$$\underline{+8} \quad \underline{-\ 6}$$
$$14$$

8. $16 - 8 = 8$

$8 + 8 =$ _____

Use the number line to answer questions 9 and 10.

9. $12 - 7 =$ _____

10. $17 - 8 =$ _____

11. Write the missing addend.

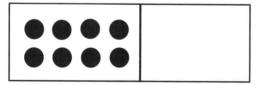

$8 +$ _____ $= 13$

12. There were 14 raisins in the box. Then Coley ate 7 raisins. How many raisins were still in the box?

_____ raisins

Name _____

Write the correct answer.

1. Write the addition sentence that tells about the picture.

_____ + _____ = _____

2. Write the addition sentence that tells about the picture.

_____ + _____ = _____

3. 7
   +8

4. 5
   +4

5. 8
   +9

6. 4
   +3

7. 9
   +5

8. 4
   +9

9. Use the picture to find the sum.

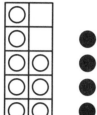

$$\begin{array}{r} 8 \\ +4 \\ \hline \end{array}$$

10. Use the picture to find the sum.

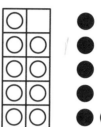

$$\begin{array}{r} 6 \\ +9 \\ \hline \end{array}$$

11. Leon saw 9 brown horses and 2 black horses. How many horses did he see?

_____ horses

12. Donna spent 8¢ for one bow and 9¢ for another bow. How much money did she spend?

_____ ¢

13.
$$\begin{array}{r} 1 \\ 9 \\ +8 \\ \hline \end{array}$$

14.
$$\begin{array}{r} 4 \\ 6 \\ +4 \\ \hline \end{array}$$

15. Jim has 7 white shirts, 3 blue shirts, and 6 green shirts. How many shirts does he have?

_____ shirts

16. Pam has 2 yellow buttons, 9 orange buttons, and 2 red buttons. How many buttons does she have?

_____ buttons

17. $\begin{array}{r} 8 \\ +7 \\ \hline 15 \end{array}$ $\qquad$ $\begin{array}{r} 15 \\ -8 \\ \hline \end{array}$	**18.** $13 - 5 = 8$ $\qquad$ $8 + 5 = \underline{}$
19. $\begin{array}{r} 7 \\ +4 \\ \hline 11 \end{array}$ $\qquad$ $\begin{array}{r} 11 \\ -7 \\ \hline \end{array}$	**20.** $12 - 7 = 5$ $\qquad$ $5 + 7 = \underline{}$
21. Write the number sentence that belongs in this fact family. $7 + 6 = 13$ $6 + 7 = 13$ $13 - 7 = 6$ $\underline{} \ O \ \underline{} = \underline{}$	**22.** Write the other number sentence that belongs in this fact family. $2 + 8 = 10$ $8 + 2 = 10$ $10 - 8 = 2$ $\underline{} \ O \ \underline{} = \underline{}$

23. Write the missing addend.

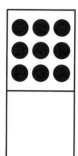

9 + ___ = 18

24. Write the missing addend.

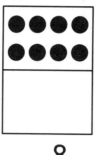

$$\begin{array}{r} 8 \\ +\,\square \\ \hline 11 \end{array}$$

_____

Use the number line to answer questions 25 and 26.

25. 16 − 8 = ___

26. 14 − 9 = ___

27.

There were 3 boys and 9 girls coloring. How many children were coloring?

____ children

28.

There were 13 monkeys in a cage. Then 4 monkeys left. How many monkeys were still in the cage?

____ monkeys

Write the correct answer.

1. How many ones are there?

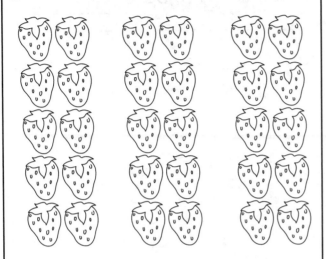

3 tens = _____ ones

2. How many ones are there?

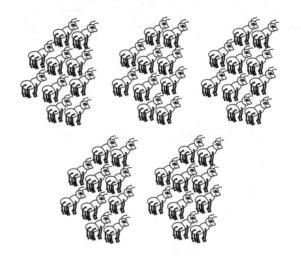

5 tens = _____ ones

3. How many tens and ones are there?

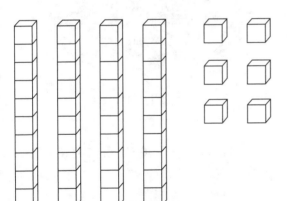

_____ tens _____ ones

4. How many tens and ones are there?

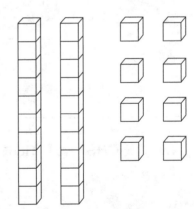

_____ tens _____ ones

5. Write the number.

8 tens 1 one = _____

6. Write the number.

6 tens 5 ones = _____

Name _____

7. Write the number.
5 tens 3 ones = _____

8. Write the number.
7 tens 2 ones = _____

9. Circle the number the model shows.

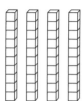

4   40   30

10. Circle the number the model shows.

7   17   71

Use these groups to help you answer questions 11 and 12.

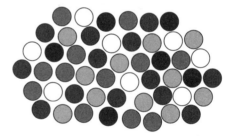

10 marbles   25 marbles   50 marbles

11. Circle the best estimate.

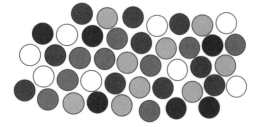

about 10 marbles
about 25 marbles
about 50 marbles

12. Circle the best estimate.

about 10 marbles
about 25 marbles
about 50 marbles

Name _____

Write the correct answer.

1. Count by fives. Write the number that comes next.

5, 10, 15, 20, _____

2. Count by tens. Write the number that comes next.

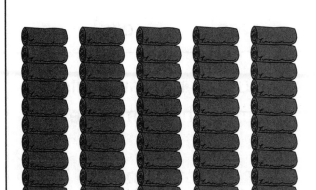

10, 20, 30, 40, _____

3. Count by fives. Write the number that comes next.

65, 70, 75, 80, _____

4. Count by tens. Write the number that comes next.

20, 30, 40, 50, _____

5. Count by twos. Write the number that comes next.

44, 46, 48, 50, _____

6. Count by threes. Write the number that comes next.

15, 18, 21, 24, _____

7. Circle even or odd.

10

even   odd

8. Circle even or odd.

13

even   odd

9. Count on by tens. Write the number that comes next.

57, 67, 77, 87, _____

10. Count back by tens. Write the number that comes next.

66, 56, 46, 36, _____

11. Circle the rule that will help you find the missing numbers.

5, 10, ___, ___, 25, 30

Count by twos.
Count by threes.
Count by fives.
Count by tens.

12. Circle the rule that will help you find the missing numbers.

71, 74, ___, 80, 83, ___

Count by twos.
Count by threes.
Count by fives.
Count by tens.

Write the correct answer.

1. Circle the number that is **greater**.

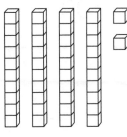 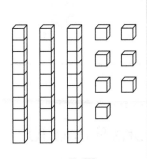 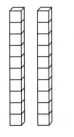

42   37

2. Circle the number that is **less**.

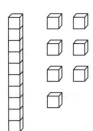

26   17

3. Write $<$ or $>$ in the circle.

6 ◯ 15

4. Write $<$ or $>$ in the circle.

51 ◯ 38

5. Write the number that is just **before** 28.

_____

28

29

6. Write the number that is **between** 34 and 36.

Harcourt Brace School Publishers

7. Write the number that is just **after** 63.

63, _____

8. Write the number that is **between** 98 and 100.

98, _____, 100

Use the pictures to answer questions 9 and 10.

| first | second | third | fourth | fifth | sixth | seventh | eighth |
| 1st | 2nd | 3rd | 4th | 5th | 6th | 7th | 8th |

9. Circle the position of .

third   fourth

fifth   sixth

10. Circle the position of .

5th   6th

7th   8th

Use the number line to answer questions 11 and 12.

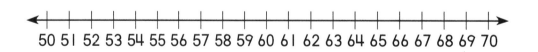

50 51 52 53 54 55 56 57 58 59 60 61 62 63 64 65 66 67 68 69 70

11. Circle the ten that 34 is closer to.

30   40

12. Circle the ten that 47 is closer to.

40   50

Name _____

Write the correct answer.

1. How many tens and ones are there?

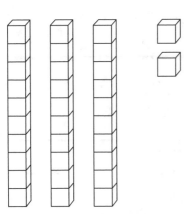

   _____ tens _____ ones

2. How many tens and ones are there?

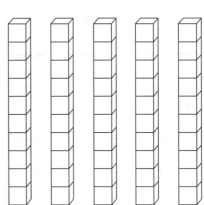

   _____ tens _____ ones

3. Write the number.

   8 tens 5 ones = _____

4. Write the number.

   4 tens 9 ones = _____

5. Count by fives. What number comes next?

   55, 60, 65, 70, _____

6. Count back by tens. What number comes next?

   66, 56, 46, 36, _____

Harcourt Brace School Publishers

7. Circle even or odd.

9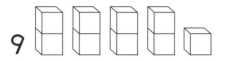

even   odd

8. Circle the rule that will help you find the missing numbers.

14, 16, ___, 20, 22

Count by twos.
Count by threes.
Count by fives.
Count by tens.

9. What number is just **after** 67?

67, _____

10. What number is **between** 92 and 94.

92, _____, 94

Use the number line to answer questions 11 and 12.

30 31 32 33 34 35 36 37 38 39 40 41 42 43 44 45 46 47 48 49 50

11. Circle the ten that 44 is closer to.

40   50

12. Circle the ten that 48 is closer to.

40   50

Harcourt Brace School Publishers

Write the correct answer.

1.
$$8$$
$$+9$$
_____

2. $15 - 8 = 7$
$7 + 8 = \underline{\ ?\ }$
_____

3. How many ones are there?

2 tens = \underline{\ ?\ } ones

_____ ones

4. Write the number

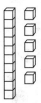

_____

5. Write the number.

4 tens 2 ones = \underline{\ ?\ }

_____

6. Write the number that is shown.

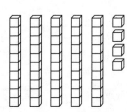

_____

Use these groups to help you answer questions 7 and 8.

 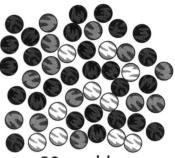

10 marbles   25 marbles   50 marbles

7. Circle the best estimate.

about 10 marbles
about 25 marbles
about 50 marbles

8. Circle the best estimate.

about 10 marbles
about 25 marbles
about 50 marbles

9. Count by twos. Write the number that comes next.

46, 48, 50, 52, _____

10. Count back by tens. Write the number that comes next.

51, 41, 31, 21, _____

11. Circle even or odd.

9

even   odd

12. Circle the rule that will help you find the missing numbers.

44, 54, ___, 74, 84, ___

Count by twos.
Count by threes.
Count by fives.
Count by tens.

13. Circle the number that is **greater**.

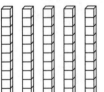   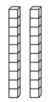

51   26

14. Circle the number that is **less**.

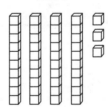   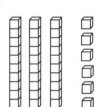

43   36

Harcourt Brace School Publishers

15. Write $<$ or $>$ in the circle.

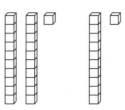

21 ◯ 11

16. Write the number.

78, ____, 80

Use the pictures below to answer questions 17 and 18.

first
1st

17. Write the position of the

_____

18. Write the position of the

_____

Use the number line to answer questions 19 and 20.

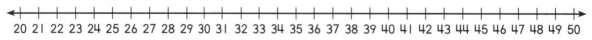

20 21 22 23 24 25 26 27 28 29 30 31 32 33 34 35 36 37 38 39 40 41 42 43 44 45 46 47 48 49 50

19. Write the ten that 22 is closest to.

_____

20. Write the ten that 36 is closest to.

_____

Name _____

11. Write the total amount.

_____ ¢

12. Write the total amount.

_____ ¢

13. Circle the group of coins that will buy  80¢ .

14. Circle the group of coins that will buy  45¢ .

Harcourt Brace School Publishers

Name _____

Write the correct answer.

1. Circle the group of coins that has the same value as

2. Circle the group of coins that has the same value as

3. Circle the group that uses fewer coins to show the same value.

Form B • Free-Response

Go on.

5. Circle the toy you could buy with this group of coins.

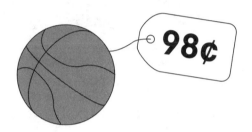

98¢

92¢

87¢

Book 80¢

6. Circle the fruit you could buy with this group of coins.

40¢

45¢

46¢

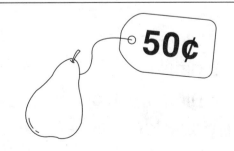

50¢

Harcourt Brace School Publishers

7. You have 55¢.

You buy 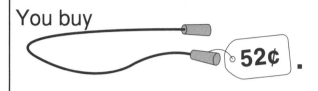 **52¢** .

53¢ ___ ___

Your change is _____ ¢.

8. You have 25¢.

You buy  **21¢** .

22¢ ___ ___ ___

Your change is _____ ¢.

9. Julie has 2 quarters, 1 dime, and 3 pennies. How much money does she have?

_____ ¢

10. Juan has 1 half-dollar, 2 dimes, and 4 pennies. How much money does he have?

_____ ¢

11. Circle the group of coins that will buy

 **35¢** .

5 nickels
3 dimes
2 dimes, 2 nickels
1 quarter, 1 dime

12. Circle the group of coins that will buy

 **80¢** .

8 nickels
2 quarters, 2 dimes
1 half-dollar, 5 nickels
3 quarters, 1 nickel

Harcourt Brace School Publishers

Name _____

Write the correct answer.
Use the calendar to answer questions 1 and 2.

October

Sunday	Monday	Tuesday	Wednesday	Thursday	Friday	Saturday
			1	2	3	4
5	6	7	8	9	10	11
12	13	14	15	16	17	18
19	20	21	22	23	24	25
26	27	28	29	30	31	

1. Write the date of the third Tuesday.

   _____

2. Write the day on which this month begins.

   _____

Use the calendar to answer questions 3 and 4.

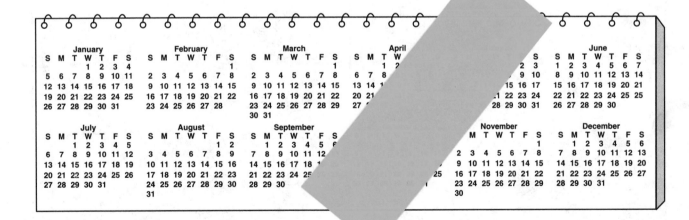

3. Write the seventh month in the year.

   _____

4. Write the month that follows April.

   _____

Harcourt Brace School Publishers

NAME Name _____

CHAPTER CHAPTER 9 TEST
PAGE 2

5. The play starts at

.

Beth gets there at

.

Is Beth early or late? Circle
your answer.

early   late

6. The circus starts at

.

Adam gets there at

.

Is Adam early or late? Circle
your answer.

early   late

7. Use the clocks. Circle the
event that came second.

8. Use the clocks. Circle the
event that came first.

Harcourt Harcourt Brace School Publishers

Form **Form B • Free-Response**   **B196**   **Go on.**

5. You have 70¢.
You buy 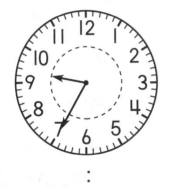 .

68¢ ___¢ ___¢
Your change is _____ ¢.

6. Mary has I half-dollar, I quarter, 2 dimes, and I penny. How much money does she have?

_____ ¢

7. What time does the clock show?

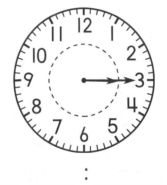

_____ : _____

8. What time does the clock show?

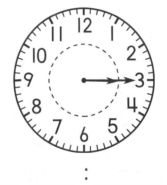

_____ : _____

9. Jack goes to a soccer game. It starts at  .

It ends 2 hours later. Write the time the game is over.

_____ : _____

10. School starts at

 .

Gina gets there at

 .

Is Gina early or late? Circle your answer.
early   late

Form B • Free-Response

Go on.

Use the schedule to answer questions 11 and 12.

Team Sports Day

8:30 – 10:00	Soccer
10:30 – 12:00	Kickball
12:00 – 1:00	Lunch
1:30 – 2:00	Rest
2:30 – 3:30	Baseball

11. What time does the mixed chorus class start? _____ : _____	12. How long does the boys' chorus class last? _____

Harcourt Brace School Publishers

Write the correct answer.

1.
$$\begin{array}{r} 5 \\ 8 \\ +5 \\ \hline \end{array}$$

2.
$$\begin{array}{r} 7 \\ 3 \\ +6 \\ \hline \end{array}$$

3. $16 - 8 =$ _____

4. $14 - 9 =$ _____

5.

There were 4 boys and 9 girls coloring. How many children were coloring?

_____ children

6.
Missing art

There were 12 bugs on a stick. Then 3 went away. How many bugs were still on the stick?

_____ bugs

7. Count by fives. Write the number that comes next.

35, 40, 45, 50, _____

8. Circle the rule that will help you find the missing numbers.

23, 26, _____, 32, 35, _____
Count by twos.
Count by threes.
Count by fives.
Count by tens.

Name _____

CUMULATIVE TEST
PAGE 2

9. Count back by tens. Write the number that comes next.

72, 62, 52, 42, _____

10. Circle even or odd.

even   odd

11. Write < or > in the circle.

7 ◯ 11

12. Write the number.

39, _____, 41

Use the pictures below to answer questions 13 and 14.

first   second   third   fourth fifth   sixth seventh eighth
1st   2nd   3rd   4th   5th   6th   7th   8th

13. Write the position of the

_____

14. Write the position of the

_____

Form B • Free-Response   B202   **Chapters 1–9**   **Go on.**

Harcourt Brace School Publishers

Write the correct answer.

15. Count on. Write the total amount.

_____ ¢

16. You have 45¢.
You buy

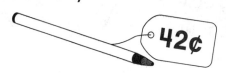

Your change is _____ ¢.

17. Circle the group of coins that will buy

18. Circle the toy you could buy with this group of coins.

19. Write the time the clock shows.

_____ : _____

20. Write the time the clock shows.

_____ : _____

Use the calendar to answer questions 21 and 22.

September

Sunday	Monday	Tuesday	Wednesday	Thursday	Friday	Saturday
1	2	3	4	5	6	7
8	9	10	11	12	13	14
15	16	17	18	19	20	21
22	23	24	25	26	27	28
29	30					

21. Write the date of the second Wednesday.

_____

22. Write the day on which this month ends.

_____

Use the schedule to answer questions 23 and 24.

Picinic Day Schedule
9:00 – 9:30   Parade
9:30 – 11:00   Races
11:00 – 12:00   Games
12:00 – 1:30   Lunch

23. Write the time the races start. _____ : _____

24. Write how long the games last. _____

Harcourt Brace School Publishers

Name _____

Name _____

Write the answer.
Use base-ten blocks to answer questions 1 and 2.

1. 8 + 6 = 14 ones

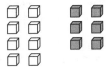

How many tens and ones?

_____ ten   _____ ones

2. 3 + 4 = 7 ones

How many tens and ones?

_____ tens   _____ ones

3. 14 + 8

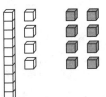

How many in all?

_____

4. 17 + 6

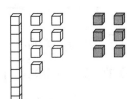

How many in all?

_____

5. 19 + 16

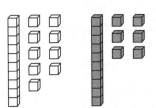

How many in all?

_____

6. 12 + 18

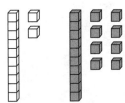

How many in all?

_____

Harcourt Brace School Publishers

7. Add.

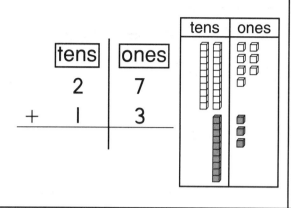

tens	ones
2	7
+ 1	3

8. Add.

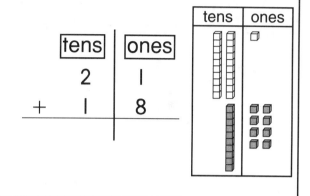

tens	ones
2	1
+ 1	8

Make a model to answer questions 9 and 10.

9. There are 17 boys and 15 girls in a race. How many children are in the race?

tens	ones
1	7
+ 1	5

_____ children

10. The pet shop has 16 goldfish and 12 redfish. How many fish does the pet shop have?

tens	ones
1	6
+ 1	2

_____ fish

Write the correct answer.
Use base-ten blocks to answer questions 1 and 2.

1.

tens	ones
□	
1	7
+	4

2.

tens	ones
□	
2	8
+	2

3.

tens	ones
□	
1	5
+	8

4.

tens	ones
□	
4	2
+	9

5.

tens	ones
4	6
+ 1	3

6.

tens	ones
2	4
+ 1	8

7.
$$\begin{array}{r} 37 \\ +39 \\ \hline \end{array}$$

8.
$$\begin{array}{r} 26 \\ +17 \\ \hline \end{array}$$

9.
$$
\begin{array}{r}
76 \\
+\ 8 \\
\hline
\end{array}
$$

10.
$$
\begin{array}{r}
58 \\
+39 \\
\hline
\end{array}
$$

11. The children in Mrs. Clark's class made 25 cards. The children in Mr. Brown's class made 36 cards. How many cards did the two classes make?

_____ cards

12. On Monday, Faye planted 24 flowers. On Tuesday, she planted 13 flowers. How many flowers did she plant in all?

_____ flowers

13. Tina baked 32 cookies for her class. She baked 44 cookies for her family. It took her 45 minutes to bake the cookies. How many cookies did Tina bake in all?

_____ cookies

14. Ray collected 28 cans on Monday. On Thursday he collected 19 cans. He went to a park on Friday. How many cans did Ray collect in all?

_____ cans

Harcourt Brace School Publishers

Name _____

Write the correct answer.

1. 13 + 16

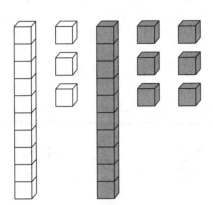

Write how many in all.

_____

2. 18 + 17

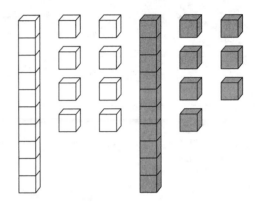

Write how many in all.

_____

Make a model to answer questions 3 and 4.

3. At the circus, there are 12 lions and 15 elephants. How many animals are at the circus?

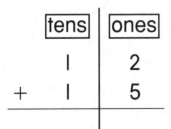

tens	ones
1	2
+ 1	5

_____ animals

4. There are 14 redbirds and 16 bluebirds in Kevin's yard. How many birds are in Kevin's yard?

tens	ones
1	4
+ 1	6

_____ birds

Form B • Free-Response

Go on.

Add. Regroup if you need to.

5.

tens	ones
2	3
+ 2	9

6.

tens	ones
4	7
+ 1	6

7.
```
  35
+  5
```

8.
```
  66
+ 18
```

9. Ryan spent $3.50 for a new bank. He put 34 pennies in the bank one week and 39 pennies in the bank the next week. How many pennies did he put in the bank?

_____ pennies

10. Sandy planted 23 pansies on Monday and 46 pansies on Tuesday. On Wednesday, she planted 12 roses. How many pansies did Sandy plant?

_____ pansies

Name _____

Choose the correct answer.

1.
$$\begin{array}{r} 4 \\ 6 \\ +\,2 \\ \hline \end{array}$$

_____

2. What is the missing addend?

[

Missing art
E062U1A-2

7 + ___ = 13

3. How many tens and ones are there?

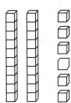

___ tens ___ ones = ___

4. Count back by fives. What number comes next?

85, 80, 75, 70, _____

5. What number is before?

_____ , 61

6. Count on. What is the total amount?

___ ¢, ___ ¢, ___ ¢, ___ ¢

7. Candy saved 1 quarter, 1 dime, 1 nickel, and 4 pennies. How much money did she save in all?

_____ ¢

8. Rob went to a baseball game. It started at

It ended 3 hours later. What time was the game over?

_____

9. Art class starts at

Tim gets there at

Is Tim early or late? Circle your answer.

early   late

10. The pet show starts at

Kathy gets there at

Is Kathy early or late? Circle your answer.

early   late

PAGE 1

Use base-ten blocks to answer questions 11 and 12.

11. $9 + 4 = 13$ ones

How many tens and ones?

_____ ten   _____ ones

12. $15 + 7$

How many in all?

_____

13. There are 14 boys and 18 girls on the playground. How many children are on the playground?

tens	ones
1	4
+1	8

_____ children

14. The flower shop has 16 red flowers and 13 yellow flowers. How many flowers does the flower shop have?.

tens	ones
1	6
+1	3

_____ flowers

Harcourt Brace School Publishers

15.

tens	ones
☐	
1	6
+	7

16.

tens	ones
1	1
+3	8

17.
$$\begin{array}{r} 26 \\ +28 \\ \hline \end{array}$$

18.
$$\begin{array}{r} 85 \\ +\ 7 \\ \hline \end{array}$$

19. The children in Mrs. Washington's class read 55 books. The students in Mrs. Johnson's class read 26 books. How many books did the two classes read?

_____ books

20. There are 18 computers in Sarah's school and 16 computers in Diane's school. How many computers are in the two schools?

_____ computers

Write the correct answer.

1. Subtract 3 ones. How many tens and ones are left?

_____ tens _____ ones

2. Subtract 7 ones. How many tens and ones are left?

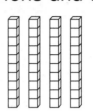

_____ tens _____ ones

3.

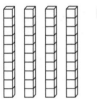

$48 - 5 =$ _____

4.

$23 - 9 =$ _____

5.

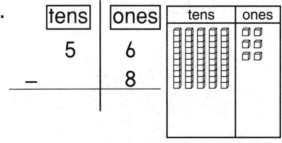

tens	ones
5	6
−	8

tens	ones

6.

tens	ones
3	2
−	5

tens	ones

7.

tens	ones
5	0
− 1	4

8.

tens	ones
4	2
− 2	4

9.

tens	ones
2	4
− 1	9

10.

tens	ones
3	0
− 1	5

Use base-ten blocks.
Choose the operation and solve. Write + or −.

11. Craig sees 24 cows and 26 pigs at a farm. How many animals does he see in all?

	tens	ones
	2	4
◯	2	6

12. Beth has 70¢. She buys a

.

How much money does Beth have left?

	tens	ones
	7	0¢
◯	1	4¢

Harcourt Brace School Publishers

Name _____

Write the answer.

1.

tens	ones

tens	ones
4	1
−	9

2.

tens	ones

tens	ones
3	4
−	6

3.

tens	ones

tens	ones
8	5
− 4	5

4.

tens	ones

tens	ones
9	6
− 7	7

5.
```
  62
- 16
```

6.
```
  55
- 17
```

7.
    71
  −19

8.
    58
  −28

9. Circle the numbers you should add to check this subtraction problem.

     92   44
   −48   +44
    44

    44   92   92
  +48   +44   +48

10. Circle the numbers you should add to check this subtraction problem.

     63   63
   −37   +26
    26

    26   26   63
  +37   +26   +37

Choose the operation and solve. Write + or −.

11. You have 75¢. You buy 38¢.

How much money do you have left?

    75¢
  ◯ 38¢

12. How much money would you need to buy 🚗 49¢ ?

    49¢
  ◯ 32¢

Harcourt Brace School Publishers

Write the correct answer.
Subtract. Regroup if you need to.

1.

TENS	ONES

tens	ones
5	1
+	8

2.

TENS	ONES

tens	ones
6	5
−	7

3.

tens	ones
3	5
− 1	9

4.

tens	ones
4	4
− 2	2

Use base-ten blocks.
Choose the operation and solve. Write + or − .

5. Pat sees 18 tigers and 25 monkeys at the zoo. How many animals does Pat see?

tens	ones
1	8
+ 2	5

_____ animals

6. Jeff has 80¢, He buys a How much money does Jeff have left?

tens	ones
8	0
+ 4	2

_____ ¢

Subtract. Regroup if you need to.

7.

TENS	ONES

tens	ones
5	0
− 2	7

8.

TENS	ONES

tens	ones
6	2
− 3	6

9.
$$\begin{array}{r} 41 \\ -27 \\ \hline \end{array}$$

10.
$$\begin{array}{r} 90 \\ -56 \\ \hline \end{array}$$

Choose the operation and solve. Write + or − .

11. You have 83¢. You buy a 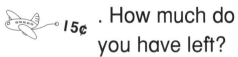 15¢ . How much do you have left?

$$\begin{array}{r} 83¢ \\ -15¢ \\ \hline ¢ \end{array}$$

12. How much money would you need to buy a ⚾ 48¢ and a ⚾ 24¢ .

$$\begin{array}{r} 48¢ \\ +24¢ \\ \hline ¢ \end{array}$$

Name _____

Write the correct answer.

1. Circle the group that uses fewer coins to show the same amount.

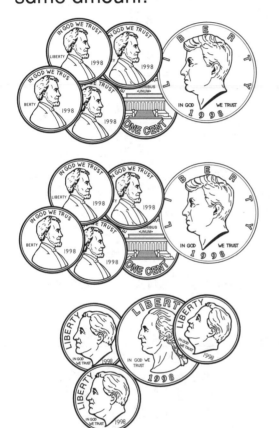

2. Circle the group that uses fewer coins to show the same amount.

3. Circle the group of coins that will buy

 25¢

4 nickels
2 dimes, 1 nickel
1 dime, 2 nickels
1 nickel, 5 pennies

4. Circle the group of coins that will buy

 60¢

8 nickels
2 quarters
1 half dollar, 1 dime
1 half dollar, 1 nickel\

Name _____

CUMULATIVE TEST
PAGE 2

5. Write the time the clock shows.

___:___

6. Subtract 5 ones. How many tens and ones are left?

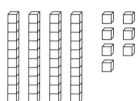

___tens ___ ones

7.

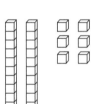

26 − 5 = ___

8.

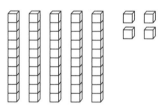

tens	ones
5	4
−	7

Form B • Free-Response   B222   **Chapters 1–13**   Go on.

Harcourt Brace School Publishers

9.

tens	ones
7	0
− 2	2

10.

tens	ones
3	6
− 1	8

Use base-ten blocks.
Choose the operation and solve. Write + or − .

11. Marcia saw 26 birds and 14 snakes at the zoo. How many animals did she see in all?

tens	ones
2	6
◯ 1	4

12. Tasha has 80¢. She buys a

55¢

How much money does Tasha have left?

tens	ones
8	0
◯ 5	5
	¢

Subtract. Regroup if you need to.

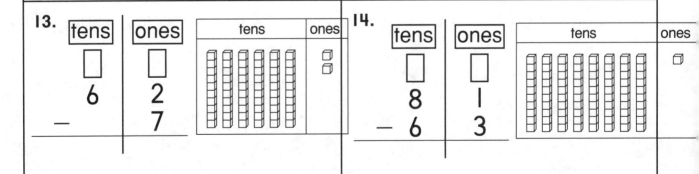

13.

tens	ones	tens	ones
☐	☐		
6	2		
−	7		

14.

tens	ones	tens	ones
☐	☐		
8	1		
− 6	3		

Harcourt Brace School Publishers

15.
$$\begin{array}{r} 74 \\ -28 \\ \hline \end{array}$$

16.
$$\begin{array}{r} 48 \\ -18 \\ \hline \end{array}$$

17. Write the numbers you should add to check this subtraction problem.

$$\begin{array}{r} 66 \\ -18 \\ \hline 48 \end{array}$$

18. Write the numbers you should add to check this subtraction problem.

$$\begin{array}{r} 53 \\ -27 \\ \hline 26 \end{array}$$

Choose the operation and solve. Write $+$ or $-$.

19. You have 55¢. You buy a

How much do you have left?

 28¢

$$\begin{array}{r} 55¢ \\ O28¢ \\ \hline \end{array}$$

20. How much money would you need to buy and? 39¢

16¢

$$\begin{array}{r} 39¢ \\ O16¢ \\ \hline \end{array}$$

Harcourt Brace School Publishers

Write the correct answer.
Use the picture to answer questions 1 and 2.

1. Write tally marks to show how many pigs there are.	2. Write tally marks to show how many cows there are.
_____	_____

Jen asked 10 friends about their favorite snack.
The tally table shows what she found.
Use the table to answer questions 3 and 4.

Favorite Snacks	
cookies	|
popcorn	||
pretzels	｜｜｜｜
fruit	||

| 3. How many children liked fruit the best?

_____ children | 4. Which snack was liked best by the most children?

_____ |

Use the table to answer questions 5 to 8.

Number of Children in the Art Contest	
Room 16	|||
Room 17	ЖЖ |
Room 18	ЖЖ ЖЖ
Room 19	|||

5. In which two rooms were the same number of children in the contest?

Rooms _____ and _____

6. How many more children from Room 18 were in the contest than from Room 17?

_____ more children

7. How many children in all were in the contest?

_____ children

8. In which room were the most children in the contest?

Room _____

Harcourt Brace School Publishers

Use the tables to answer questions 9 to 12.

Favorite Games in Room 19	
jump rope	ⵌ l
tag	ⵌ ll
races	ⵌ lll
kickball	lll

Favorite Games in Room 20	
jump rope	ⵌ ⵌ
tag	llll
races	lll
kickball	ⵌ ll

9. How many children in Room 19 like tag best? _____ children	10. In which room do more children like races best? Room _____
11. How many children are in Room 20? _____ children	12. Which game got the most votes in all? _____

Name _____

Write the correct answer.
Use the graph to answer questions 1 to 4.

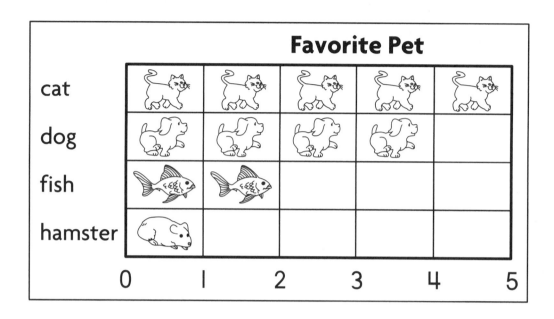

1. Which is the favorite pet of the most people?

_____

2. Which is the favorite pet of the fewest people?

_____

3. How many more people like dogs than like fish?

_____ more

4. How many fewer people like hamsters than like cats?

_____ fewer

Harcourt Brace School Publishers

Name _____

Use the graph to answer questions 5 to 8.

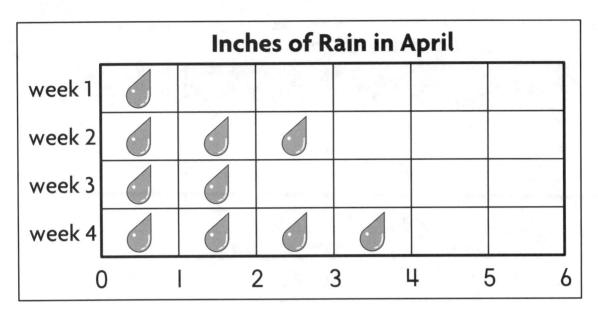

Each ⬤ stands for 2 inches of rain.

5. Which week had 4 inches of rain? week _____		**6.** Which week had the fewest inches of rain? week _____
7. Which week had the most inches of rain? week _____		**8.** How many inches of rain were there in week 2? _____ inches

Harcourt Brace School Publishers

Name _____

Use the graph to answer questions 9 to 14.

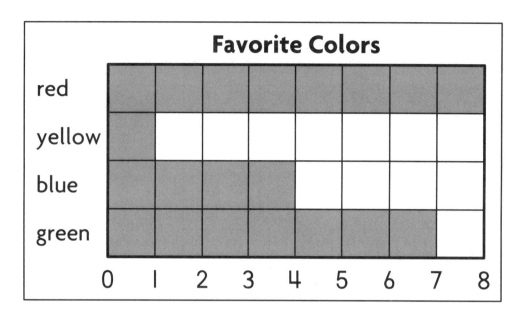

Favorite Colors

9. How many fewer people like green the best than red?

_____ fewer

10. How many people like blue the best?

_____ people

11. Which color do the most people like the best?

_____

12. Which color do the fewest people like the best?

_____

13. How many more people like green the best than like blue the best?

_____ more

14. How many fewer people like yellow than like red the best?

_____ fewer

Stop!

Name _____

Write the correct answer.
Use the picture to answer questions 1 to 4.

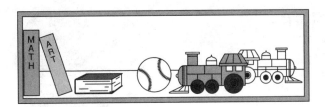

1. Circle the group of objects you are certain to find on the shelf.

2. Circle the group of objects it is impossible to find on the shelf.

3. Circle the group of objects you are certain to find on the shelf.

 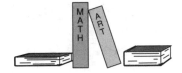

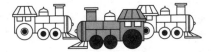

4. Circle the group of objects it is impossible to find on the shelf.

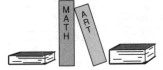

Use the table to answer questions 5 and 6.
This table shows the outcomes of 10 spins on the spinner.

Color	Tally Marks
black	卌 |||
white	||

5. Which color did the spinner stop on more often?

_____

6. How many times did the spinner stop on white?

_____ times

7. There are 4 triangles, 4 circles, and 12 squares in a bag. Which shape will be pulled out most often?

_____

8. This spinner can stop on 1, 2, or 3. Which number will it stop on most often?

_____

9. Circle the bag a ball will be pulled from least often.

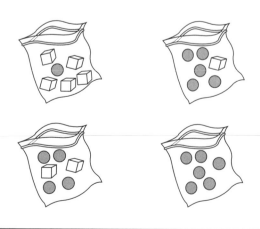

10. This spinner can stop on 1, 2, or 3. Which will it stop on most often?

_____

Stop!

Harcourt Brace School Publishers

Write the correct answer.
Use the tables to answer questions 1 to 4.

Boys' Favorite Song	Tally Marks	Totals
Bingo	✔✔✔✔✔ ✔✔	
This Old Man	✔✔✔✔	
Row Your Boat	✔✔	
Yankee Doodle	✔	

Girls' Favorite Song	Tally Marks	Totals
Bingo	✔✔✔✔✔ ✔	
This Old Man	✔✔✔✔✔	
Row Your Boat	✔✔	
Yankee Doodle	✔	

1. How many boys liked "Row your Boat" the best?

   _____ boys

2. In which group do more children like "This Old Man" the best? Write **boys** or **girls**.

   _____

3. How many boys and girls are there in all?

   _____ boys and _____ girls

4. Which song got the most votes in both groups?

   _____

Name _____

Use the graph to answer questions 5 and 6.

Our Favorite Drink

Milk	
Soda	
Water	
Lemonade	

5. Which drink is the favorite of the most people?

_____

6 How many fewer people like lemonade than like milk?

_____ fewer

Use the picture to answer questions 7 and 8.

7. Circle which group of coins you are certain to find on the tray.

8. Circle which group of coins it is impossible to find on the tray.

Form B   B234

Harcourt Brace School Publishers

Write the correct answer.

1. Use the picture to find the sum.

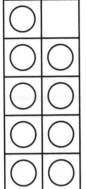

9
+4
___

2. Circle the rule that will help you find the missing numbers.

12, 14, ___, 18, 20,

Count by twos.
Count by threes.
Count by fives.
Count by tens.

3. Joel goes to a ball game. It starts at

It ends 2 hours later.
Write the time the game is over.

_____ : _____

4. Leah planted 41 seeds on Monday and 39 seeds on Wednesday. On Tuesday, she cooked 2 cakes. How many seeds did Leah plant?

_____ seeds

Jill asked 4 friends how many children were in their families.
The tally table shows what she found.
Use the table to answer questions 5 to 8.

Number of Children in Family	Tally Marks	Totals
Carl	ⵁⵁⵁⵁⵁ ⵁ	6
Mindy	|||	3
Linda	||||	4
Mathew	||	2

5. How many children are in Linda's family?

___ children

6. How many children are in the largest family?

___

7. How many people have more than 2 in their family?

___ people

8. How many more children are in Linda's family than in Matthew's family?

___ more

Use the graph to answer questions 9 and 10.

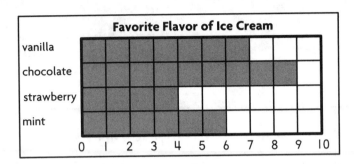

Favorite Flavor of Ice Cream

vanilla	
chocolate	
strawberry	
mint	

0 1 2 3 4 5 6 7 8 9 10

9. How many people like chocolate the best? ___ people	10. How many more people like mint than like strawberry? ___ more people

Use the graph to answer questions 11 and 12.

Favorite Lunch

sandwich	
pizza	
salad	
soup	

0   1   2   3   4   5

11. How many more people like sandwiches than like soup? ___ more	12. Which is the favorite lunch of the most people? _____

Harcourt Brace School Publishers

Name _____

Use the table to answer questions 13 and 14.
This table shows the outcomes of 10 spins.

Pattern	Tally Marks
dots	卌 II
stripes	III

---

13. Write which pattern the pointer stopped on more often. Write **dots** or **stripes**.

_____

14. How many times did the pointer stop on stripes?

___ times

---

15. In a bag there are 3 red markers, 4 green markers, and 15 yellow markers. Which color will be pulled out most often?

_____

16. This pointer can stop on 1, 2, or 3. Which number will it stop on most often?

_____

---

17. Circle the bag you think a cube will be pulled from least often.

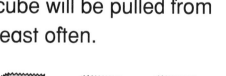

18. The pointer can stop on 1, 2, or 3. Which do you think it will stop on least often?

_____

Harcourt Brace School Publishers

Name _____

Write the correct answer.

1. Circle the object shaped like this solid figure.

2. Circle the object shaped like this solid figure.

3. Circle the object shaped like this solid figure.

4. Circle the solid figure that is the same shape as this solid figure.

5. Circle the solid figure that has all flat faces and can be stacked.

6. Circle the solid figure that has no flat faces and can be rolled.

Harcourt Brace School Publishers

Name _____

7. Circle the solid figure that has 5 flat faces and can slide.

8. Circle the solid figure that can roll and slide.

9. Circle the solid figure missing in the pattern.

10. Circle the solid figure missing in the pattern.

11. Circle the plane figure you could trace from the solid figure.

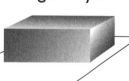

12. Circle the plane figure you could trace from the solid figure.

Harcourt Brace School Publishers

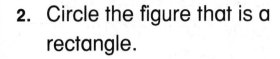

Write the correct answer.

1. Circle the figure that is a triangle.

2. Circle the figure that is a rectangle.

3. How many sides does this figure have?

_____ sides

4. How many corners does this figure have?

_____ corners

5. Circle the figure that has 5 sides and 5 corners.

6. Circle the figure that has 3 sides and 3 corners.

Name _____

7. Circle the drawing that shows how you can cut this figure to make 2 rectangles.

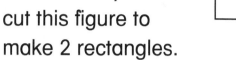

8. Circle the drawing that shows how you can cut this figure to make 2 triangles.

9. Circle the figures that are the same size and shape.

10. Circle the figure that is the same size and shape as this figure.

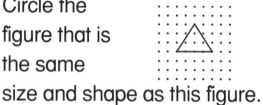

11. Circle the figure that will fit.

12. Circle the figure that will fit.

Harcourt Brace School Publishers

Name _____

Circle the correct answer.

---

1. Circle the picture that has symmetry.

2. Circle the picture that does NOT have symmetry.

---

3. Circle the picture that has symmetry.

4. Circle the picture that does NOT have symmetry.

Form B • Free-Response　　　　**B243**　　　　**Go on.**

5. Circle the picture that shows the line of symmetry.

 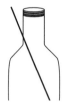

6. Circle the picture that shows the line of symmetry.

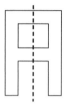

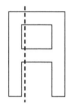

7. Circle the word that names the move.

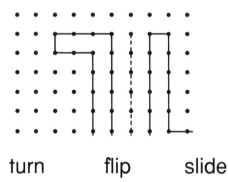

turn   flip   slide

8. Circle the word that names the move.

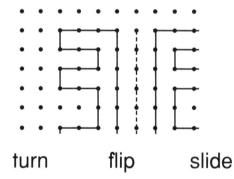

turn   flip   slide

9. Circle the word that names the move.

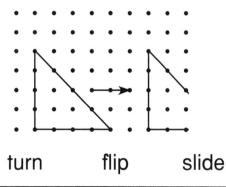

turn   flip   slide

10. Circle the word that names the move.

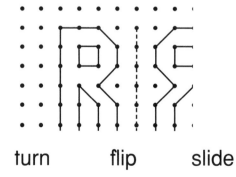

turn   flip   slide

Name _____

Write the correct answer.

1. Circle the object that is shaped like this solid figure.

2. Circle the solid figure that can stack and roll.

3. Circle the solid figure that comes next in the pattern.

4. Circle the plane figure you could trace from the solid figure.

 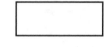

OVERSET

5. How many sides and corners does the figure have?

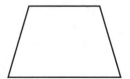

_____ sides _____ corners

Harcourt Brace School Publishers

7. Circle the figure that will fit.

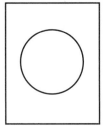
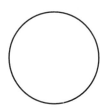

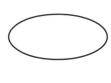

8. Circle the picture that shows the line of symmetry for the letter C.

9. Which word names the move? Write **turn, flip,** or **slide**.

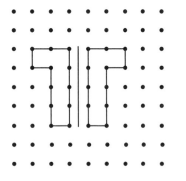

_____

10. Which word names the move? Write **turn, flip**, or **slide**.

_____

Name _____

Write the correct answer.

1. Write the total amount.

_____ ¢

2. Write the total amount.

_____ ¢

Use the tables to answer questions 3 and 4.

Favorite Subject in Room 27	Tally Marks
Reading	Ж III
Math	Ж Ж
Science	Ж II
Spelling	IIII

Favorite Subject in Room 28	Tally Marks
Reading	Ж Ж
Math	Ж II
Science	Ж I
Spelling	Ж

3. Write how many children in Room 28 like reading best.

_____ children

4. Write in which room the most children like math best.

Room _____

5. Draw the minute hand to show the time.

10:05

6. Draw the minute hand to show the time.

1:45

7. Circle the solid figure that has six flat faces and can be stacked.

8. Circle the solid figure that has two flat faces and can be stacked.

9. Draw the solid figure that is missing in the pattern.

_____

10. Draw the plane figure you could trace from the solid figure.

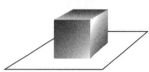

_____

11. Circle the object shaped like this solid figure.

12. Write how many sides this figure has.

_____ sides

13. Circle the drawing that shows how you can cut this figure to make 2 squares.

14. Circle the figure that will fit.

Name _____

CUMULATIVE TEST
PAGE 4

15. Draw a rectangle.

16. Draw a triangle.

17. Draw a line of symmetry on this picture.

18. Draw a line of symmetry on this picture.

19. Write the word that names the move. Write **turn**, **flip**, or **slide**.

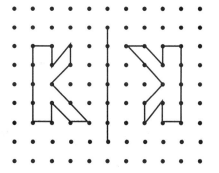

_____

20. Write the word that names the move. Write **turn**, **flip**, or **slide**.

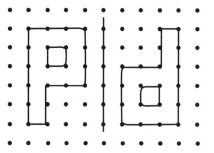

_____

Harcourt Brace School Publishers

Form B • Free-Response   B250   **Chapters 1–19**   Stop!

Name _____

Write the correct answer.
Use an inch ruler.

---

1. About how many paper clips long is this earthworm?

about _____ paper clips

---

2. About how many paper clips long are these scissors?

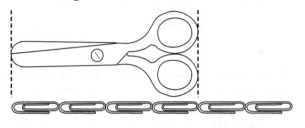

about _____ paper clips

---

3. Which is the best estimate for how long this dog biscuit is?

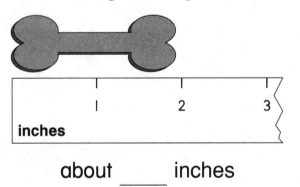

about _____ inches

---

4. About how long is this nail?

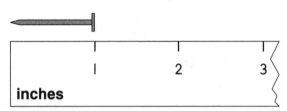

about _____ inch

---

5. How long is this stick of candy?

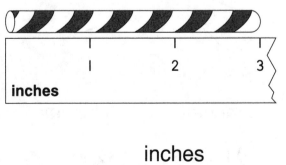

_____ inches

---

6. How long is this leaf?

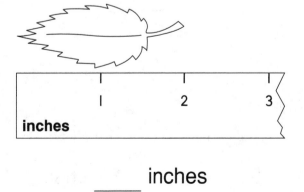

_____ inches

Form B • Free-Response   B251   **Go on.**

7. Circle about how long a car is.

less than 1 foot
about 1 foot
more than 1 foot

8. Circle about how long a pencil is.

less than 1 foot
about 1 foot
more than 1 foot

9. Circle which object is more than 1 foot long.

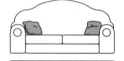   

10. Circle which object is about 1 foot long.

11. Circle how long this path is.

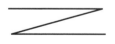

1 inch   3 inches

5 inches   8 inches

12. Circle how long this path is.

4 inches   8 inches

10 inches   12 inches

Stop!

Name _____

Write the correct answer.
Use a centimeter ruler.

1. How long is this feather?

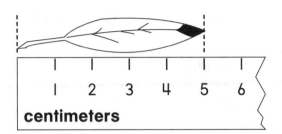

about _____ centimeters

2. How long is this bug?

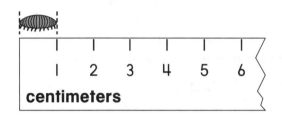

about _____ centimeter

3. How long is this toy car?

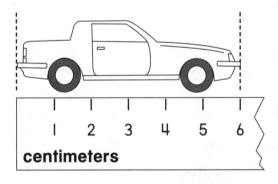

about _____ centimeters

4. How long is this caterpillar?

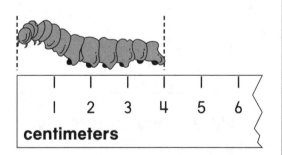

about _____ centimeters

Harcourt Brace School Publishers

For questions 5 and 6, use a decimeter ruler.

```
    1    2    3    4    5    6    7    8    9    10
centimeters
```

---

5. Circle the one that is about a decimeter long.

a car

a lizard

an elephant's trunk

a baseball bat

6. Circle the one that is less than a decimeter long.

an ant

a lamp

a magazine

a school bus

---

7. How many centimeters is it around the figure?

_____ centimeters

8. How many centimeters is it around the figure?

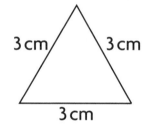

3 cm   3 cm

3 cm

_____ centimeters

---

9. How many squares will fit in the figure?

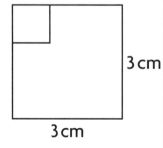

3 cm

3 cm

_____ squares

10. How many squares will fit in the figure?

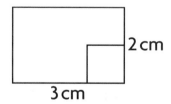

2 cm

3 cm

_____ squares

Name _____

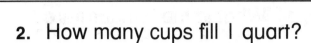
Write the correct answer.

1. How many cups fill 1 pint?

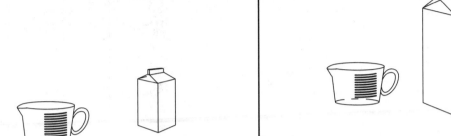

_____ cups

2. How many cups fill 1 quart?

_____ cups

3. How many cups fill 3 pints?

_____ cups

4. Which object weighs less than 1 pound?

a carrot   a table

a chair   a lamp

5. About how much does this desk weigh?

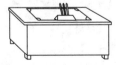

less than 1 pound

more than 1 pound

6. About how much does this shoelace weigh?

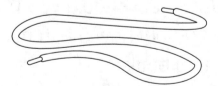

less than 1 pound

more than 1 pound

Harcourt Brace School Publishers

Name _____

7. What is the temperature?

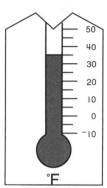

_____ °F

8. What is the temperature?

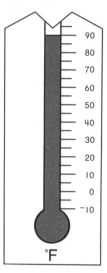

_____ °F

9. What is the temperature?

_____ °F

10. Which tool should you use to find out how tall you are?

MISSING ART

cup

ruler

thermometer

11. Which tool should you use to find out how much milk is in a bottle?

cup

ruler

thermometer

12. Which tool should Sue use to find out how cold it is outside?

cup

ruler

thermometer

Stop!

Harcourt Brace School Publishers

Name _____

Write the correct answer.

1. How many equal parts are there?

_____ equal parts

2. How many equal parts are there?

_____ equal parts

3. What part is colored?

$\frac{1}{6}$ $\frac{1}{3}$

$\frac{1}{4}$ $\frac{1}{2}$

4. Which picture shows $\frac{1}{2}$?

5. Which fraction tells what part is colored?

$\frac{1}{6}$ $\frac{1}{3}$

$\frac{1}{4}$ $\frac{1}{2}$

6. Which fraction tells what part is colored?

$\frac{1}{6}$ $\frac{1}{3}$

$\frac{1}{4}$ $\frac{1}{2}$

Form B • Free-Response   B257   Go on.

7. What fraction of the figure is colored?

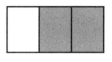

$\dfrac{1}{6}$ $\dfrac{2}{4}$

$\dfrac{1}{2}$ $\dfrac{2}{3}$

8. What figure shows $\dfrac{3}{4}$ colored?

9. Which fraction of the group of triangles is black?

$\dfrac{1}{4}$ $\dfrac{1}{2}$

$\dfrac{2}{3}$ $\dfrac{5}{6}$

10. Which fraction of the circle is white?

$\dfrac{1}{6}$ $\dfrac{1}{4}$

$\dfrac{3}{4}$ $\dfrac{4}{6}$

11. Shawn cut a sandwich in fourths. Then he ate 2 pieces. What part did Shawn eat?

$\dfrac{1}{6}$ $\dfrac{1}{4}$

$\dfrac{1}{3}$ $\dfrac{1}{2}$

12. Three children share 6 cupcakes. Each gets an equal part of the group. What part does one child get?

$\dfrac{1}{6}$ $\dfrac{1}{4}$

$\dfrac{1}{3}$ $\dfrac{1}{2}$

Harcourt Brace School Publishers

Name _____

Write the correct answer.

1. About how many paper clips long is the ribbon?

about _____ paper clips

2. How long is the nail?

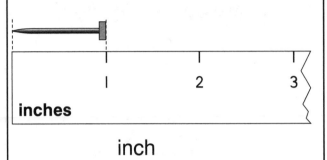

inches

_____ inch

3. Circle the object that is more than 1 foot long.

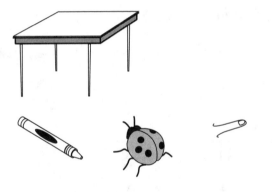

4. How long is the toy car?

about _____ centimeters

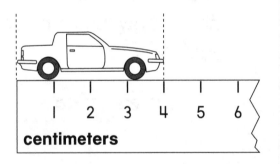

centimeters

5. How many centimeters is it around the figure.

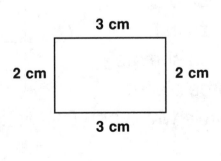

3 cm

2 cm   2 cm

3 cm

_____ centimeters

6. How many squares will fit in the figure?

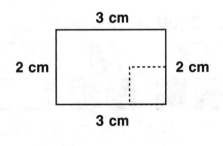

3 cm

2 cm   2 cm

3 cm

_____ squares

Harcourt Brace School Publishers

7. About how much does this carrot weigh? Circle the answer.

less than I pound

more than I pound

8. What is the temperature?

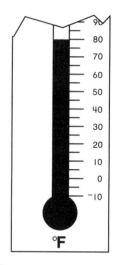

_____° F

9. What tool should Ben use to find out how long a piece of rope is?

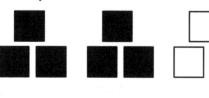

cup

ruler

thermometer

10. What part is colored?

$\frac{1}{4}$ $\frac{1}{3}$

$\frac{1}{2}$ $\frac{1}{6}$

11. Which fraction of the group of squares is black?

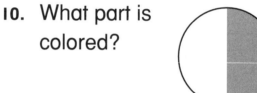

$\frac{3}{4}$ $\frac{2}{3}$ $\frac{1}{4}$ $\frac{1}{6}$

12. Debbie cut a pizza in fourths. Then she ate three pieces. Circle which part Debbie ate.

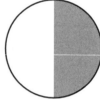

$\frac{3}{4}$ $\frac{2}{3}$ $\frac{4}{6}$ $\frac{1}{4}$

Stop!

Write the correct answer.

1. $14 - 6 = 8$ $8 + 6 =$ ___	2. Write the number that is **between** 77 and 79. 77, ___, 79
3. Juan has 1 half dollar, 2 nickels, and 2 pennies. How much money does he have? _____ ¢	4. $\begin{array}{r} 65 \\ -16 \\ \hline \end{array}$
5. Write about how many paper clips long this bean is.  about _____ paper clips	6. Write about how long this nail is. inches about ____ inches

Name _____

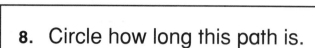

7. Write how long this bandage is.

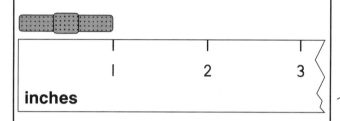

_____ inch

8. Circle how long this path is.

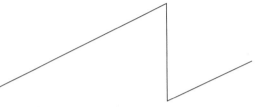

1 inch   2 inches

3 inches   4 inches

9. Write how long this ant is.

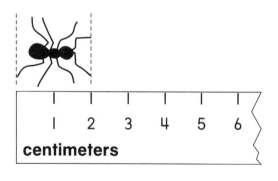

about _____ centimeters

10. Write how many centimeters it is around the figure.

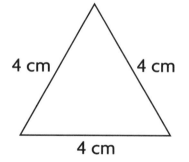

4 cm   4 cm

4 cm

_____ centimeters

Harcourt Brace School Publishers

Write the correct answer.

1. How many hundreds are there?

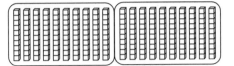

_____ hundreds

2. How many ones are there?

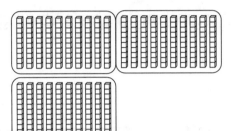

_____ ones

3. How many hundreds, tens, and ones are there?

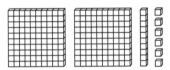

___ hundreds ___ ten ___ ones

4. What number does the model show?

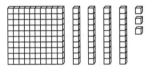

_____

5. What number does the model show?

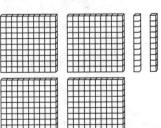

_____

6. What is the number?

9 ones + 7 hundreds + 1 ten

_____

7. Jessica has 5 hundreds, 9 tens, and 4 ones. What number is she showing?

_____

8. Mark has 8 tens, 6 hundreds, and 0 ones. What number is he showing?

_____

9. Which number does the model show?

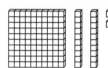

12   123

132   222

10. Which number does the model show?

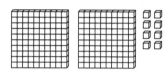

28   82

208   802

11. How many equal $1.00?

_____ nickels

12. Which coins equal $1.00?

Harcourt Brace School Publishers

Write the correct answer.

1. Compare the two models. Circle the model showing the **greater** number.

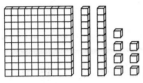

2. Compare the two models. Circle the model showing the number that is **less**.

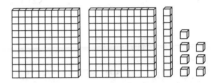

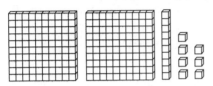

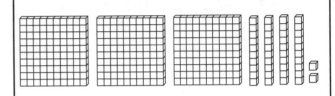

3. Circle the **greater** number.

   995   959

4. Circle the **greater** number.

   636   663

5. Circle the number that is **less**.

   780   870

6. Circle the number that is **less**.

   541   514

7. Joe read 126 books. Dan read 162 books. Who read the greater number of books?

   _____

8. Eli has 392 pennies. Beth has 405 pennies. Who has the number of pennies that is less?

   _____

9. Write **greater** or **less** to complete this sentence.

57 is _____ than 570.

10. Write $>$ or $<$ to fill the circle.

900 ◯ 899

11. The number that is just **after** 249 is _____ .

12. The number that is just **before** 480 is _____ .

13. Write the number that belongs in the blank.

629, _____, 631

14. Write the number that belongs in the blank.

_____, 200

15. Write the numbers 500, 540, 505, and 560 in order from least to greatest.

_____, _____, _____, _____

16. Write the numbers 302, 320, 230, and 203 in order from least to greatest.

_____, _____, _____, _____

Stop!

Harcourt Brace School Publishers

Name _____

Write the correct answer.

1. | hundreds | tens | ones |
   |:---:|:---:|:---:|
   | | □ | |
   | 2 | 4 | 6 |
   | + 1 | 2 | 4 |

2. | hundreds | tens | ones |
   |:---:|:---:|:---:|
   | □ | □ | |
   | 3 | 7 | 5 |
   | + 3 | 6 | 1 |

3.
```
  4 0 3
+ 1 5 8
```

4.
```
  5 4 2
+ 3 6 4
```

5. | hundreds | tens | ones |
   |:---:|:---:|:---:|
   | | □ | □ |
   | 9 | 8 | 4 |
   | − 5 | 2 | 7 |

6. | hundreds | tens | ones |
   |:---:|:---:|:---:|
   | □ | □ | |
   | 5 | 3 | 8 |
   | − 2 | 4 | 3 |

Harcourt Brace School Publishers

Name _____

7.
$$\begin{array}{r} 7\ 6\ 1 \\ -\ 6\ 7\ 0 \\ \hline \end{array}$$

8.
$$\begin{array}{r} 8\ 2\ 7 \\ -\ 4\ 8\ 2 \\ \hline \end{array}$$

9.
$$\begin{array}{r} \$2.\ 0\ 2 \\ +\ \ 3.\ 2\ 6 \\ \hline \$ \end{array}$$

10.
$$\begin{array}{r} \$6.\ 5\ 6 \\ -\ \ 2.\ 7\ 5 \\ \hline \$ \end{array}$$

11. Kimi had $9.93. She spent $7.69 on a gift. Write how much money she has left.

_____ $ _____

12. Bryan earned $2.98 on Friday and $1.40 on Saturday. Write how much money he earned in all.

_____ $ _____

Write the correct answer.

1. Write how many hundreds, tens, and ones are there.

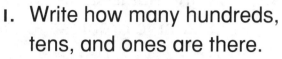
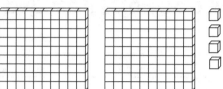

___ hundreds ___ tens ___ ones

2. Write the number the model shows.

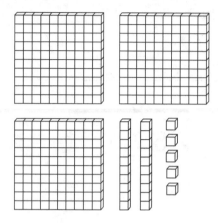

_____

3. Joan has 7 ones, 8 hundreds, and 6 tens. Write the number she is showing.

_____

4. How many equal $1.00?

_____ dimes

5. Circle the **greater** number.

699   700

6. Circle the number that is **less**.

401   410

7. Write the number that belongs in the blank.

723, _____, 725

8. Write the numbers in order from least to greatest.

685, 601, 692, 619

_____, _____, _____, _____

9.
$$538 \\ +257$$

9.
$$826 \\ -682$$

11. Chuck had $5.15. He spent $3.06 on a toy. How much money does he have left?

$_____

12. Katie earned $3.65 on Monday and $2.80 on Tuesday. How much money did she earn in all?

$_____

Harcourt Brace School Publishers

Write the correct answer.

1. Write the addition sentence that tells about the picture.

___ + ___ = ___

2. Write the missing addend.

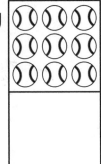

9 + ___ = 17

3. Write the number that is just **after** 82.

82, ___

4. Jim has 1 half-dollar, 1 quarter, 1 dime, and 3 pennies. How much money does he have?

___ ¢

5.

tens	ones
3	8
+ 2	7

6.

tens	ones
□	□
5	0
−1	7

Use the picture to answer questions 7 and 8.

7. Circle the group of toys you are certain to find on the shelf.

8. Circle the group of toys it is impossible to find on the shelf.

9. Write the number.

9 ones + 6 hundreds + 4 tens

_____

10. Write how many equal $1.00.

_____ pennies

11. Jessica has 7 hundreds, 3 tens, and 5 ones. Write the number she is showing.

_____

12. Mark has 4 tens, 8 hundreds, and 0 ones. Write the number he is showing.

_____

13. Circle the **greater** number.

807   870

14. Circle the number that is **less**.

159   591

15. Write **greater** or **less** to complete this sentence.

16 is _____ than 160.

16. Write the number that belongs in the blank.

729, _____, 731

17.

hundreds	tens	ones
	☐	
5	3	8
+ 3	2	6

18.

hundreds	tens	ones
	☐	☐
7	5	2
− 4	3	6

19.

$$634$$
$$+172$$

20.

$$515$$
$$-430$$

21. Kara had $7.25. She spent $5.28 on a gift. Write how much money she has left.

$ _____

22. Max earned $2.60 on Saturday and $1.75 on Sunday. Write how much money in all he earned.

$ _____

Name _____

Write the correct answer.

1. How many in all?

   3 groups of 2

   $2 + 2 + 2 =$ _____

2. How many in all?

   4 groups of 3

   $3 + 3 + 3 + 3 =$ _____

3. Look at the picture and the number sentence. Circle another number sentence that goes with the picture.

   $2 + 2 + 2 + 2 = 8$

   - - - - - - - - - -

   $2 - 2 = 0$
   $2 + 2 = 4$
   $4 \times 2 = 8$
   $8 + 2 = 10$

4. Look at the picture and the number sentence. Circle another number sentence that goes with the picture.

   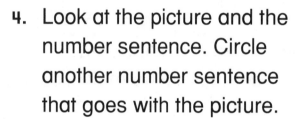

   $5 + 5 + 5 = 15$

   - - - - - - - - - -

   $15 - 5 = 10$
   $5 + 5 = 10$
   $9 + 6 = 15$
   $3 \times 5 = 15$

5.

   $2 \times 6 =$ _____

6.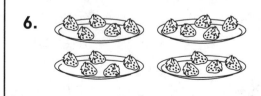

   $4 \times 5 =$ _____

Form B • Free-Response

Go on.

7. Write the multiplication sentence that goes with the picture.

___ × ___ = ___

8. Write the multiplication sentence that goes with the picture.

___ × ___ = ___

9. Write the number that completes the multiplication sentence.

3 × 3 = ___

10. Write the number that completes the multiplication sentence.

4 × 3 = ___

11. There are 5 children at a playground. Each child has 5 marbles. Write the number sentence that tells how many marbles they have in all.

___ × ___ = ___ marbles

12. There are 4 cats. Each cat has 2 kittens. Write how many kittens there are in all.

___ × ___ = ___ kittens

Harcourt Brace School Publishers

Write the correct answer.

1. 2 equal groups

How many are in each group?

_____ in each group

2. 3 equal groups

How many are in each group?

_____ in each group

3. 3 equal groups

How many are in each group?

_____ in each group

4. 2 equal groups

How many are in each group?

_____ in each group

5. How many equal groups are there?

_____ groups

6. How many equal groups are there?

_____ groups

Form B • Free-Response

Go on.

7. Groups of 3

How many equal groups are there?

_____ groups

8. Groups of 2

How many equal groups are there?

_____ groups

Solve.

9. There are 10 carrots. There are 5 children. Each child has the same number of carrots. How many carrots does each child have?

_____ carrots

10. James had 8 tickets. He gave each an equal number to 2 friends. How many tickets did each friend get?

_____ tickets

11. Jane had 10 cookies. She gave away 7 cookies. How many cookies does she have left?

_____ cookies

12. There are 4 children. Each child buys a toy that costs $4.00. How much money do they spend in all?

$ _____

Harcourt Brace School Publishers

Name _____

Write the correct answer.

1. Write how many in all.

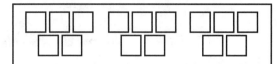

$$5 + 5 + 5 = \underline{\quad}$$

2. Write how many in all.

$$2 + 2 = \underline{\quad}$$

3. Write the multiplication sentence that goes with the picture.

$$\underline{\quad} \times \underline{\quad} = \underline{\quad}$$

4. Write the multiplication sentence that goes with the picture.

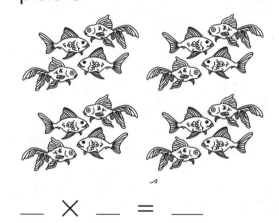

$$\underline{\quad} \times \underline{\quad} = \underline{\quad}$$

5. There are 4 children playing. Each child has 4 blocks. Write the multiplication sentence that tells how many blocks they have in all.

$$\underline{\quad} \times \underline{\quad} = \underline{\quad}$$

6. There are 2 bags. Each bag has 5 peanuts. Write how many peanuts there are in all.

$$\underline{\quad} \text{ peanuts}$$

7. 2 equal groups

How many are in each group?

___ in each group

8. 3 equal groups

How many are in each group?

___ in each group

9. Groups of 3

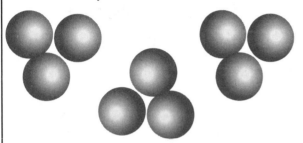

How many equal groups are there?

___ groups

10. Groups of 2

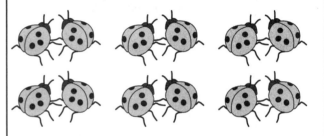

How many equal groups are there?

___ groups

Solve.

11. There are 15 toys. There are 5 children. Each child has the same number of toys. How many toys does each child have?

___ toys

12. Janet gave 14 stickers to 2 friends. She gave each friend an equal number. How many stickers did each friend get?

___ stickers

Name _____

Write the correct answer.
Use base-ten blocks to answer questions 1 and 2.

1. $\begin{array}{r} 47 \\ +36 \\ \hline \end{array}$	2. $\begin{array}{r} 28 \\ +12 \\ \hline \end{array}$

Use base-ten blocks.
Choose the operation and solve. Write $+$ or $-$.

3. Grandma has 34 flowers in her front yard and 27 flowers in her back yard. How many flowers does she have in all?

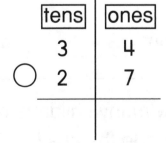

tens	ones
3	4
○ 2	7

4. Cheryl has 50¢. She buys a

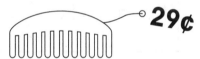

29¢

How much money does Cheryl have left?

tens	ones
5	0¢
○ 2	9¢

Harcourt Brace School Publishers

| 5. $\begin{array}{r} 51 \\ -26 \\ \hline \end{array}$ | 6. $\begin{array}{r} 73 \\ -44 \\ \hline \end{array}$ |

Use the graph to answer questions 7 to 10.

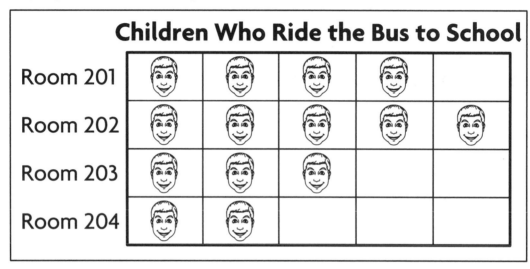

Children Who Ride the Bus to School

Each [face] stands for 3 students.

| 7. Which room has 12 children who ride the bus?

Room _____ | 8. Which room has the fewest number of children riding the bus?

Room _____ |
| 9. Which room has the most children riding the bus?

Room _____ | 10. How many children in Room 203 ride the bus?

_____ children |

Harcourt Brace School Publishers

11. **How many in all?**

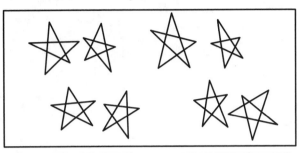

2 + 2 + 2 + 2 = ___

12.

5 × 3 = ___

13. Write the number that completes the multiplication sentence.

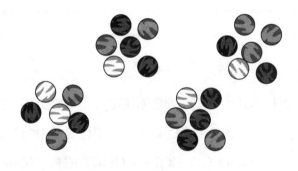

4 × 6 = ___

14. Write the number that completes the multiplication sentence.

3 × 2 = ___

15. There are 4 children in a car. Each child has 3 toys. Write the number sentence that tells how many toys they have in all.

___ × ___ = ___ toys

16. There are 7 cups on the table. Each cup has 4 lollipops. How many lollipops are there in all?

___ × ___ = ___ lollipops

17. 5 equal groups

How many are in each group?

_____ in each group

18. Groups of 2

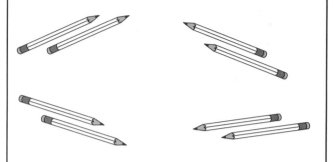

How many equal groups are there?

_____ groups

Solve.

19. There are 8 cookies. There are 4 children. Each child has the same number of cookies. How many cookies does each child have?

_____ cookies

20. John gives 6 dog biscuits to his 2 dogs. He gives each dog an equal number. How many dog biscuits does each dog get?

_____ dog biscuits

21. Mrs. Jones had 20 stickers. She gave away 10 stickers. How many stickers does she have left?

_____ stickers

22. There are 5 children. Each child buys a book that costs $1.00. How much money in all do they spend?

$ _____

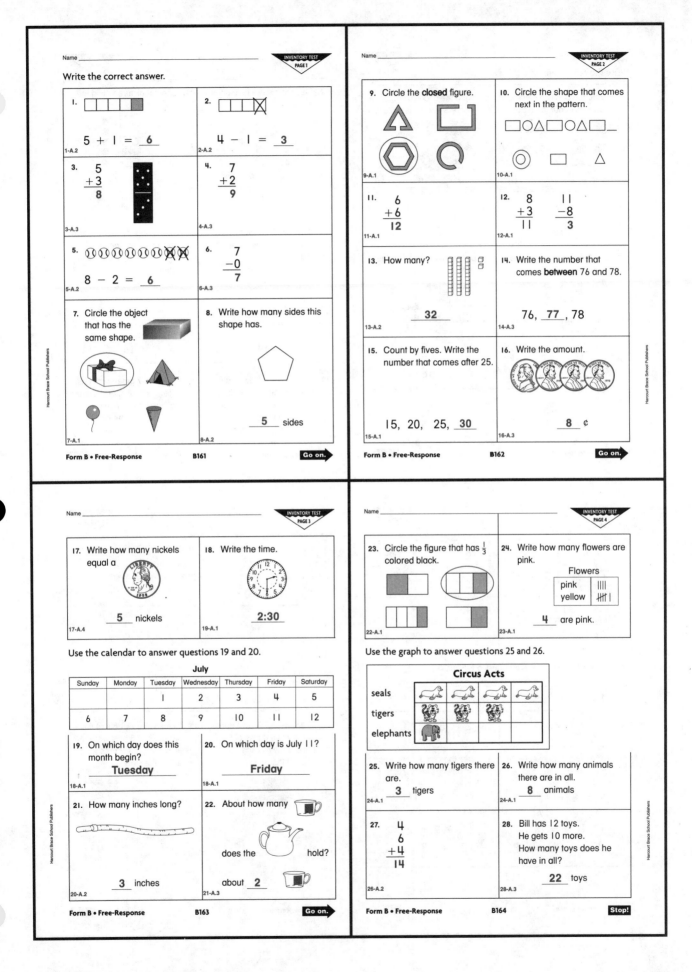

Name _____

INVENTORY TEST PAGE 1

Write the correct answer.

1. $5 + 1 = \underline{6}$
1-A.2

2. $4 - 1 = \underline{3}$
2-A.2

3. $\begin{array}{r} 5 \\ +3 \\ \hline 8 \end{array}$
3-A.3

4. $\begin{array}{r} 7 \\ +2 \\ \hline 9 \end{array}$
4-A.3

5. $8 - 2 = \underline{6}$
5-A.2

6. $\begin{array}{r} 7 \\ -0 \\ \hline 7 \end{array}$
6-A.3

7. Circle the object that has the same shape.
7-A.1

8. Write how many sides this shape has.

$\underline{5}$ sides
8-A.2

Form B • Free-Response   B161   **Go on.**

Name _____

INVENTORY TEST PAGE 2

9. Circle the **closed** figure.
9-A.1

10. Circle the shape that comes next in the pattern.

□ ○ △ □ ○ △ □ _
10-A.1

11. $\begin{array}{r} 6 \\ +6 \\ \hline 12 \end{array}$
11-A.1

12. $\begin{array}{r} 8 \\ +3 \\ \hline 11 \end{array}$ $\begin{array}{r} 11 \\ -8 \\ \hline 3 \end{array}$
12-A.1

13. How many?

$\underline{32}$
13-A.2

14. Write the number that comes **between** 76 and 78.

$76, \underline{77}, 78$
14-A.3

15. Count by fives. Write the number that comes after 25.

$15, 20, 25, \underline{30}$
15-A.1

16. Write the amount.

$\underline{8}$ ¢
16-A.3

Form B • Free-Response   B162   **Go on.**

Name _____

INVENTORY TEST PAGE 3

17. Write how many nickels equal a

$\underline{5}$ nickels
17-A.4

18. Write the time.

$2:30$
19-A.1

Use the calendar to answer questions 19 and 20.

July

Sunday	Monday	Tuesday	Wednesday	Thursday	Friday	Saturday
		1	2	3	4	5
6	7	8	9	10	11	12

19. On which day does this month begin?
Tuesday
18-A.1

20. On which day is July 11?
Friday
18-A.1

21. How many inches long?

$\underline{3}$ inches
20-A.2

22. About how many does the hold?

about $\underline{2}$
21-A.3

Form B • Free-Response   B163   **Go on.**

Name _____

INVENTORY TEST PAGE 4

23. Circle the figure that has $\frac{1}{3}$ colored black.
22-A.1

24. Write how many flowers are pink.

Flowers

pink	llll
yellow	Ⓗ Ⓛ l

$\underline{4}$ are pink.
23-A.1

Use the graph to answer questions 25 and 26.

Circus Acts

seals				
tigers				
elephants				

25. Write how many tigers there are.
$\underline{3}$ tigers
24-A.1

26. Write how many animals there are in all.
$\underline{8}$ animals
24-A.1

27. $\begin{array}{r} 4 \\ 6 \\ +4 \\ \hline 14 \end{array}$
26-A.2

28. Bill has 12 toys. He gets 10 more. How many toys does he have in all?

$\underline{22}$ toys
28-A.3

Form B • Free-Response   B164   **Stop!**

Harcourt Brace School Publishers

Free-Response Format • Test Answers

287

Write the correct answer.

1. Write the addition sentence that tells about the picture.

___7___ + ___7___ = ___14___

2. Write the addition sentence that tells about the picture.

___9___ + ___9___ = ___18___

3.
```
  6
+7
―――
 13
```

4.
```
  6
+5
―――
 11
```

5. Use the picture to find the sum.

```
  9
+4
―――
 13
```

6. Use the picture to find the sum.

```
  9
+7
―――
 16
```

7.
```
  6
+9
―――
 15
```

8.
```
  8
+9
―――
 17
```

---

9. Use the picture to find the sum.

```
  9
+3
―――
 12
```

10. Use the picture to find the sum.

```
  7
+5
―――
 12
```

11. Jim saw 3 red birds and 8 blue birds. How many birds did he see?

___11___ birds

12. Anna spent 7¢ for one shell and 8¢ for another shell. How much money did she spend?

___15___ ¢

13.
```
  8
  2
+4
―――
 14
```

14.
```
  5
  5
+6
―――
 16
```

15. Jade has 4 yellow boats, 4 green boats, and 9 blue boats. How many boats does she have?

___17___ boats

16. Jess has 7 green balloons, 3 pink balloons, and 2 blue balloons. How many balloons does he have?

___12___ balloons

Write the correct answer.

1.
```
  7      11
+4      -4
――      ――
 11       7
```

2. $16 - 7 = 9$

$9 + 7 = $ ___16___

3.
```
  8      13
+5      -5
――      ――
 13       8
```

4. $14 - 5 = 9$

$9 + 5 = $ ___14___

Use the number line to answer questions 5 and 6.

```
0  1  2  3  4  5  6  7  8  9  10 11 12 13 14 15 16 17 18
```

5. $15 - 9 = $ ___6___

6. $12 - 5 = $ ___7___

7. Write the number sentence that belongs in this fact family.

$9 + 8 = 17$
$8 + 9 = 17$
$17 - 9 = 8$
___17___ − ___8___ = ___9___

8. Write the number sentence that belongs in this fact family.

$9 + 2 = 11$
$11 - 2 = 9$
$11 - 9 = 2$
___2___ + ___9___ = ___11___

---

9. Write the missing addend.

```
  8
+7
――
 15
```

10. Write the missing addend.

```
  6
+8
――
 14
```

11. There were 7 brown ducks and 6 white ducks at the pond. How many ducks were at the pond?

___13___ ducks

12. There were 11 bats at the store. Then 8 bats were sold. How many bats were still at the store?

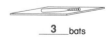

___3___ bats

Free-Response Format • Test Answers

Harcourt Brace School Publishers

Write the correct answer.

1. Write the addition sentence that tells about the picture.

___5___ + ___5___ = ___10___

1-A.1

2. Use the picture to find the sum.

$$\begin{array}{r} 9 \\ +3 \\ \hline 12 \end{array}$$

1-A.1

3. Anna has 5 green bows and 9 blue bows. How many bows does she have?

___14___ bows

1-A.1

4. Jake spent 9¢ for a pencil and 4¢ for paper. How much money did he spend?

___13___ ¢

1-A.1

5.
$$\begin{array}{r} 8 \\ 6 \\ +4 \\ \hline 18 \end{array}$$

1-A.2

6.
$$\begin{array}{r} 4 \\ 4 \\ +9 \\ \hline 17 \end{array}$$

1-A.2

Form B • Free-Response   B169   **Go on.**

7.
$$\begin{array}{r} 6 \\ +8 \\ \hline 14 \end{array} \qquad \begin{array}{r} 14 \\ -6 \\ \hline 8 \end{array}$$

2-A.1

8. $16 - 8 = 8$

$8 + 8 = $ ___16___

2-A.1

Use the number line to answer questions 9 and 10.

$$\overset{0\ 1\ 2\ 3\ 4\ 5\ 6\ 7\ 8\ 9\ 10\ 11\ 12\ 13\ 14\ 15\ 16\ 17\ 18}{\longleftarrow|\,|\,|\,|\,|\,|\,|\,|\,|\,|\,|\,|\,|\,|\,|\,|\,|\,|\,|\longrightarrow}$$

9. $12 - 7 = $ ___5___

2-A.2

10. $17 - 8 = $ ___9___

2-A.2

11. Write the missing addend.

$8 + $ ___5___ $ = 13$

2-A.1

12. There were 14 raisins in the box. Then Coley ate 7 raisins. How many raisins were still in the box?

___7___ raisins

2-A.3

Form B • Free-Response   B170   **Stop!**

Write the correct answer.

1. Write the addition sentence that tells about the picture.

___5___ + ___5___ = ___10___

1-A.1

2. Write the addition sentence that tells about the picture.

___8___ + ___8___ = ___16___

1-A.1

3.
$$\begin{array}{r} 7 \\ +8 \\ \hline 15 \end{array}$$

1-A.1

4.
$$\begin{array}{r} 5 \\ +4 \\ \hline 9 \end{array}$$

1-A.1

5.
$$\begin{array}{r} 8 \\ +9 \\ \hline 17 \end{array}$$

1-A.1

6.
$$\begin{array}{r} 4 \\ +3 \\ \hline 7 \end{array}$$

1-A.1

7.
$$\begin{array}{r} 9 \\ +5 \\ \hline 14 \end{array}$$

1-A.1

8.
$$\begin{array}{r} 4 \\ +9 \\ \hline 13 \end{array}$$

1-A.1

Form B • Free-Response   B171   **Chapters 1–2**   **Go on.**

---

9. Use the picture to find the sum.

$$\begin{array}{r} 8 \\ +4 \\ \hline 12 \end{array}$$

1-A.1

10. Use the picture to find the sum.

$$\begin{array}{r} 6 \\ +9 \\ \hline 15 \end{array}$$

1-A.1

11. Leon saw 9 brown horses and 2 black horses. How many horses did he see?

___11___ horses

1-A.1

12. Donna spent 8¢ for one bow and 9¢ for another bow. How much money did she spend?

___17___ ¢

1-A.1

13.
$$\begin{array}{r} 1 \\ 9 \\ +8 \\ \hline 18 \end{array}$$

1-A.2

14.
$$\begin{array}{r} 4 \\ 6 \\ +4 \\ \hline 14 \end{array}$$

1-A.2

15. Jim has 7 white shirts, 3 blue shirts, and 6 green shirts. How many shirts does he have?

___16___ shirts

1-A.2

16. Pam has 2 yellow buttons, 9 orange buttons, and 2 red buttons. How many buttons does she have?

___13___ buttons

1-A.2

Form B • Free-Response   B172   **Chapters 1–2**   **Go on.**

Free-Response Format • Test Answers

289

Name _____

17. $\begin{array}{r} 8 \\ +7 \\ \hline 15 \end{array}$ $\begin{array}{r} 15 \\ -8 \\ \hline 7 \end{array}$ 2-A.1	18. $13 - 5 = 8$ $8 + 5 = \underline{13}$ 2-A.1
19. $\begin{array}{r} 7 \\ +4 \\ \hline 11 \end{array}$ $\begin{array}{r} 11 \\ -7 \\ \hline 4 \end{array}$ 2-A.1	20. $12 - 7 = 5$ $5 + 7 = \underline{12}$ 2-A.1
21. Write the number sentence that belongs in this fact family. $7 + 6 = 13$ $6 + 7 = 13$ $13 - 7 = 6$ $\underline{13} \ominus \underline{6} = \underline{7}$ 2-A.1	22. Write the other number sentence that belongs in this fact family. $2 + 8 = 10$ $8 + 2 = 10$ $10 - 8 = 2$ $\underline{10} \ominus \underline{2} = \underline{8}$ 2-A.1

Form B • Free-Response   B173   Chapters 1–2   **Go on.**

Name _____

23. Write the missing addend. 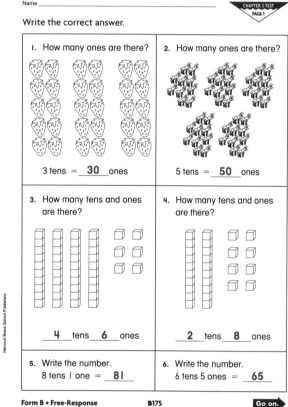 $9 + \underline{9} = 18$ 2-A.1	24. Write the missing addend. 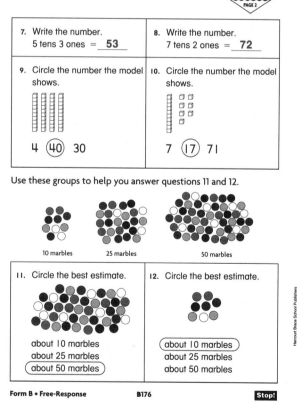 $\begin{array}{r} 8 \\ +\Box \\ \hline 11 \end{array}$ $\underline{3}$ 2-A.1

Use the number line to answer questions 25 and 26.

0 1 2 3 4 5 6 7 8 9 10 11 12 13 14 15 16 17 18

25. $16 - 8 = \underline{8}$ 2-A.2	26. $14 - 9 = \underline{5}$ 2-A.2
27. There were 3 boys and 9 girls coloring. How many children were coloring? $\underline{12}$ children 2-A.3	28. There were 13 monkeys in a cage. Then 4 monkeys left. How many monkeys were still in the cage? $\underline{9}$ monkeys 2-A.3

Form B • Free-Response   B174   Chapters 1–2   **Stop!**

Name _____

Write the correct answer.

1. How many ones are there? 3 tens = $\underline{30}$ ones	2. How many ones are there? 5 tens = $\underline{50}$ ones
3. How many tens and ones are there? $\underline{4}$ tens $\underline{6}$ ones	4. How many tens and ones are there? $\underline{2}$ tens $\underline{8}$ ones
5. Write the number. 8 tens 1 one = $\underline{81}$	6. Write the number. 6 tens 5 ones = $\underline{65}$

Form B • Free-Response   B175   **Go on.**

Name _____

7. Write the number. 5 tens 3 ones = $\underline{53}$	8. Write the number. 7 tens 2 ones = $\underline{72}$
9. Circle the number the model shows. 4 (40) 30	10. Circle the number the model shows. 7 (17) 71

Use these groups to help you answer questions 11 and 12.

10 marbles   25 marbles   50 marbles

11. Circle the best estimate. about 10 marbles about 25 marbles (about 50 marbles)	12. Circle the best estimate. (about 10 marbles) about 25 marbles about 50 marbles

Form B • Free-Response   B176   **Stop!**

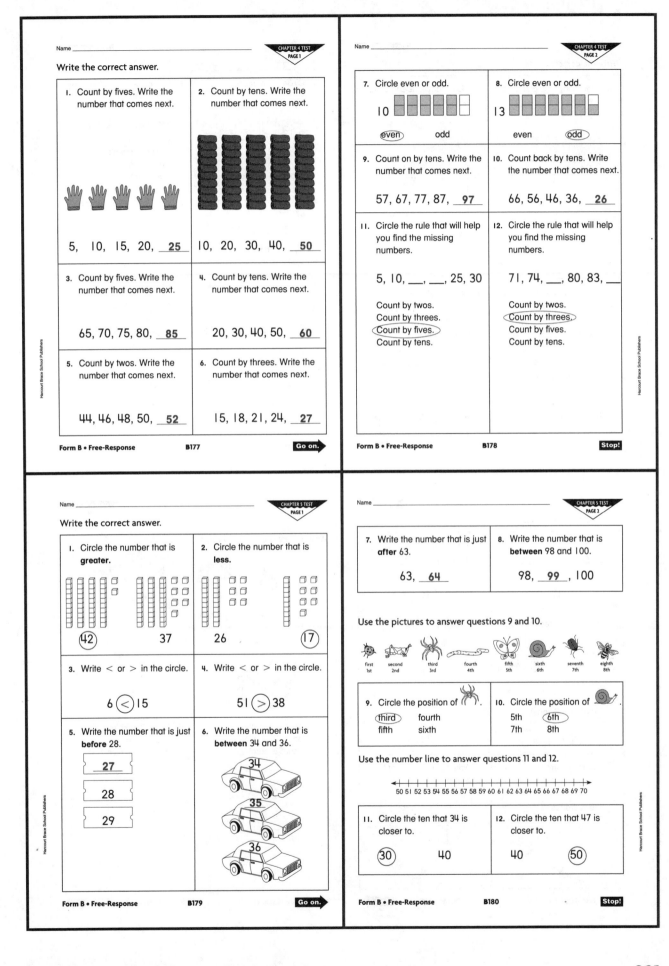

Name _____

Write the correct answer.

1. Count by fives. Write the number that comes next.

5, 10, 15, 20, __25__

2. Count by tens. Write the number that comes next.

10, 20, 30, 40, __50__

3. Count by fives. Write the number that comes next.

65, 70, 75, 80, __85__

4. Count by tens. Write the number that comes next.

20, 30, 40, 50, __60__

5. Count by twos. Write the number that comes next.

44, 46, 48, 50, __52__

6. Count by threes. Write the number that comes next.

15, 18, 21, 24, __27__

Form B • Free-Response   B177   **Go on.**

Name _____

7. Circle even or odd.

10

(even)   odd

8. Circle even or odd.

13

even   (odd)

9. Count on by tens. Write the number that comes next.

57, 67, 77, 87, __97__

10. Count back by tens. Write the number that comes next.

66, 56, 46, 36, __26__

11. Circle the rule that will help you find the missing numbers.

5, 10, ___, ___, 25, 30

Count by twos.
Count by threes.
(Count by fives.)
Count by tens.

12. Circle the rule that will help you find the missing numbers.

71, 74, ___, 80, 83, ___

Count by twos.
(Count by threes.)
Count by fives.
Count by tens.

Form B • Free-Response   B178   **Stop!**

Name _____

Write the correct answer.

1. Circle the number that is **greater**.

(42)   37

2. Circle the number that is **less**.

26   (17)

3. Write < or > in the circle.

6 (<) 15

4. Write < or > in the circle.

51 (>) 38

5. Write the number that is just **before** 28.

__27__
28
29

6. Write the number that is **between** 34 and 36.

34
35
36

Form B • Free-Response   B179   **Go on.**

Name _____

7. Write the number that is just **after** 63.

63, __64__

8. Write the number that is **between** 98 and 100.

98, __99__, 100

Use the pictures to answer questions 9 and 10.

first second third fourth fifth sixth seventh eighth
1st   2nd   3rd   4th   5th   6th   7th   8th

9. Circle the position of the spider.

(third)   fourth
fifth   sixth

10. Circle the position of the snail.

5th   (6th)
7th   8th

Use the number line to answer questions 11 and 12.

50 51 52 53 54 55 56 57 58 59 60 61 62 63 64 65 66 67 68 69 70

11. Circle the ten that 34 is closer to.

(30)   40

12. Circle the ten that 47 is closer to.

40   (50)

Form B • Free-Response   B180   **Stop!**

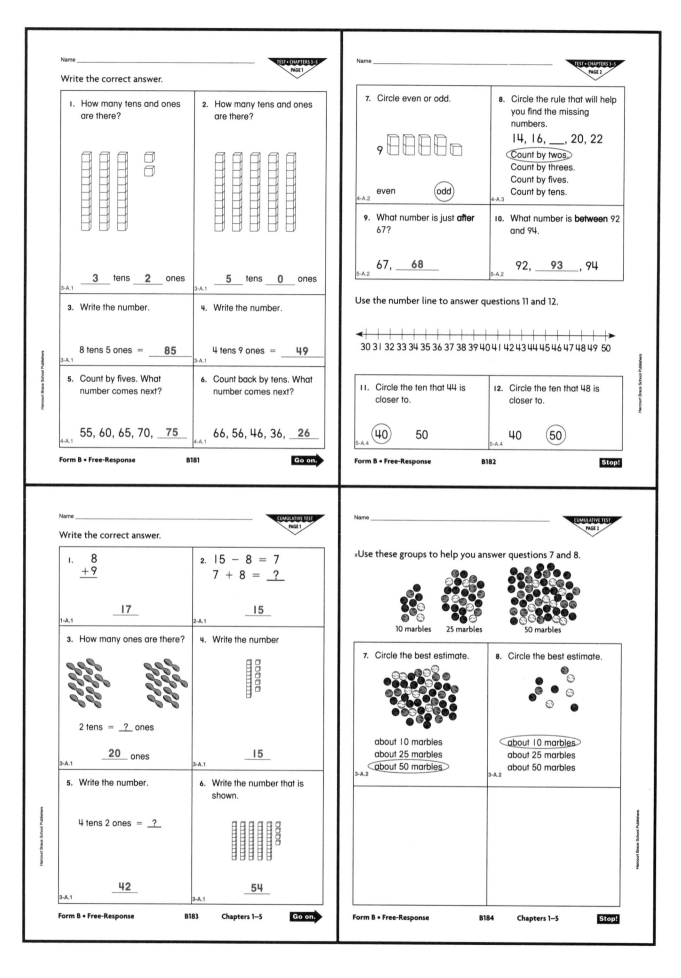

Free-Response Format • Test Answers

9. Count by twos. Write the number that comes next.

46, 48, 50, 52, __54__

4-A.1

10. Count back by tens. Write the number that comes next.

51, 41, 31, 21, __11__

4-A.1

11. Circle even or odd.

9

even (odd)

4-A.2

12. Circle the rule that will help you find the missing numbers.

44, 54, ___, 74, 84, ___

Count by twos.
Count by threes.
Count by fives.
(Count by tens.)

4-A.3

13. Circle the number that is **greater**.

(51)　26

5-A.1

14. Circle the number that is **less**.

43　(36)

5-A.1

Form B • Free-Response　　B185　　Chapters 1–5　　**Go on.**

15. Write < or > in the circle.

21 (>) 11

5-A.1

16. Write the number.

78, __79__, 80

5-A.2

Use the pictures below to answer questions 17 and 18.

first
1st

17. Write the position of the

__second or 2nd__

5-A.3

18. Write the position of the

__fifth or 5th__

5-A.3

Use the number line to answer questions 19 and 20.

20 21 22 23 24 25 26 27 28 29 30 31 32 33 34 35 36 37 38 39 40 41 42 43 44 45 46 47 48 49 50

19. Write the ten that 22 is closest to.

__20__

5-A.4

20. Write the ten that 36 is closest to.

__40__

5-A.4

Form B • Free-Response　　B186　　Chapters 1–5　　**Stop!**

Write the correct answer.

1. Count on. Write the total amount.

__11__ ¢

2. Count on. Write the total amount.

__16__ ¢

3. Count on. Write the total amount.

__22__ ¢

4. Count on. Write the total amount.

__31__ ¢

5. Count on. Write the total amount.

__40__ ¢

6. Count on. Write the total amount.

__51__ ¢

Form B • Free-Response　　B187　　**Go on.**

7. Circle the answer that shows the coins in order from greatest to least value.

8. Circle the answer that shows the coins in order from greatest to least value.

9. Write the total amount.

__61__ ¢

10. Write the total amount.

__50__ ¢

Form B • Free-Response　　B188　　**Go on.**

Free-Response Format • Test Answers

293

Harcourt Brace School Publishers

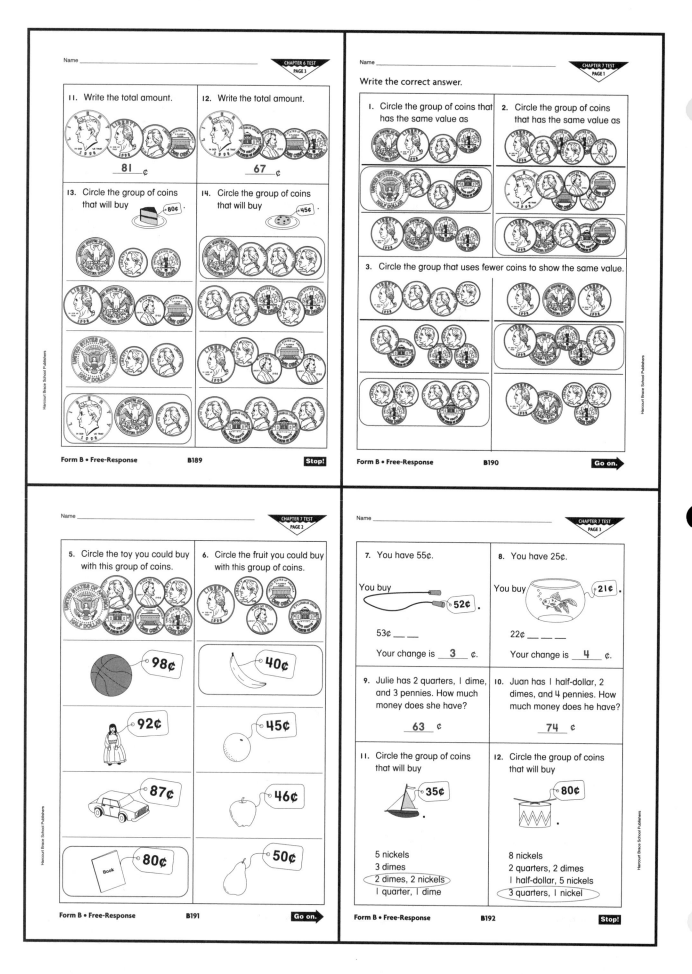

CHAPTER 6 TEST
PAGE 3

11. Write the total amount.

___81___ ¢

12. Write the total amount.

___67___ ¢

13. Circle the group of coins that will buy [80¢ cake]

14. Circle the group of coins that will buy [45¢ cookie]

Form B • Free-Response   B189   Stop!

CHAPTER 7 TEST
PAGE 1

Write the correct answer.

1. Circle the group of coins that has the same value as

2. Circle the group of coins that has the same value as

3. Circle the group that uses fewer coins to show the same value.

Form B • Free-Response   B190   Go on.

CHAPTER 7 TEST
PAGE 2

5. Circle the toy you could buy with this group of coins.

98¢ basketball
92¢ doll
87¢ car
80¢ Book

6. Circle the fruit you could buy with this group of coins.

40¢ banana
45¢ orange
46¢ apple
50¢ pear

Form B • Free-Response   B191   Go on.

CHAPTER 7 TEST
PAGE 3

7. You have 55¢.
You buy [52¢]
53¢ __ __
Your change is ___3___ ¢.

8. You have 25¢.
You buy [21¢]
22¢ __ __ __
Your change is ___4___ ¢.

9. Julie has 2 quarters, 1 dime, and 3 pennies. How much money does she have?
___63___ ¢

10. Juan has 1 half-dollar, 2 dimes, and 4 pennies. How much money does he have?
___74___ ¢

11. Circle the group of coins that will buy [35¢ sailboat]
5 nickels
3 dimes
(2 dimes, 2 nickels)
1 quarter, 1 dime

12. Circle the group of coins that will buy [80¢ drum]
8 nickels
2 quarters, 2 dimes
1 half-dollar, 5 nickels
(3 quarters, 1 nickel)

Form B • Free-Response   B192   Stop!

Free-Response Format • Test Answers

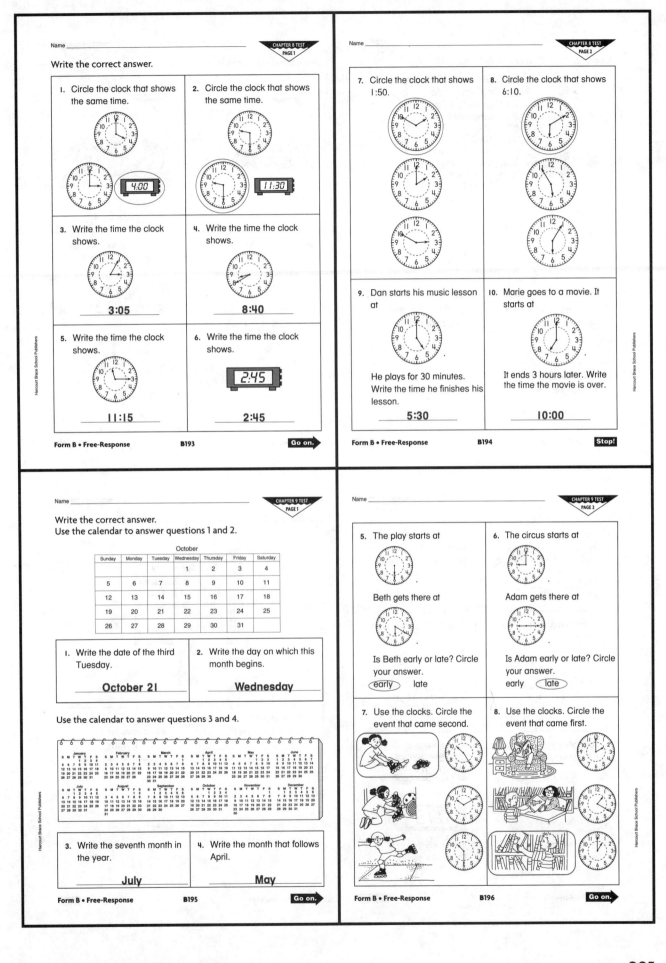

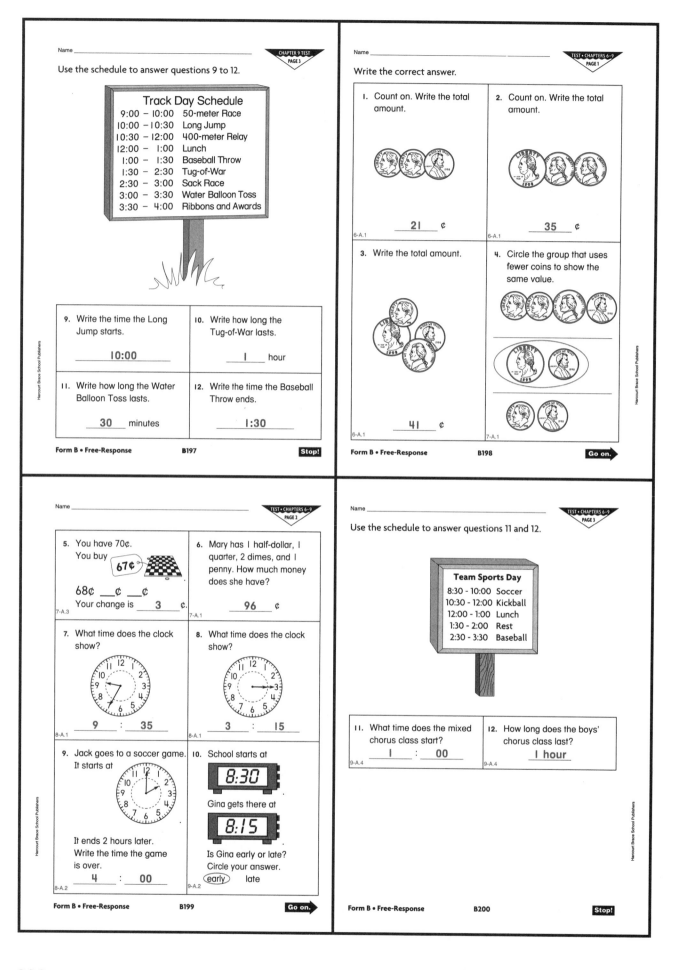

Use the schedule to answer questions 9 to 12.

Track Day Schedule
9:00 – 10:00   50-meter Race
10:00 – 10:30   Long Jump
10:30 – 12:00   400-meter Relay
12:00 – 1:00   Lunch
1:00 – 1:30   Baseball Throw
1:30 – 2:30   Tug-of-War
2:30 – 3:00   Sack Race
3:00 – 3:30   Water Balloon Toss
3:30 – 4:00   Ribbons and Awards

9. Write the time the Long Jump starts.

_____ 10:00 _____

10. Write how long the Tug-of-War lasts.

_____ 1 _____ hour

11. Write how long the Water Balloon Toss lasts.

_____ 30 _____ minutes

12. Write the time the Baseball Throw ends.

_____ 1:30 _____

Form B • Free-Response   B197   **Stop!**

Write the correct answer.

1. Count on. Write the total amount.

_____ 21 _____ ¢

6-A.1

2. Count on. Write the total amount.

_____ 35 _____ ¢

6-A.1

3. Write the total amount.

_____ 41 _____ ¢

6-A.1

4. Circle the group that uses fewer coins to show the same value.

7-A.1

Form B • Free-Response   B198   **Go on.**

---

5. You have 70¢. You buy [67¢]

68¢ ___ ¢ ___ ¢
Your change is _____ 3 _____ ¢.

7-A.3

6. Mary has 1 half-dollar, 1 quarter, 2 dimes, and 1 penny. How much money does she have?

_____ 96 _____ ¢

7-A.1

7. What time does the clock show?

_____ 9 _____ : _____ 35 _____

8-A.1

8. What time does the clock show?

_____ 3 _____ : _____ 15 _____

8-A.1

9. Jack goes to a soccer game. It starts at

It ends 2 hours later. Write the time the game is over.

_____ 4 _____ : _____ 00 _____

8-A.2

10. School starts at

[8:30]

Gina gets there at

[8:15]

Is Gina early or late? Circle your answer.

(early)   late

9-A.2

Form B • Free-Response   B199   **Go on.**

Use the schedule to answer questions 11 and 12.

Team Sports Day
8:30 - 10:00   Soccer
10:30 - 12:00   Kickball
12:00 - 1:00   Lunch
1:30 - 2:00   Rest
2:30 - 3:30   Baseball

11. What time does the mixed chorus class start?

_____ 1 _____ : _____ 00 _____

9-A.4

12. How long does the boys' chorus class last?

_____ 1 hour _____

9-A.4

Form B • Free-Response   B200   **Stop!**

Free-Response Format • Test Answers

Write the correct answer.

1. $\begin{array}{r} 5 \\ 8 \\ +5 \\ \hline 18 \end{array}$	2. $\begin{array}{r} 7 \\ 3 \\ +6 \\ \hline 16 \end{array}$
1-A.2	1-A.2

3. $16 - 8 = \underline{\ 8\ }$ 2-A.2	4. $14 - 9 = \underline{\ 5\ }$ 2-A.2

5.  There were 4 boys and 9 girls coloring. How many children were coloring? $\underline{\ 13\ }$ children 2-A.2	6. Missing art There were 12 bugs on a stick. Then 3 went away. How many bugs were still on the stick? $\underline{\ 9\ }$ bugs 2-A.2

7. Count by fives. Write the number that comes next. 35, 40, 45, 50, $\underline{\ 55\ }$ 4-A.1	8. Circle the rule that will help you find the missing numbers. 23, 26, ____, 32, 35, ____ Count by twos. Count by threes. ⟨Count by fives.⟩ Count by tens. 4-A.3

Form B • Free-Response   B201   Chapters 1–9   **Go on.**

---

9. Count back by tens. Write the number that comes next. 72, 62, 52, 42, $\underline{\ 32\ }$ 4-A.1	10. Circle even or odd. ⟨even⟩ odd 4-A.2

11. Write < or > in the circle. 7 ⊙ 11 5-A.1	12. Write the number. 39, $\underline{\ 40\ }$, 41 5-A.2

Use the pictures below to answer questions 13 and 14.

| first | second | third | fourth | fifth | sixth | seventh | eighth |
| 1st | 2nd | 3rd | 4th | 5th | 6th | 7th | 8th |

13. Write the position of the $\underline{\text{sixth or 6th}}$ 5-A.3	14. Write the position of the $\underline{\text{fourth or 4th}}$ 5-A.3

Form B • Free-Response   B202   Chapters 1–9   **Go on.**

Write the correct answer.

15. Count on. Write the total amount. $\underline{\ 31\ }$ ¢ 6-A.1	16. You have 45¢. You buy •42¢ Your change is $\underline{\ 3\ }$ ¢. 7-A.3

17. Circle the group of coins that will buy •55¢ 6-A.2	18. Circle the toy you could buy with this group of coins. •95¢ •89¢ •75¢ 7-A.2

Form B • Free-Response   B203   Chapters 1–9   **Go on.**

---

19. Write the time the clock shows. $\underline{4} : \underline{05}$ 8-A.1	20. Write the time the clock shows. $\underline{6} : \underline{45}$ 8-A.1

Use the calendar to answer questions 21 and 22.

September

Sunday	Monday	Tuesday	Wednesday	Thursday	Friday	Saturday
1	2	3	4	5	6	7
8	9	10	11	12	13	14
15	16	17	18	19	20	21
22	23	24	25	26	27	28
29	30					

21. Write the date of the second Wednesday. **September 10** 9-A.1	22. Write the day on which this month ends. **Tuesday 10** 9-A.1

Use the schedule to answer questions 23 and 24.

Picnic Day Schedule
9:00 – 9:30   Parade
9:30 – 11:00 Races
11:00 – 12:00 Games
12:00 – 1:30 Lunch

23. Write the time the races start. $\underline{9} : \underline{30}$ 9-A.4	24. Write how long the games last. **1 hour** 9-A.4

Form B • Free-Response   B204   Chapters 1–9   **Stop!**

Free-Response Format • Test Answers

Write the answer.
Use base-ten blocks to answer questions 1 and 2.

1. $8 + 6 = 14$ ones

How many tens and ones?

___1___ ten ___4___ ones

2. $3 + 4 = 7$ ones

How many tens and ones?

___0___ tens ___7___ ones

3. $14 + 8$

How many in all?
22

4. $17 + 6$

How many in all?
23

5. $19 + 16$

How many in all?
35

6. $12 + 18$

How many in all?
30

7. Add.

tens	ones
2	7
+ 1	3
4	**0**

8. Add.

tens	ones
2	1
+ 1	8
3	**9**

Make a model to answer questions 9 and 10.

9. There are 17 boys and 15 girls in a race. How many children are in the race?

tens	ones
1	7
+ 1	5

___32___ children

10. The pet shop has 16 goldfish and 12 redfish. How many fish does the pet shop have?

tens	ones
1	6
+ 1	2

___28___ fish

Write the correct answer.
Use base-ten blocks to answer questions 1 and 2.

1.
tens	ones
1	7
+	4
2	**1**

2.
tens	ones
2	8
+	2
3	**0**

3.
tens	ones
1	5
+	8
2	**3**

4.
tens	ones
4	2
+	9
5	**1**

5.
tens	ones
4	6
+ 1	3
5	**9**

6.
tens	ones
2	4
+ 1	8
4	**2**

7. 37
$+39$
$\overline{76}$

8. 26
$+17$
$\overline{43}$

9. 76
$+ 8$
$\overline{84}$

10. 58
$+39$
$\overline{97}$

11. The children in Mrs. Clark's class made 25 cards. The children in Mr. Brown's class made 36 cards. How many cards did the two classes make?

___61___ cards

12. On Monday, Faye planted 24 flowers. On Tuesday, she planted 13 flowers. How many flowers did she plant in all?

___37___ flowers

13. Tina baked 32 cookies for her class. She baked 44 cookies for her family. It took her 45 minutes to bake the cookies. How many cookies did Tina bake in all?

___76___ cookies

14. Ray collected 28 cans on Monday. On Thursday he collected 19 cans. He went to a park on Friday. How many cans did Ray collect in all?

___47___ cans

Free-Response Format • Test Answers

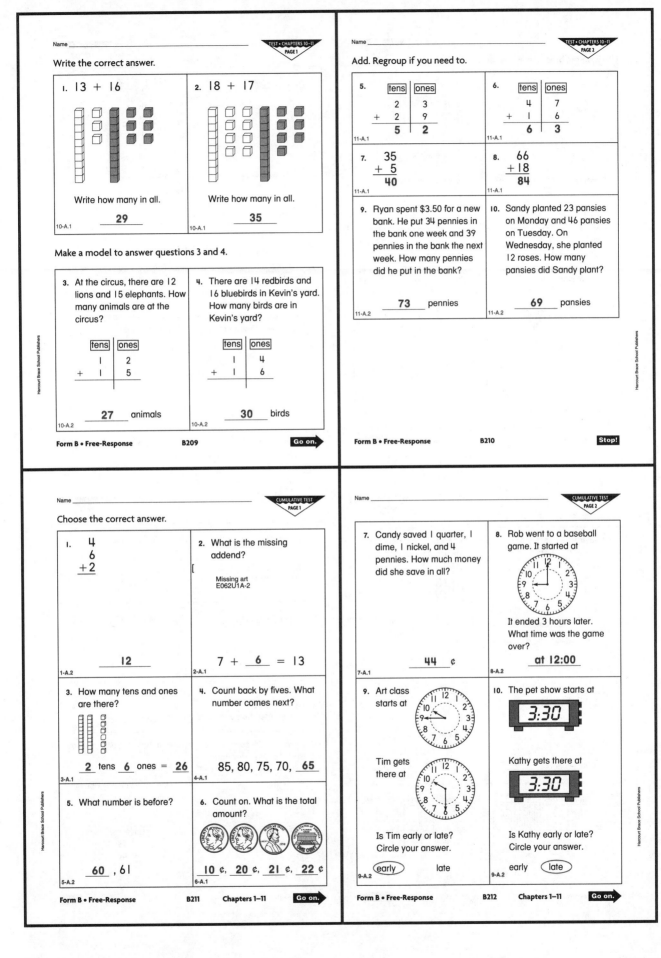

Page 1 (TEST • CHAPTERS 10–11)

Write the correct answer.

1. $13 + 16$

Write how many in all.

29

10-A.1

2. $18 + 17$

Write how many in all.

35

10-A.1

Make a model to answer questions 3 and 4.

3. At the circus, there are 12 lions and 15 elephants. How many animals are at the circus?

tens	ones
1	2
+ 1	5

27 animals

10-A.2

4. There are 14 redbirds and 16 bluebirds in Kevin's yard. How many birds are in Kevin's yard?

tens	ones
1	4
+ 1	6

30 birds

10-A.2

Page 2 (TEST • CHAPTERS 10–11)

Add. Regroup if you need to.

5.

tens	ones
2	3
+ 2	9
5	**2**

11-A.1

6.

tens	ones
4	7
+ 1	6
6	**3**

11-A.1

7.
35
$+ 5$
40

11-A.1

8.
66
$+18$
84

11-A.1

9. Ryan spent $3.50 for a new bank. He put 34 pennies in the bank one week and 39 pennies in the bank the next week. How many pennies did he put in the bank?

73 pennies

11-A.2

10. Sandy planted 23 pansies on Monday and 46 pansies on Tuesday. On Wednesday, she planted 12 roses. How many pansies did Sandy plant?

69 pansies

11-A.2

Page 1 (CUMULATIVE TEST)

Choose the correct answer.

1.
4
6
$+2$
____
12

1-A.2

2. What is the missing addend?

Missing art
E062U1A-2

$7 + \underline{6} = 13$

2-A.1

3. How many tens and ones are there?

2 tens **6** ones = **26**

3-A.1

4. Count back by fives. What number comes next?

85, 80, 75, 70, **65**

4-A.1

5. What number is before?

60 , 61

5-A.2

6. Count on. What is the total amount?

10 ¢, **20** ¢, **21** ¢, **22** ¢

6-A.1

Page 2 (CUMULATIVE TEST)

7. Candy saved 1 quarter, 1 dime, 1 nickel, and 4 pennies. How much money did she save in all?

44 ¢

7-A.1

8. Rob went to a baseball game. It started at

It ended 3 hours later. What time was the game over?

at 12:00

8-A.2

9. Art class starts at

Tim gets there at

Is Tim early or late? Circle your answer.

(early)   late

9-A.2

10. The pet show starts at

3:30

Kathy gets there at

3:30

Is Kathy early or late? Circle your answer.

early   (late)

9-A.2

Free-Response Format • Test Answers

Harcourt Brace School Publishers

Name _____

Use base-ten blocks to answer questions 11 and 12.

11. $9 + 4 = 13$ ones

How many tens and ones?

__1__ ten __3__ ones

10-A.1

12. $15 + 7$

How many in all?

__22__

10-A.1

13. There are 14 boys and 18 girls on the playground. How many children are on the playground?

tens	ones
1	4
+1	8

__32__ children

10-A.2

14. The flower shop has 16 red flowers and 13 yellow flowers. How many flowers does the flower shop have?.

tens	ones
1	6
+1	3

__29__ flowers

10-A.2

Form B • Free-Response   B213   Chapters 1–11   Go on.

Name _____

15.

tens	ones
☐	
1	6
+	7
2	3

11-A.1

16.

tens	ones
1	1
+3	8
4	9

11-A.1

17.
$$26 + 28 = 54$$

11-A.1

18.
$$85 + 7 = 92$$

11-A.1

19. The children in Mrs. Washington's class read 55 books. The students in Mrs. Johnson's class read 26 books. How many books did the two classes read?

__81__ books

11-A.1

20. There are 18 computers in Sarah's school and 16 computers in Diane's school. How many computers are in the two schools?

__34__ computers

11-A.2

Form B • Free-Response   B214   Chapters 1–11   Stop!

Name _____

Write the correct answer.

1. Subtract 3 ones. How many tens and ones are left?

__2__ tens __2__ ones

2. Subtract 7 ones. How many tens and ones are left?

__3__ tens __4__ ones

3.
$$48 - 5 = 43$$

4.
$$23 - 9 = 14$$

5.

tens	ones		tens	ones
5	6			
–	8			
4	8			

6.

tens	ones		tens	ones
3	2			
–	5			
2	7			

Form B • Free-Response   B215   Go on.

Name _____

7.

tens	ones
5	0
– 1	4
3	6

8.

tens	ones
4	2
– 2	4
1	8

9.

tens	ones
2	4
– 1	9
	5

10.

tens	ones
3	0
– 1	5
1	5

Use base-ten blocks.
Choose the operation and solve. Write + or −.

11. Craig sees 24 cows and 26 pigs at a farm. How many animals does he see in all?

tens	ones
2	4
⊕ 2	6
5	0

12. Beth has 70¢. She buys a 14¢. How much money does Beth have left?

tens	ones
7	0¢
⊖ 1	4¢
5	6

Form B • Free-Response   B216   Stop!

---

300   **Free-Response Format • Test Answers**

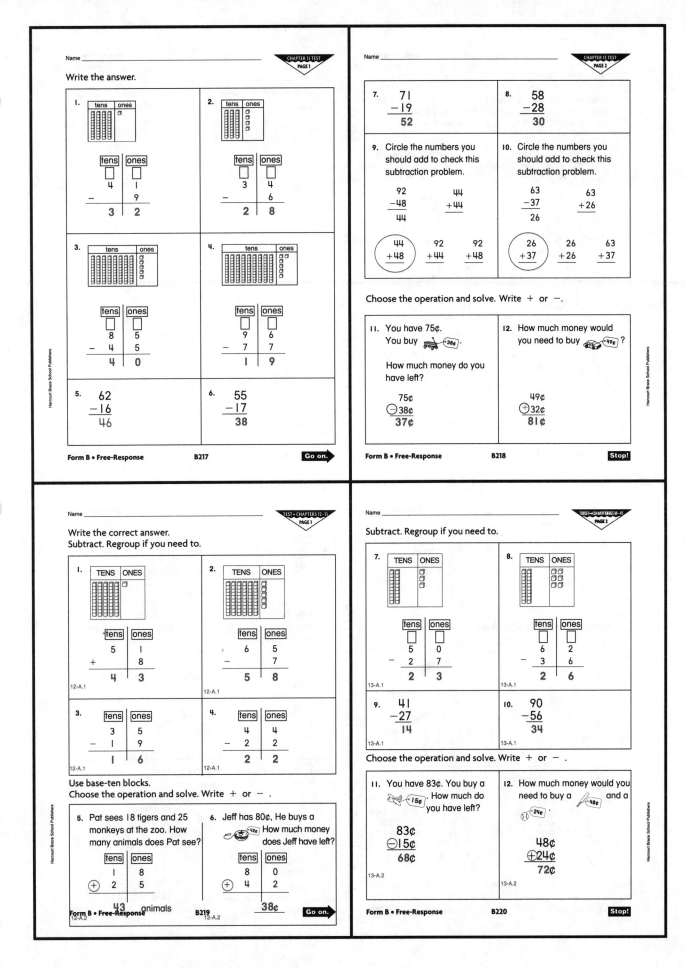

Name

Write the answer.

1.
tens	ones

tens	ones
4	1
−	9
3	2

2.
tens	ones

tens	ones
3	4
−	6
2	8

3.
tens	ones

tens	ones
8	5
− 4	5
4	0

4.
tens	ones

tens	ones
9	6
− 7	7
1	9

5.
$$\begin{array}{r} 62 \\ -16 \\ \hline 46 \end{array}$$

6.
$$\begin{array}{r} 55 \\ -17 \\ \hline 38 \end{array}$$

Form B • Free-Response   B217   Go on. ▶

Name

7.
$$\begin{array}{r} 71 \\ -19 \\ \hline 52 \end{array}$$

8.
$$\begin{array}{r} 58 \\ -28 \\ \hline 30 \end{array}$$

9. Circle the numbers you should add to check this subtraction problem.

$$\begin{array}{r} 92 \\ -48 \\ \hline 44 \end{array} \qquad \begin{array}{r} 44 \\ +44 \\ \hline \end{array}$$

$$\boxed{\begin{array}{r} 44 \\ +48 \end{array}} \qquad \begin{array}{r} 92 \\ +44 \end{array} \qquad \begin{array}{r} 92 \\ +48 \end{array}$$

10. Circle the numbers you should add to check this subtraction problem.

$$\begin{array}{r} 63 \\ -37 \\ \hline 26 \end{array} \qquad \begin{array}{r} 63 \\ +26 \\ \hline \end{array}$$

$$\boxed{\begin{array}{r} 26 \\ +37 \end{array}} \qquad \begin{array}{r} 26 \\ +26 \end{array} \qquad \begin{array}{r} 63 \\ +37 \end{array}$$

Choose the operation and solve. Write + or −.

11. You have 75¢. You buy [38¢]. How much money do you have left?

$$\begin{array}{r} 75¢ \\ \ominus 38¢ \\ \hline 37¢ \end{array}$$

12. How much money would you need to buy [49¢]?

$$\begin{array}{r} 49¢ \\ \oplus 32¢ \\ \hline 81¢ \end{array}$$

Form B • Free-Response   B218   Stop!

Name

Write the correct answer.
Subtract. Regroup if you need to.

1.
TENS	ONES

tens	ones
5	1
+	8
4	3

12-A.1

2.
TENS	ONES

tens	ones
6	5
−	7
5	8

12-A.1

3.
tens	ones
3	5
− 1	9
1	6

12-A.1

4.
tens	ones
4	4
− 2	2
2	2

12-A.1

Use base-ten blocks.
Choose the operation and solve. Write + or −.

5. Pat sees 18 tigers and 25 monkeys at the zoo. How many animals does Pat see?

tens	ones
1	8
⊕ 2	5
4	3

43 animals

12-A.2

6. Jeff has 80¢. He buys a [42¢]. How much money does Jeff have left?

tens	ones
8	0
⊕ 4	2
	38¢

Form B • Free-Response   B219   12-A.2   Go on. ▶

Name

Subtract. Regroup if you need to.

7.
TENS	ONES

tens	ones
5	0
− 2	7
2	3

13-A.1

8.
TENS	ONES

tens	ones
6	2
− 3	6
2	6

13-A.1

9.
$$\begin{array}{r} 41 \\ -27 \\ \hline 14 \end{array}$$
13-A.1

10.
$$\begin{array}{r} 90 \\ -56 \\ \hline 34 \end{array}$$
13-A.1

Choose the operation and solve. Write + or −.

11. You have 83¢. You buy a [15¢]. How much do you have left?

$$\begin{array}{r} 83¢ \\ \ominus 15¢ \\ \hline 68¢ \end{array}$$

13-A.2

12. How much money would you need to buy a [48¢] and a [24¢].

$$\begin{array}{r} 48¢ \\ \oplus 24¢ \\ \hline 72¢ \end{array}$$

13-A.2

Form B • Free-Response   B220   Stop!

Free-Response Format • Test Answers

301

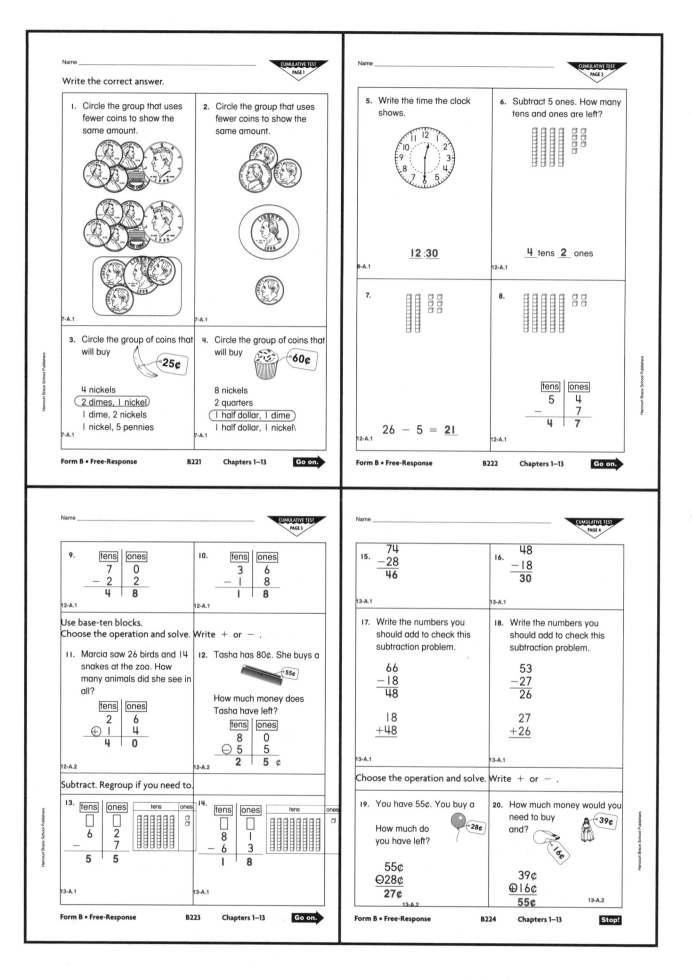

Free-Response Format • Test Answers

Write the correct answer.
Use the picture to answer questions 1 and 2.

1. Write tally marks to show how many pigs there are.

IIII

2. Write tally marks to show how many cows there are.

III

Jen asked 10 friends about their favorite snack.
The tally table shows what she found.
Use the table to answer questions 3 and 4.

Favorite Snacks	
cookies	I
popcorn	II
pretzels	HH
fruit	II

3. How many children liked fruit the best?

__2__ children

4. Which snack was liked best by the most children?

__pretzels__

Go on.

Use the table to answer questions 5 to 8.

Number of Children in the Art Contest	
Room 16	III
Room 17	HH I
Room 18	HH HH
Room 19	III

5. In which two rooms were the same number of children in the contest?

Rooms __16__ and __19__

6. How many more children from Room 18 were in the contest than from Room 17?

__4__ more children

7. How many children in all were in the contest?

__22__ children

8. In which room were the most children in the contest?

Room __18__

Go on.

Use the tables to answer questions 9 to12.

Favorite Games in Room 19	
jump rope	HH I
tag	HH II
races	HH III
kickball	III

Favorite Games in Room 20	
jump rope	HH HH
tag	IIII
races	III
kickball	HH II

9. How many children in Room 19 like tag best?

__7__ children

10. In which room do more children like races best?

Room __19__

11. How many children are in Room 20?

__24__ children

12. Which game got the most votes in all?

__jump rope__

Stop!

Write the correct answer.
Use the graph to answer questions 1 to 4.

Favorite Pet

1. Which is the favorite pet of the most people?

__cat__

2. Which is the favorite pet of the fewest people?

__hamster__

3. How many more people like dogs than like fish?

__2__ more

4. How many fewer people like hamsters than like cats?

__4__ fewer

Go on.

Free-Response Format • Test Answers

CHAPTER 15 TEST
PAGE 2

Use the graph to answer questions 5 to 8.

Inches of Rain in April

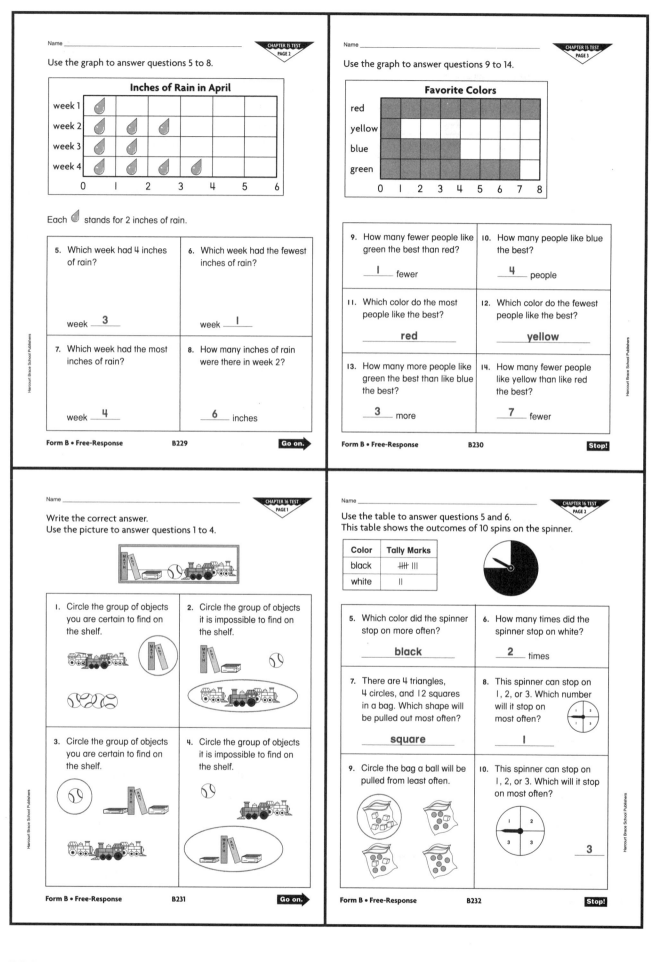

	0	1	2	3	4	5	6
week 1							
week 2							
week 3							
week 4							

Each 💧 stands for 2 inches of rain.

5. Which week had 4 inches of rain? week __3__	6. Which week had the fewest inches of rain? week __1__
7. Which week had the most inches of rain? week __4__	8. How many inches of rain were there in week 2? __6__ inches

Form B • Free-Response B229 Go on.

Name _____

CHAPTER 15 TEST
PAGE 3

Use the graph to answer questions 9 to 14.

Favorite Colors

	0	1	2	3	4	5	6	7	8
red									
yellow									
blue									
green									

9. How many fewer people like green the best than red? __1__ fewer	10. How many people like blue the best? __4__ people
11. Which color do the most people like the best? __red__	12. Which color do the fewest people like the best? __yellow__
13. How many more people like green the best than like blue the best? __3__ more	14. How many fewer people like yellow than like red the best? __7__ fewer

Form B • Free-Response B230 Stop!

Name _____

CHAPTER 16 TEST
PAGE 1

Write the correct answer.
Use the picture to answer questions 1 to 4.

1. Circle the group of objects you are certain to find on the shelf.	2. Circle the group of objects it is impossible to find on the shelf.
3. Circle the group of objects you are certain to find on the shelf.	4. Circle the group of objects it is impossible to find on the shelf.

Form B • Free-Response B231 Go on.

Name _____

CHAPTER 16 TEST
PAGE 2

Use the table to answer questions 5 and 6.
This table shows the outcomes of 10 spins on the spinner.

Color	Tally Marks
black	卌 III
white	II

5. Which color did the spinner stop on more often? __black__	6. How many times did the spinner stop on white? __2__ times
7. There are 4 triangles, 4 circles, and 12 squares in a bag. Which shape will be pulled out most often? __square__	8. This spinner can stop on 1, 2, or 3. Which number will it stop on most often? __1__
9. Circle the bag a ball will be pulled from least often.	10. This spinner can stop on 1, 2, or 3. Which will it stop on most often? __3__

Form B • Free-Response B232 Stop!

Free-Response Format • Test Answers

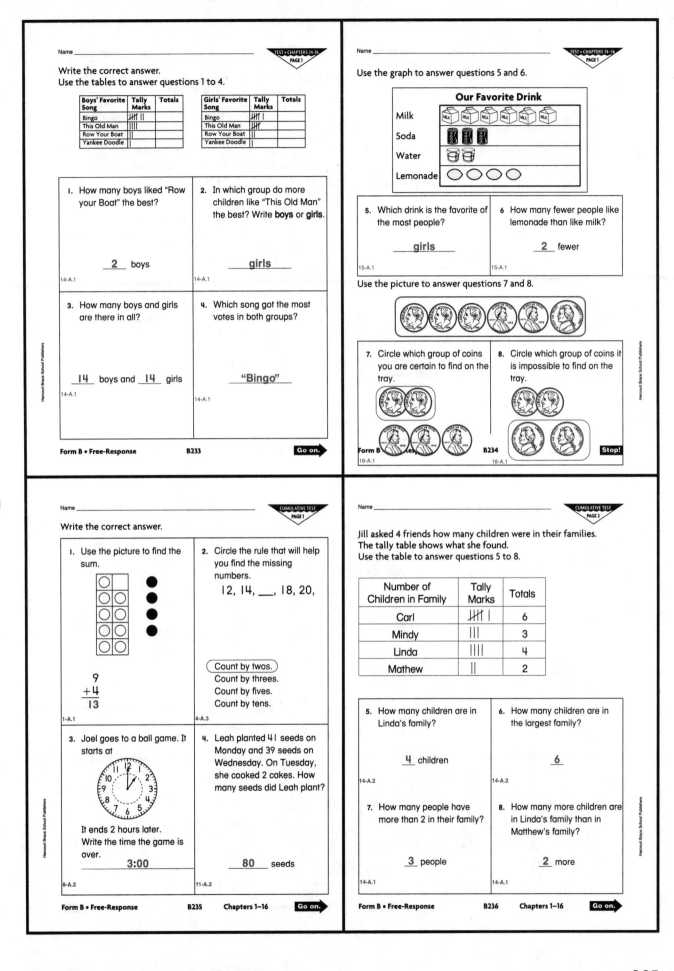

Write the correct answer.
Use the tables to answer questions 1 to 4.

Boys' Favorite Song	Tally Marks	Totals
Bingo	JHT II	
This Old Man	IIIII	
Row Your Boat	II	
Yankee Doodle	II	

Girls' Favorite Song	Tally Marks	Totals
Bingo	JHT I	
This Old Man	JHT	
Row Your Boat	II	
Yankee Doodle	II	

1. How many boys liked "Row your Boat" the best?

  ___2___ boys

14-A.1

2. In which group do more children like "This Old Man" the best? Write **boys** or **girls**.

  ___girls___

14-A.1

3. How many boys and girls are there in all?

  _14_ boys and _14_ girls

14-A.1

4. Which song got the most votes in both groups?

  ___"Bingo"___

14-A.1

Form B • Free-Response   B233   Go on. ▶

Use the graph to answer questions 5 and 6.

Our Favorite Drink

Milk · Soda · Water · Lemonade

5. Which drink is the favorite of the most people?

  ___girls___

15-A.1

6. How many fewer people like lemonade than like milk?

  ___2___ fewer

15-A.1

Use the picture to answer questions 7 and 8.

7. Circle which group of coins you are certain to find on the tray.

8. Circle which group of coins it is impossible to find on the tray.

Form B   B234   **Stop!**

16-A.1   16-A.1

Write the correct answer.

1. Use the picture to find the sum.

  $\begin{array}{r} 9 \\ +4 \\ \hline 13 \end{array}$

1-A.1

2. Circle the rule that will help you find the missing numbers.

  12, 14, ___, 18, 20,

  (Count by twos.)
  Count by threes.
  Count by fives.
  Count by tens.

4-A.3

3. Joel goes to a ball game. It starts at

  It ends 2 hours later.
  Write the time the game is over.
  ___3:00___

8-A.2

4. Leah planted 41 seeds on Monday and 39 seeds on Wednesday. On Tuesday, she cooked 2 cakes. How many seeds did Leah plant?

  ___80___ seeds

11-A.2

Form B • Free-Response   B235   **Chapters 1–16**   Go on. ▶

Jill asked 4 friends how many children were in their families. The tally table shows what she found.
Use the table to answer questions 5 to 8.

Number of Children in Family	Tally Marks	Totals
Carl	JHT I	6
Mindy	III	3
Linda	IIII	4
Mathew	II	2

5. How many children are in Linda's family?

  ___4___ children

14-A.2

6. How many children are in the largest family?

  ___6___

14-A.2

7. How many people have more than 2 in their family?

  ___3___ people

14-A.1

8. How many more children are in Linda's family than in Matthew's family?

  ___2___ more

14-A.1

Form B • Free-Response   B236   **Chapters 1–16**   Go on. ▶

Free-Response Format • Test Answers   **305**

Use the graph to answer questions 9 and 10.

Favorite Flavor of Ice Cream

vanilla
chocolate
strawberry
mint

0 1 2 3 4 5 6 7 8 9 10

9. How many people like chocolate the best?	10. How many more people like mint than like strawberry?
9 people	**2** more people
15-A.1	15-A.1

Use the graph to answer questions 11 and 12.

Favorite Lunch

sandwich
pizza
salad
soup

0 1 2 3 4 5

11. How many more people like sandwiches than like soup?	12. Which is the favorite lunch of the most people?
2 more	**pizza**
15-A.1	15-A.2

Form B • Free-Response B237 **Chapters 1–16** Go on.

Use the table to answer questions 13 and 14.
This table shows the outcomes of 10 spins.

Pattern	Tally Marks
dots	JHT II
stripes	III

13. Write which pattern the pointer stopped on more often. Write **dots** or **stripes**.	14. How many times did the pointer stop on stripes?
dots	**3** times
16-A.2	16-A.2

15. In a bag there are 3 red markers, 4 green markers, and 15 yellow markers. Which color will be pulled out most often?	16. This pointer can stop on 1, 2, or 3. Which number will it stop on most often?
yellow	**1**
16-A.1	16-A.1

17. Circle the bag you think a cube will be pulled from least often.	18. The pointer can stop on 1, 2, or 3. Which do you think it will stop on least often?
	3
16-A.1	16-A.1

Form B • Free-Response B238 **Chapters 1–16** Stop!

Write the correct answer.

1. Circle the object shaped like this solid figure.	2. Circle the object shaped like this solid figure.

3. Circle the object shaped like this solid figure.	4. Circle the solid figure that is the same shape as this solid figure.

5. Circle the solid figure that has all flat faces and can be stacked.	6. Circle the solid figure that has no flat faces and can be rolled.

Form B • Free-Response B239 Go on.

7. Circle the solid figure that has 5 flat faces and can slide.	8. Circle the solid figure that can roll and slide.

9. Circle the solid figure missing in the pattern.	10. Circle the solid figure missing in the pattern.

11. Circle the plane figure you could trace from the solid figure.	12. Circle the plane figure you could trace from the solid figure.

Form B • Free-Response B240 Stop!

Free-Response Format • Test Answers

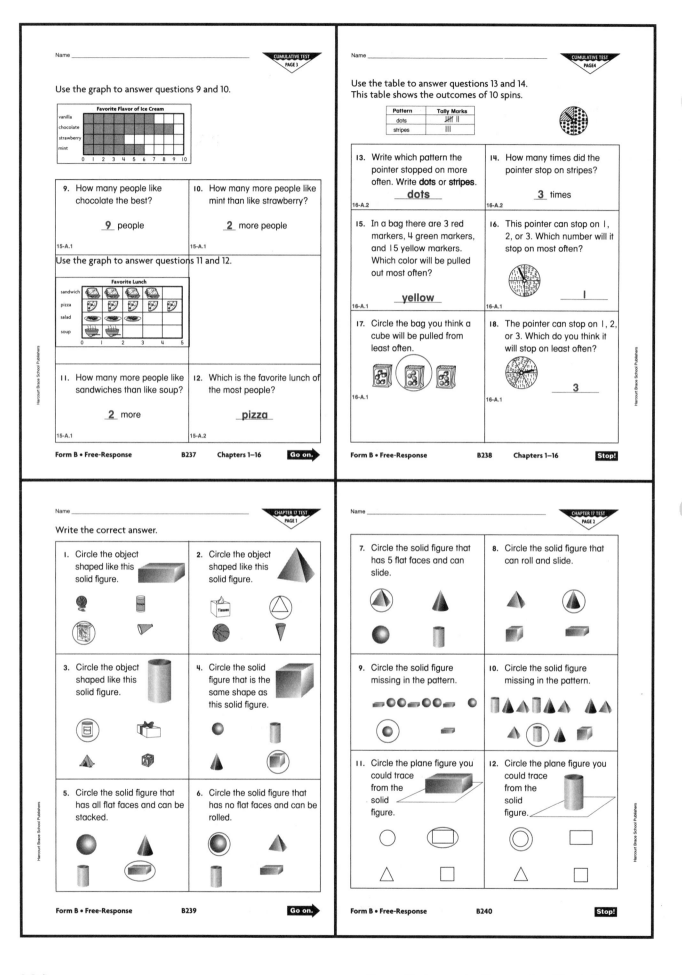

Write the correct answer.

1. Circle the figure that is a triangle.

2. Circle the figure that is a rectangle.

3. How many sides does this figure have?

___6___ sides

4. How many corners does this figure have?

___4___ corners

5. Circle the figure that has 5 sides and 5 corners.

6. Circle the figure that has 3 sides and 3 corners.

---

7. Circle the drawing that shows how you can cut this figure to make 2 rectangles.

8. Circle the drawing that shows how you can cut this figure to make 2 triangles.

9. Circle the figures that are the same size and shape.

10. Circle the figure that is the same size and shape as this figure.

11. Circle the figure that will fit.

12. Circle the figure that will fit.

Circle the correct answer.

1. Circle the picture that has symmetry.

2. Circle the picture that does NOT have symmetry.

3. Circle the picture that has symmetry.

4. Circle the picture that does NOT have symmetry.

---

5. Circle the picture that shows the line of symmetry.

6. Circle the picture that shows the line of symmetry.

7. Circle the word that names the move.

turn   flip   slide

8. Circle the word that names the move.

turn   (flip)   slide

9. Circle the word that names the move.

turn   flip   (slide)

10. Circle the word that names the move.

turn   (flip)   slide

Free-Response Format • Test Answers

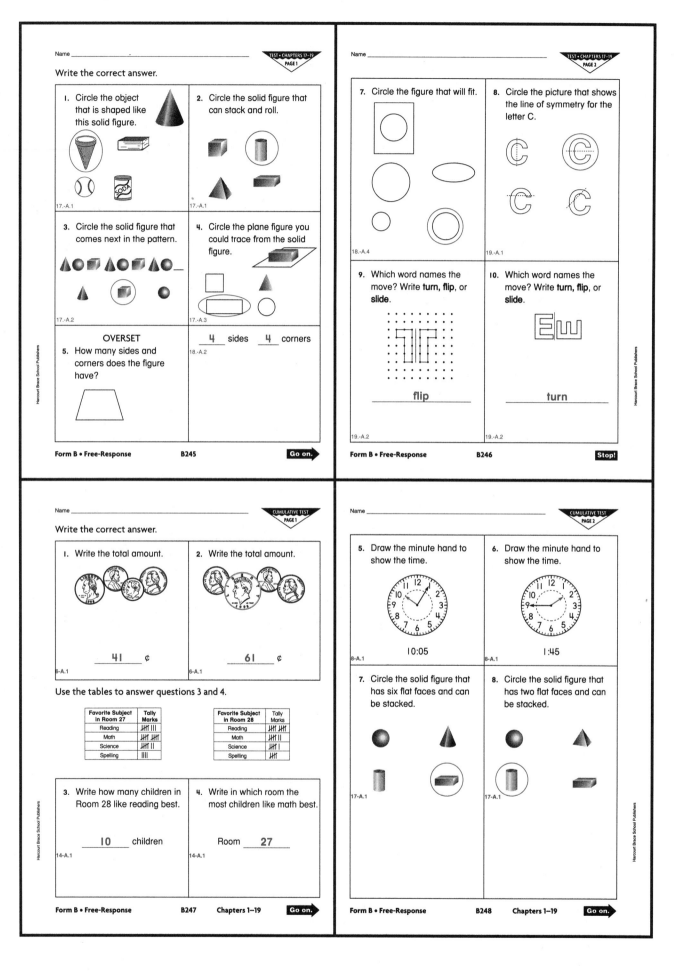

Free-Response Format • Test Answers

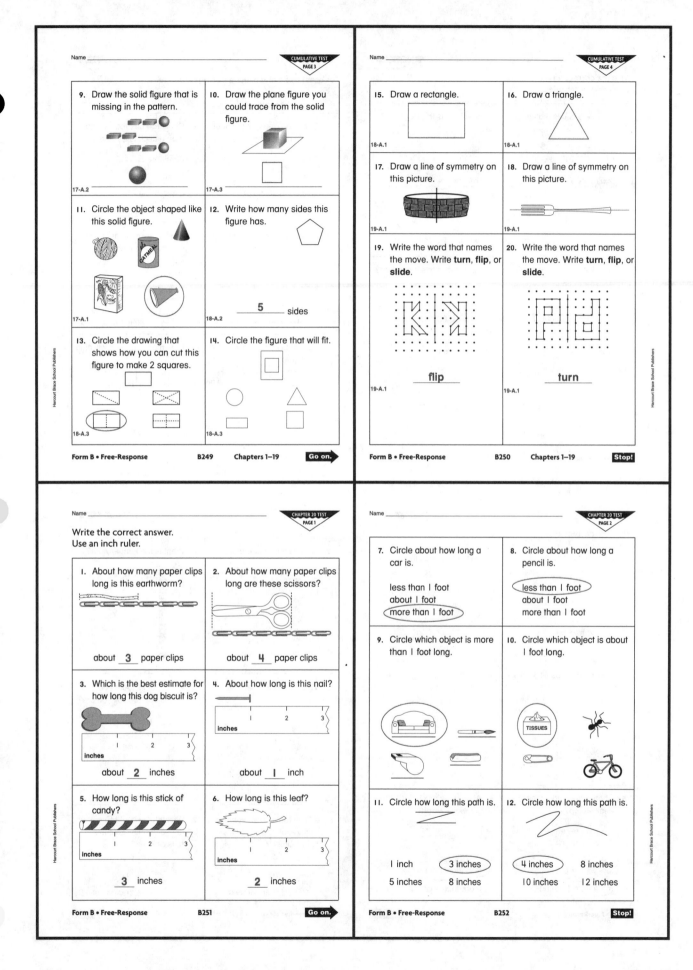

9. Draw the solid figure that is missing in the pattern.

17-A.2 _____

10. Draw the plane figure you could trace from the solid figure.

17-A.3 _____

11. Circle the object shaped like this solid figure.

17-A.1

12. Write how many sides this figure has.

____5____ sides

18-A.2

13. Circle the drawing that shows how you can cut this figure to make 2 squares.

18-A.3

14. Circle the figure that will fit.

18-A.3

15. Draw a rectangle.

18-A.1

16. Draw a triangle.

18-A.1

17. Draw a line of symmetry on this picture.

19-A.1

18. Draw a line of symmetry on this picture.

19-A.1

19. Write the word that names the move. Write **turn**, **flip**, or **slide**.

____flip____

19-A.1

20. Write the word that names the move. Write **turn**, **flip**, or **slide**.

____turn____

19-A.1

Write the correct answer.
Use an inch ruler.

1. About how many paper clips long is this earthworm?

about __3__ paper clips

2. About how many paper clips long are these scissors?

about __4__ paper clips

3. Which is the best estimate for how long this dog biscuit is?

about __2__ inches

4. About how long is this nail?

about __1__ inch

5. How long is this stick of candy?

__3__ inches

6. How long is this leaf?

__2__ inches

7. Circle about how long a car is.

less than 1 foot
about 1 foot
more than 1 foot

8. Circle about how long a pencil is.

less than 1 foot
about 1 foot
more than 1 foot

9. Circle which object is more than 1 foot long.

10. Circle which object is about 1 foot long.

11. Circle how long this path is.

1 inch   3 inches
5 inches   8 inches

12. Circle how long this path is.

4 inches   8 inches
10 inches   12 inches

Free-Response Format • Test Answers

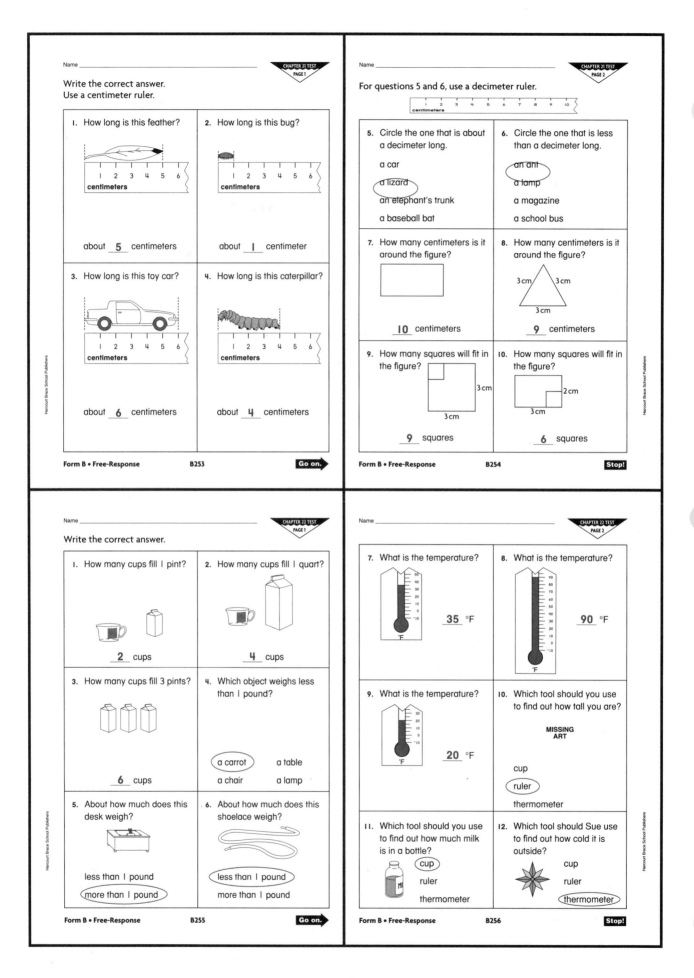

Page 1 (top left)

Write the correct answer.
Use a centimeter ruler.

1. How long is this feather?

about __5__ centimeters

2. How long is this bug?

about __1__ centimeter

3. How long is this toy car?

about __6__ centimeters

4. How long is this caterpillar?

about __4__ centimeters

Page 2 (top right)

For questions 5 and 6, use a decimeter ruler.

5. Circle the one that is about a decimeter long.

a car
(a lizard)
an elephant's trunk
a baseball bat

6. Circle the one that is less than a decimeter long.

(an ant)
a lamp
a magazine
a school bus

7. How many centimeters is it around the figure?

__10__ centimeters

8. How many centimeters is it around the figure?

3 cm   3 cm
3 cm

__9__ centimeters

9. How many squares will fit in the figure?

3 cm
3 cm

__9__ squares

10. How many squares will fit in the figure?

2 cm
3 cm

__6__ squares

Page 1 (bottom left)

Write the correct answer.

1. How many cups fill 1 pint?

__2__ cups

2. How many cups fill 1 quart?

__4__ cups

3. How many cups fill 3 pints?

__6__ cups

4. Which object weighs less than 1 pound?

(a carrot)   a table
a chair   a lamp

5. About how much does this desk weigh?

less than 1 pound
(more than 1 pound)

6. About how much does this shoelace weigh?

(less than 1 pound)
more than 1 pound

Page 2 (bottom right)

7. What is the temperature?

__35__ °F

8. What is the temperature?

__90__ °F

9. What is the temperature?

__20__ °F

10. Which tool should you use to find out how tall you are?

MISSING ART

cup
(ruler)
thermometer

11. Which tool should you use to find out how much milk is in a bottle?

(cup)
ruler
thermometer

12. Which tool should Sue use to find out how cold it is outside?

cup
ruler
(thermometer)

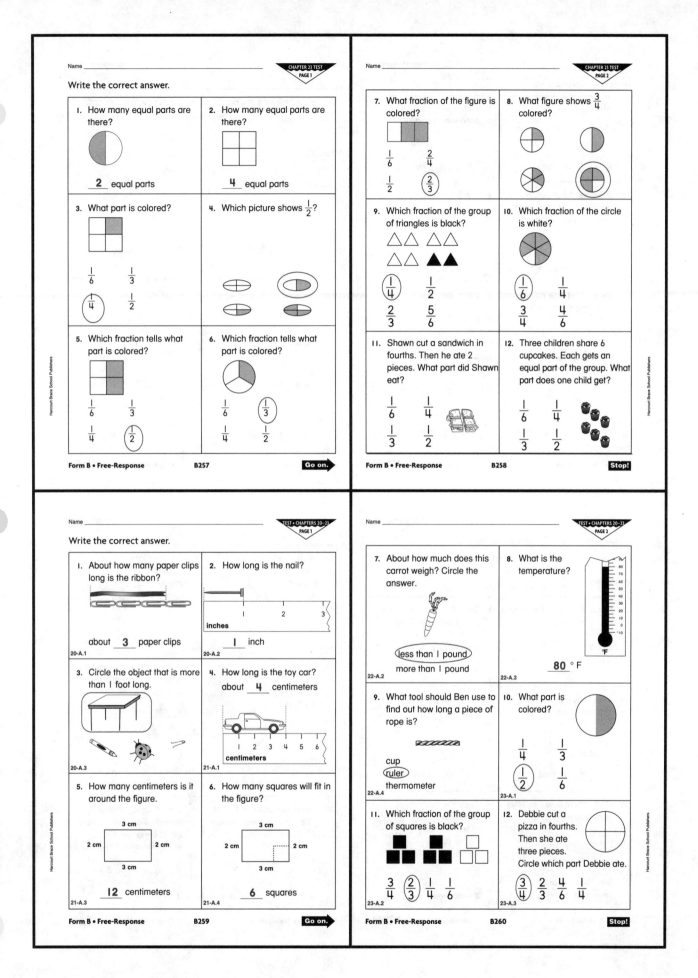

Name _____

Write the correct answer.

1. How many equal parts are there?

   2 equal parts

2. How many equal parts are there?

   4 equal parts

3. What part is colored?

   $\frac{1}{6}$ $\frac{1}{3}$
   ⬤$\frac{1}{4}$ $\frac{1}{2}$

4. Which picture shows $\frac{1}{2}$?

5. Which fraction tells what part is colored?

   $\frac{1}{6}$ $\frac{1}{3}$
   $\frac{1}{4}$ ⬤$\frac{1}{2}$

6. Which fraction tells what part is colored?

   $\frac{1}{6}$ ⬤$\frac{1}{3}$
   $\frac{1}{4}$ $\frac{1}{2}$

Form B • Free-Response   B257   Go on.

Name _____

7. What fraction of the figure is colored?

   $\frac{1}{6}$ $\frac{2}{4}$
   $\frac{1}{2}$ ⬤$\frac{2}{3}$

8. What figure shows $\frac{3}{4}$ colored?

9. Which fraction of the group of triangles is black?

   ⬤$\frac{1}{4}$ $\frac{1}{2}$
   $\frac{2}{3}$ $\frac{5}{6}$

10. Which fraction of the circle is white?

    ⬤$\frac{1}{6}$ $\frac{1}{4}$
    $\frac{3}{4}$ $\frac{4}{6}$

11. Shawn cut a sandwich in fourths. Then he ate 2 pieces. What part did Shawn eat?

    $\frac{1}{6}$ $\frac{1}{4}$
    $\frac{1}{3}$ ⬤$\frac{1}{2}$

12. Three children share 6 cupcakes. Each gets an equal part of the group. What part does one child get?

    $\frac{1}{6}$ $\frac{1}{4}$
    ⬤$\frac{1}{3}$ $\frac{1}{2}$

Form B • Free-Response   B258   Stop!

Name _____

Write the correct answer.

1. About how many paper clips long is the ribbon?

   about **3** paper clips
   20-A.1

2. How long is the nail?

   1 inch
   inches
   20-A.2

3. Circle the object that is more than 1 foot long.
   20-A.3

4. How long is the toy car?

   about **4** centimeters
   centimeters
   21-A.1

5. How many centimeters is it around the figure.

   3 cm
   2 cm   2 cm
   3 cm

   12 centimeters
   21-A.3

6. How many squares will fit in the figure?

   3 cm
   2 cm   2 cm
   3 cm

   6 squares
   21-A.4

Form B • Free-Response   B259   Go on.

Name _____

7. About how much does this carrot weigh? Circle the answer.

   ⬭less than 1 pound
   more than 1 pound
   22-A.2

8. What is the temperature?

   80 °F
   22-A.3

9. What tool should Ben use to find out how long a piece of rope is?

   cup
   ⬭ruler
   thermometer
   22-A.4

10. What part is colored?

    $\frac{1}{4}$ $\frac{1}{3}$
    ⬤$\frac{1}{2}$ $\frac{1}{6}$
    23-A.1

11. Which fraction of the group of squares is black?

    $\frac{3}{4}$ ⬤$\frac{2}{3}$ $\frac{1}{4}$ $\frac{1}{6}$
    23-A.2

12. Debbie cut a pizza in fourths. Then she ate three pieces. Circle which part Debbie ate.

    ⬤$\frac{3}{4}$ $\frac{2}{3}$ $\frac{4}{6}$ $\frac{1}{4}$
    23-A.3

Form B • Free-Response   B260   Stop!

Free-Response Format • Test Answers

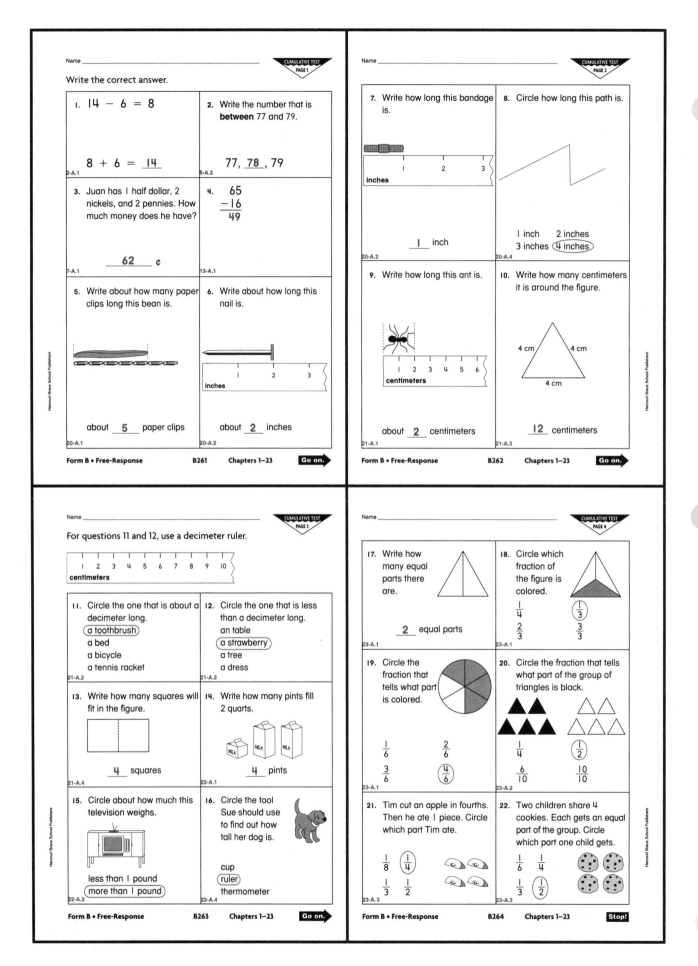

Free-Response Format • Test Answers

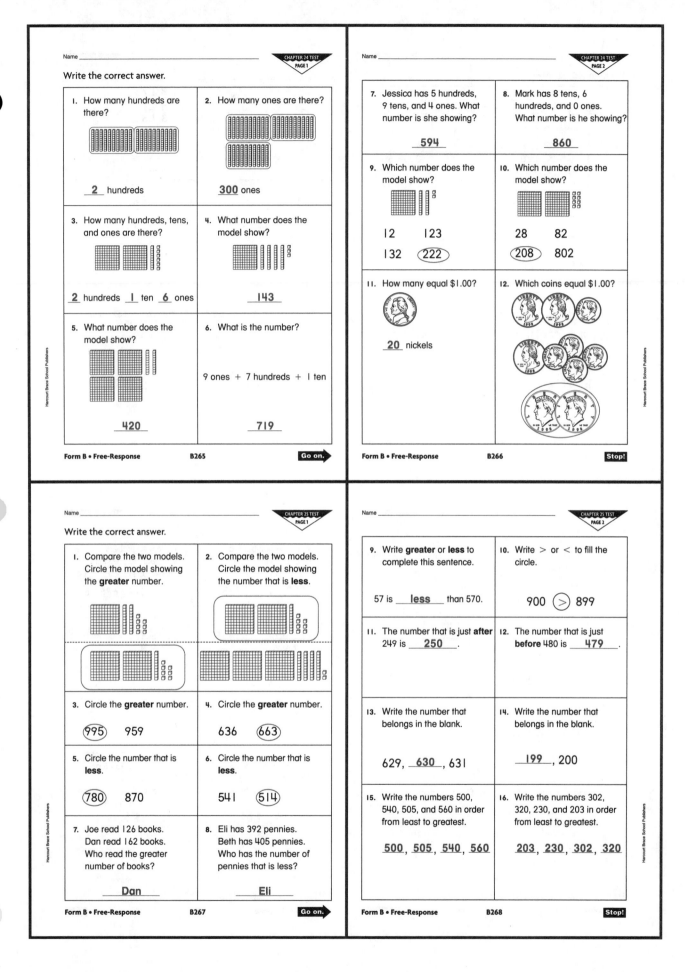

Write the correct answer.

1. How many hundreds are there?

  __2__ hundreds

2. How many ones are there?

  300 ones

3. How many hundreds, tens, and ones are there?

  2 hundreds **1** ten **6** ones

4. What number does the model show?

  __143__

5. What number does the model show?

  __420__

6. What is the number?

  9 ones + 7 hundreds + 1 ten

  __719__

7. Jessica has 5 hundreds, 9 tens, and 4 ones. What number is she showing?

  __594__

8. Mark has 8 tens, 6 hundreds, and 0 ones. What number is he showing?

  __860__

9. Which number does the model show?

  12   123
  132   (222)

10. Which number does the model show?

  28   82
  (208)   802

11. How many equal $1.00?

  __20__ nickels

12. Which coins equal $1.00?

Write the correct answer.

1. Compare the two models. Circle the model showing the **greater** number.

2. Compare the two models. Circle the model showing the number that is **less**.

3. Circle the **greater** number.

  (995)   959

4. Circle the **greater** number.

  636   (663)

5. Circle the number that is **less**.

  (780)   870

6. Circle the number that is **less**.

  541   (514)

7. Joe read 126 books. Dan read 162 books. Who read the greater number of books?

  __Dan__

8. Eli has 392 pennies. Beth has 405 pennies. Who has the number of pennies that is less?

  __Eli__

9. Write **greater** or **less** to complete this sentence.

  57 is __less__ than 570.

10. Write > or < to fill the circle.

  900 (>) 899

11. The number that is just **after** 249 is __250__.

12. The number that is just **before** 480 is __479__.

13. Write the number that belongs in the blank.

  629, __630__, 631

14. Write the number that belongs in the blank.

  __199__, 200

15. Write the numbers 500, 540, 505, and 560 in order from least to greatest.

  __500__, __505__, __540__, __560__

16. Write the numbers 302, 320, 230, and 203 in order from least to greatest.

  __203__, __230__, __302__, __320__

Free-Response Format • Test Answers

Write the correct answer.

1.

hundreds	tens	ones
	□	
2	4	6
+ 1	2	4
3	7	0

2.

hundreds	tens	ones
□	□	
3	7	5
+ 3	6	1
7	3	6

3.
```
  403
 +158
  561
```

4.
```
  542
 +364
  906
```

5.

hundreds	tens	ones
	□	□
9	8	4
− 5	2	7
4	5	7

6.

hundreds	tens	ones
□	□	
5	3	8
− 2	4	3
2	9	5

Form B • Free-Response   B269   Go on.

7.
```
  761
 −670
   91
```

8.
```
  827
 −482
  345
```

9.
```
  $2.02
 + 3.26
  $5.28
```

10.
```
  $6.56
 − 2.75
  $3.81
```

11. Kimi had $9.93. She spent $7.69 on a gift. Write how much money she has left.

$2.24

12. Bryan earned $2.98 on Friday and $1.40 on Saturday. Write how much money he earned in all.

$4.38

Form B • Free-Response   B270   Stop!

Write the correct answer.

1. Write how many hundreds, tens, and ones are there.

<u>2</u> hundreds <u>0</u> tens <u>4</u> ones
24-A.1

2. Write the number the model shows.

325
24-A.1

3. Joan has 7 ones, 8 hundreds, and 6 tens. Write the number she is showing.

867
24-A.1

4. How many equal $1.00?

<u>10</u> dimes
24-A.2

5. Circle the **greater** number.

699 (700)
25-A.1

6. Circle the number that is **less**.

(401) 410
25-A.1

Form B • Free-Response   B271   Go on.

---

7. Write the number that belongs in the blank.

723, <u>724</u>, 725
25-A.2

8. Write the numbers in order from least to greatest.

685, 601, 692, 619

<u>601</u>, <u>619</u>, <u>685</u>, <u>692</u>
25-A.3

9.
```
  538
 +257
  795
```
26-A.1

9.
```
  826
 −682
  144
```
26-A.1

11. Chuck had $5.15. He spent $3.06 on a toy. How much money does he have left?

$ <u>2.09</u>
26-A.3

12. Katie earned $3.65 on Monday and $2.80 on Tuesday. How much money did she earn in all?

$ <u>6.45</u>
26-A.3

Form B • Free-Response   B272   Stop!

Free-Response Format • Test Answers

Write the correct answer.

1. Write the addition sentence that tells about the picture.

$\underline{7} + \underline{7} = \underline{14}$

1-A.1

2. Write the missing addend.

$9 + \underline{8} = 17$

2-A.1

3. Write the number that is just **after** 82.

82, **83**

5-A.2

4. Jim has 1 half-dollar, 1 quarter, 1 dime, and 3 pennies. How much money does he have?

88 ¢

7-A.1

5.

tens	ones
3	8
+ 2	7
6	**5**

11-A.1

6.

tens	ones
5	0
- 1	7
3	**3**

13-A.1

Use the picture to answer questions 7 and 8.

7. Circle the group of toys you are certain to find on the shelf.

16-A.1

8. Circle the group of toys it is impossible to find on the shelf.

16-A.1

9. Write the number.

9 ones + 6 hundreds + 4 tens
649

24-A.1

10. Write how many equal $1.00.

100 pennies

24-A.2

11. Jessica has 7 hundreds, 3 tens, and 5 ones. Write the number she is showing.

735

24-A.1

12. Mark has 4 tens, 8 hundreds, and 0 ones. Write the number he is showing.

840

24-A.1

13. Circle the **greater** number.

807   (870)

25-A.1

14. Circle the number that is **less**.

(159)   591

25-A.1

15. Write **greater** or **less** to complete this sentence.

16 is **less** than 160.

25-A.1

16. Write the number that belongs in the blank.

729, **730**, 731

25-A.2

17.

hundreds	tens	ones
5	3	8
+ 3	2	6
8	6	4

26-A.1

18.

hundreds	tens	ones
7	5	2
- 4	3	6
3	1	6

26-A.2

19.

$\begin{array}{r} 634 \\ +172 \\ \hline 806 \end{array}$

26-A.1

20.

$\begin{array}{r} 515 \\ -430 \\ \hline 85 \end{array}$

26-A.2

21. Kara had $7.25. She spent $5.28 on a gift. Write how much money she has left.

$ **1.97**

26-A.3

22. Max earned $2.60 on Saturday and $1.75 on Sunday. Write how much money in all he earned.

$ **4.35**

26-A.3

Free-Response Format • Test Answers

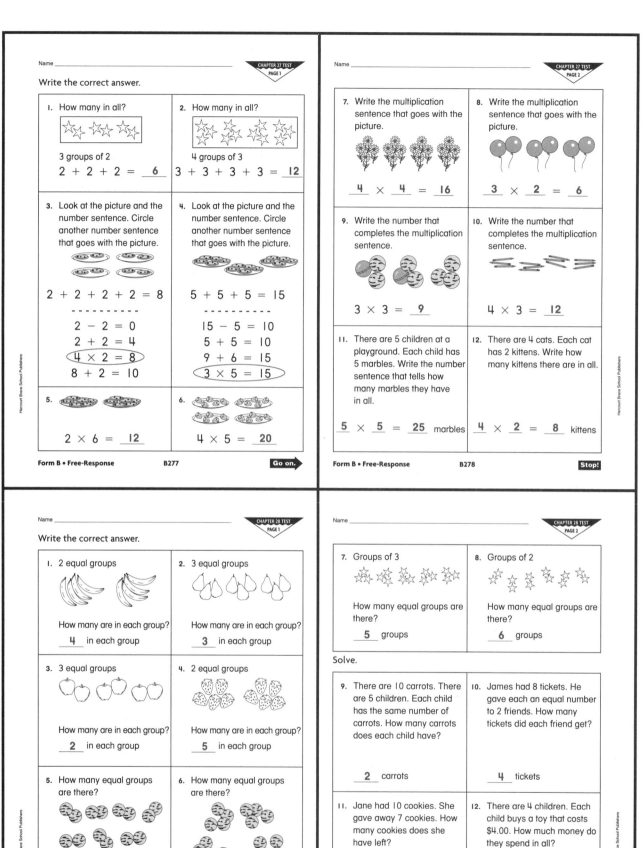

Free-Response Format • Test Answers

Write the correct answer.

1. Write how many in all.

[□□□ □□□ □□□]

$5 + 5 + 5 = \underline{15}$

27-A.1

2. Write how many in all.

[□□ □□]

$2 + 2 = \underline{4}$

27-A.1

3. Write the multiplication sentence that goes with the picture.

✰✰ ✰✰✰ ✰✰ ✰✰✰

$\underline{4} \times \underline{3} = \underline{12}$

27-A.2

4. Write the multiplication sentence that goes with the picture.

$\underline{5} \times \underline{4} = \underline{20}$

27-A.2

5. There are 4 children playing. Each child has 4 blocks. Write the multiplication sentence that tells how many blocks they have in all.

$\underline{4} \times \underline{4} = \underline{16}$

27-A.3

6. There are 2 bags. Each bag has 5 peanuts. Write how many peanuts there are in all.

$\underline{10}$ peanuts

27-A.3

7. 2 equal groups

How many are in each group?
$\underline{4}$ in each group

28-A.1

8. 3 equal groups

How many are in each group?
$\underline{2}$ in each group

28-A.1

9. Groups of 3

How many equal groups are there?
$\underline{3}$ groups

28-A.1

10. Groups of 2

How many equal groups are there?
$\underline{6}$ groups

28-A.1

Solve.

11. There are 15 toys. There are 5 children. Each child has the same number of toys. How many toys does each child have?

$\underline{3}$ toys

28-A.2

12. Janet gave 14 stickers to 2 friends. She gave each friend an equal number. How many stickers did each friend get?

$\underline{7}$ stickers

28-A.2

Write the correct answer.
Use base-ten blocks to answer questions 1 and 2.

1.
$\begin{array}{r} 47 \\ +36 \\ \hline 83 \end{array}$

11-A.1

2.
$\begin{array}{r} 28 \\ +12 \\ \hline 40 \end{array}$

11-A.1

Use base-ten blocks.
Choose the operation and solve. Write + or −.

3. Grandma has 34 flowers in her front yard and 27 flowers in her back yard. How many flowers does she have in all?

tens	ones
3	4
⊕ 2	7
6	1

11-A.1

4. Cheryl has 50¢. She buys a

29¢

How much money does Cheryl have left?

tens	ones
5	0¢
⊖ 2	9¢
2	1¢

11-A.1

5.
$\begin{array}{r} 51 \\ -26 \\ \hline 25 \end{array}$

13-A.1

6.
$\begin{array}{r} 73 \\ -44 \\ \hline 29 \end{array}$

13-A.1

Use the graph to answer questions 7 to 10.

Children Who Ride the Bus to School					
Room 201	😊	😊	😊	😊	
Room 202	😊	😊	😊	😊	😊
Room 203	😊	😊	😊		
Room 204	😊	😊			

Each 😊 stands for 3 students.

7. Which room has 12 children who ride the bus?

Room $\underline{201}$

15-A.1

8. Which room has the fewest number of children riding the bus?

Room $\underline{204}$

15-A.1

9. Which room has the most children riding the bus?

Room $\underline{202}$

15-A.1

10. How many children in Room 203 ride the bus?

$\underline{9}$ children

15-A.1

Free-Response Format • Test Answers

317

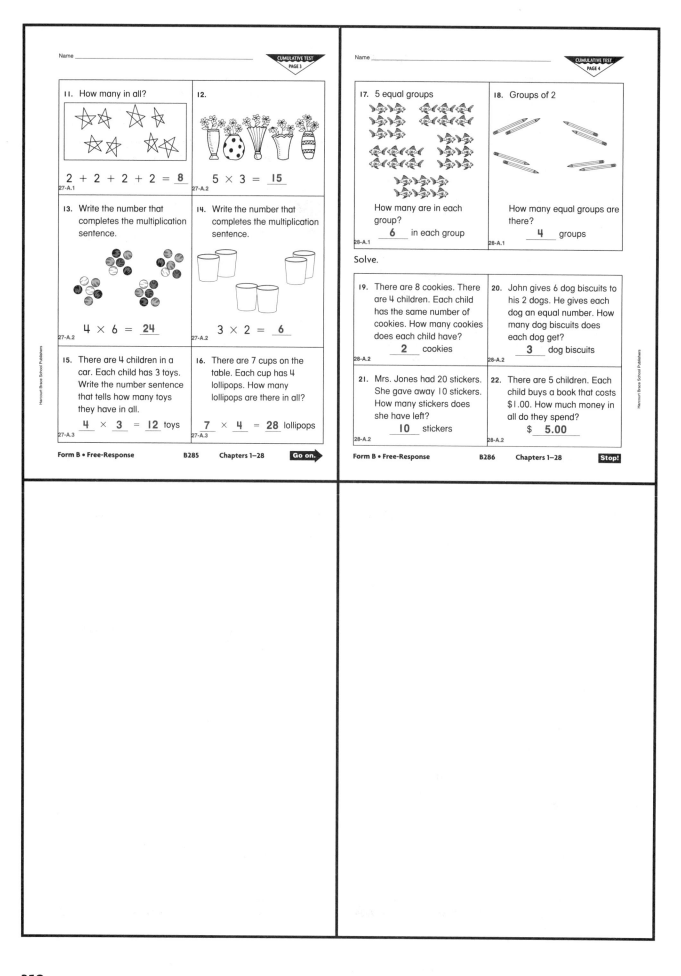

11. How many in all?

$2 + 2 + 2 + 2 = \underline{8}$
27-A.1

12.

$5 \times 3 = \underline{15}$
27-A.2

13. Write the number that completes the multiplication sentence.

$4 \times 6 = \underline{24}$
27-A.2

14. Write the number that completes the multiplication sentence.

$3 \times 2 = \underline{6}$
27-A.2

15. There are 4 children in a car. Each child has 3 toys. Write the number sentence that tells how many toys they have in all.

$\underline{4} \times \underline{3} = \underline{12}$ toys
27-A.3

16. There are 7 cups on the table. Each cup has 4 lollipops. How many lollipops are there in all?

$\underline{7} \times \underline{4} = \underline{28}$ lollipops
27-A.3

17. 5 equal groups

How many are in each group?
$\underline{6}$ in each group
28-A.1

18. Groups of 2

How many equal groups are there?
$\underline{4}$ groups
28-A.1

Solve.

19. There are 8 cookies. There are 4 children. Each child has the same number of cookies. How many cookies does each child have?
$\underline{2}$ cookies
28-A.2

20. John gives 6 dog biscuits to his 2 dogs. He gives each dog an equal number. How many dog biscuits does each dog get?
$\underline{3}$ dog biscuits
28-A.2

21. Mrs. Jones had 20 stickers. She gave away 10 stickers. How many stickers does she have left?
$\underline{10}$ stickers
28-A.2

22. There are 5 children. Each child buys a book that costs $1.00. How much money in all do they spend?
$ \underline{5.00}$
28-A.2

Free-Response Format • Test Answers

Management Forms

Test Answer Sheet

This copying master is an individual recording sheet for up to 50 items on the multiple-choice (standardized) format tests.

Grading Made Easy

This percent converter can be used for all quizzes and tests. The percents given are based on all problems having equal value. Percents are rounded to the nearest whole percent giving the benefit of 0.5 percent.

Individual Record Form

One copying master for each content cluster of chapters is provided. Criterion scores for each learning goal are given for the chapter test. The student's total scores are recorded at the top of the page for chapter tests, the multi-chapter test and the cumulative test. The scores for each learning goal can also be recorded. You can use the Review Options that are listed on the form to assign additional review for the student unable to pass the test.

Formal Assessment Class Record Form

The scores for all the tests can be recorded for your class on these record forms. The Criterion Score for each test is given.

Learning Goals

The learning goals for the entire grade level are provided. These goals are referenced throughout the program. Each test item is referenced to a learning goal. You may wish to use these pages to cross-reference the Math Advantage Learning Goals with local, district, or statewide benchmarks.

Name_____ Date_____

Test Answer Sheet

MATHEMATICS ADVANTAGE

Test Title_____

1. Ⓐ Ⓑ Ⓒ Ⓓ
2. Ⓐ Ⓑ Ⓒ Ⓓ
3. Ⓐ Ⓑ Ⓒ Ⓓ
4. Ⓐ Ⓑ Ⓒ Ⓓ
5. Ⓐ Ⓑ Ⓒ Ⓓ

6. Ⓐ Ⓑ Ⓒ Ⓓ
7. Ⓐ Ⓑ Ⓒ Ⓓ
8. Ⓐ Ⓑ Ⓒ Ⓓ
9. Ⓐ Ⓑ Ⓒ Ⓓ
10. Ⓐ Ⓑ Ⓒ Ⓓ

11. Ⓐ Ⓑ Ⓒ Ⓓ
12. Ⓐ Ⓑ Ⓒ Ⓓ
13. Ⓐ Ⓑ Ⓒ Ⓓ
14. Ⓐ Ⓑ Ⓒ Ⓓ
15. Ⓐ Ⓑ Ⓒ Ⓓ

16. Ⓐ Ⓑ Ⓒ Ⓓ
17. Ⓐ Ⓑ Ⓒ Ⓓ
18. Ⓐ Ⓑ Ⓒ Ⓓ
19. Ⓐ Ⓑ Ⓒ Ⓓ
20. Ⓐ Ⓑ Ⓒ Ⓓ

21. Ⓐ Ⓑ Ⓒ Ⓓ
22. Ⓐ Ⓑ Ⓒ Ⓓ
23. Ⓐ Ⓑ Ⓒ Ⓓ
24. Ⓐ Ⓑ Ⓒ Ⓓ
25. Ⓐ Ⓑ Ⓒ Ⓓ

26. Ⓐ Ⓑ Ⓒ Ⓓ
27. Ⓐ Ⓑ Ⓒ Ⓓ
28. Ⓐ Ⓑ Ⓒ Ⓓ
29. Ⓐ Ⓑ Ⓒ Ⓓ
30. Ⓐ Ⓑ Ⓒ Ⓓ

31. Ⓐ Ⓑ Ⓒ Ⓓ
32. Ⓐ Ⓑ Ⓒ Ⓓ
33. Ⓐ Ⓑ Ⓒ Ⓓ
34. Ⓐ Ⓑ Ⓒ Ⓓ
35. Ⓐ Ⓑ Ⓒ Ⓓ

36. Ⓐ Ⓑ Ⓒ Ⓓ
37. Ⓐ Ⓑ Ⓒ Ⓓ
38. Ⓐ Ⓑ Ⓒ Ⓓ
39. Ⓐ Ⓑ Ⓒ Ⓓ
40. Ⓐ Ⓑ Ⓒ Ⓓ

41. Ⓐ Ⓑ Ⓒ Ⓓ
42. Ⓐ Ⓑ Ⓒ Ⓓ
43. Ⓐ Ⓑ Ⓒ Ⓓ
44. Ⓐ Ⓑ Ⓒ Ⓓ
45. Ⓐ Ⓑ Ⓒ Ⓓ

46. Ⓐ Ⓑ Ⓒ Ⓓ
47. Ⓐ Ⓑ Ⓒ Ⓓ
48. Ⓐ Ⓑ Ⓒ Ⓓ
49. Ⓐ Ⓑ Ⓒ Ⓓ
50. Ⓐ Ⓑ Ⓒ Ⓓ

Total Number of Test Items

Number of Test Items Wrong

	4	5	6	7	8	9	10	11	12	13	14	15	16	17	18	19	20	21	22	23	24	25	26	27	28	29	30
1	75	80	83	86	88	89	90	91	92	92	93	93	94	94	94	95	95	95	95	96	96	96	96	96	96	97	97
2	50	60	67	71	75	78	80	82	83	85	86	87	88	88	89	89	89	90	90	91	91	92	92	93	93	93	93
3	25	40	50	57	63	67	70	73	75	77	79	80	81	82	83	84	85	86	86	87	88	88	88	89	89	90	90
4	0	20	33	43	50	56	60	64	67	69	71	73	75	76	78	79	80	81	82	83	83	84	85	85	86	86	87
5		0	17	29	38	44	50	55	58	62	64	67	69	71	72	74	75	76	77	78	79	80	81	81	82	83	83
6			0	14	25	33	40	45	50	54	57	60	63	65	67	68	70	71	73	74	75	76	77	78	79	79	80
7				0	13	22	30	36	42	46	50	53	56	59	61	63	65	67	68	70	71	72	73	74	75	76	77
8					0	11	20	27	33	38	43	47	50	53	56	58	60	62	64	65	67	68	69	70	71	72	73
9						0	10	18	25	31	36	40	44	47	50	53	55	57	59	61	63	64	65	67	68	69	70
10							0	9	17	23	29	33	38	41	44	47	50	52	55	57	58	60	62	63	64	66	67
11								0	8	15	21	27	31	35	39	42	45	48	50	52	54	56	58	59	61	62	63
12									0	8	14	20	25	29	33	37	40	43	45	48	50	52	54	56	57	59	60
13										0	7	13	19	24	28	32	35	38	41	43	46	48	50	52	54	55	57
14											0	7	13	18	22	26	30	33	36	39	42	44	46	48	50	52	53
15												0	6	12	17	21	25	29	32	35	38	40	42	44	46	48	50
16													0	6	11	16	20	24	27	30	33	36	38	41	43	45	47
17														0	6	11	15	19	23	26	29	32	35	37	39	41	43
18															0	5	10	14	18	22	25	28	31	33	36	38	40
19																0	5	10	14	17	21	24	27	30	32	34	37
20																	0	5	9	13	17	20	23	26	29	31	33
21																		0	5	9	13	16	19	22	25	28	0
22																			0	4	8	12	15	19	21	24	27
23																				0	4	8	12	15	18	21	23
24																					0	4	8	11	14	17	20
25																						0	4	7	11	14	17
26																							0	4	7	10	13
27																								0	4	7	10
28																									0	3	8
29																										0	3
30																											0
31																											
32																											

MATH ADVANTAGE

Individual Record Form

GRADE 2 • Chapters 1-2

Child's Name _____

Test	Chapter 1	Chapter 2	Chapters 1-2	Cum Chs 1-2
Date				
Score				

LEARNING GOALS

		CHAPTER TEST				REVIEW OPTIONS				
		Test Items			**Criterion**	**Lesson**	**Teacher's Edition**	**Workbooks**		
Goal #	**Learning Goal**	**Concept**	**Skills**	**PSolv**	**Scores**	**page #**		**P**	**R**	**E**
1-A.1	To use mental math strategies to add basic facts with sums to 18	1-2	3-4		10/12	27-28	p. 25C: BB	1.1	1.1	1.1
		5-6	7-8			29-30	p. 39C: PG	1.2	1.2	1.2
		9-10				31-32	p. 25D: LCC	1.3	1.3	1.3
						33-34		1.4	1.4	1.4
1-A.2	To find sums of 3 addends	13-14		15-16	3/4	35-36	p. 35A: AOC 2	1.5	1.5	1.5
2-A.1	To use inverse operations to relate addition and subtraction	1-4	7-8		7/8	41-42	p. 39D: LCC	2.1	2.1	2.1
			9-10			45-46	p. 41A: AOC 1	2.3	2.3	2.3
						47-48		2.4	2.4	2.4
2-A.2	To use a number line to subtract	5-6			2/2	43-44	p. 43A: AOC 3	2.2	2.2	2.2
2-A.3	To choose the operation to solve problems			11-12	2/2	49-50	p. 49A: AOC 1	2.5	2.5	2.5

Key: AOC–Activity Options Column   **BB**–Bulletin Board   **PG**–Practice Game   **LCC**–Learning Center Card   **Tech-GSL**–Technology, Grow Slide Level

Individual Record Form

GRADE 2 • Chapters 3-5

MATH ADVANTAGE

Child's Name _____

Test	Chapter 3	Chapter 4	Chapter 5	Chapters 3-5	Cum Chs 3-5
Date					
Score					

LEARNING GOALS

Goal #	Learning Goal	CHAPTER TEST — Test Items: Concept	Skills	PSolv	Criterion Scores	Lesson page #	Teacher's Edition	Workbooks P	R	E
3-A.1	To group by tens and ones to 100	1-2 3-4	5-8		9/10	59-60 61-62 63-64 65-66	p. 71C: PG p. 57D: LCC	3.1 3.2 3.3 3.4	3.1 3.2 3.3 3.4	3.1 3.2 3.3 3.4
3-A.2	To use a benchmark to estimate a quantity	11-12		9/10	2/2	67-68	p. 67A: AOC 1, AOC 2 AOC 3	3.5	3.5	3.5
4-A.1	To skip count by twos, threes, fives, and tens	1-2	3-4 5-6 9-10		7/8	73-74 75-76 79-80	p. 71D: LCC p. 76A: Reteach	4.1 4.2 4.4	4.1 4.2 4.4	4.1 4.2 4.4
4-A.2	To identify numbers as odd or even	7-8			2/2	77-78	p. 57C: BB	4.3	4.3	4.3
4-A.3	To look for a number pattern to solve problems			11-12	2/2	81-82	p. 82A: Enrichment	4.5	4.5	4.5
5-A.1	To compare two numbers using the > or < symbols	1-2	3-4		3/4	87-88 89-90	p. 88A: Reteach p. 90A: Tech-GSL N	5.1 5.2	5.1 5.2	5.1 5.2
5-A.2	To identify a number before, after, or between other numbers	5-6	7-8		3/4	91-92	p. 92A: Enrichment	5.3	5.3	5.3
5-A.3	To identify ordinal positions to twentieth		9-10		2/2	93-94	p. 93A: AOC 1	5.4	5.4	5.4
5-A.4	To use a number line to determine which ten a number is closer to		11-12		2/2	95-96	p. 95A: AOC 1	5.5	5.5	5.5

Key: AOC–Activity Options Column **BB**–Bulletin Board **PG**–Practice Game **LCC**–Learning Center Card **Tech-GSL**–Technology, Grow Slide Level

Individual Record Form

GRADE 2 • Chapters 6-9

Child's Name _____

MATH ADVANTAGE

Test	Chapter 6	Chapter 7	Chapter 8	Chapter 9	Chapters 6-9	Cum Chs 6-9
Date						
Score						

LEARNING GOALS / CHAPTER TEST / REVIEW OPTIONS

Goal #	Learning Goal	Concept	Skills	PSolv	Criterion Scores	Lesson page #	Teacher's Edition	P	R	E
6-A.1	To count on to identify amounts of money using coins		1-4 5-6 9-10 11-12		10/12	105-106 107-108 109-110 111-112	p. 103D: LCC p. 105A: AOC 2 p. 108A: Tech-GSL F	6.1 6.2 6.3 6.4	6.1 6.2 6.3 6.4	6.1 6.2 6.3 6.4
6-A.2	To act out and solve problems by using coins	5-6		13-14	2/2	113-114	p. 113A: AOC 3	6.5	6.5	6.5
7-A.1	To use coins to show amounts to 99¢		1-2 3-4	9-12	9/12	119-120 121-122 127-128	p. 103C: BB p. 121A: AOC 3	7.1 7.2 7.5	7.1 7.2 7.5	7.1 7.2 7.5
7-A.2	To count coins and identify objects that can be bought with that amount		5-6		2/2	123-124	p. 123A: AOC 2	7.3	7.3	7.3
7-A.3	To figure change by counting on with pennies	7-8			2/2	125-126	p. 117D: LCC	7.4	7.4	7.4
8-A.1	To tell time to the hour, half-hour, 5 minutes, and 15 minutes	3-4 5-6	1-2 7-8		6/8	133-134 135-136 137-138 139-140	p. 131C: PG p. 131D: LCC	8.1 8.2 8.3 8.4	8.1 8.2 8.3 8.4	8.1 8.2 8.3 8.4
8-A.2	To solve problems using elapsed time			9-10	2/2	141-142	p. 142A: Reteach	8.5	8.5	8.5
9-A.1	To read and use a calendar		1-2 3-4		3/4	147-148 149-150	p. 145C: BB p. 145D: LCC	9.1 9.2	9.1 9.2	9.1 9.2
9-A.2	To use clocks and elapsed time to solve problems	5-6			2/2	151-152	p. 151A: AOC 2	9.3	9.3	9.3
9-A.3	To sequence a series of events		7-8		2/2	153-154	p. 154A: Enrichment	9.4	9.4	9.4
9-A.4	To use a schedule to solve problems			9-12	3/4	155-156	p. 156A: Reteach	9.5	9.5	9.5

Key: AOC–Activity Options Column **BB**–Bulletin Board **PG**–Practice Game **LCC**–Learning Center Card **Tech-GSL**–Technology, Grow Slide Level

Individual Record Form

GRADE 2 • Chapters 10-11

Child's Name _____

MATH ADVANTAGE

Test	Chapter 10	Chapter 11	Chapters 10-11	Cum Chs 10-11
Date				
Score				

LEARNING GOALS

Goal #	Learning Goal	CHAPTER TEST — Test Items: Concept	Skills	PSolv	Criterion Scores	REVIEW OPTIONS — Lesson page #	Teacher's Edition	Workbooks P	R	E
10-A.1	To model one- and two-digit addition problems with and without regrouping	1-2 3-4 5-6 7-8			6/8	165-166 167-168 169-170 171-172	p. 163D: LCC p. 166A: Tech-GSL J	10.1 10.2 10.3 10.4	10.1 10.2 10.3 10.4	10.1 10.2 10.3 10.4
10-A.2	To make a model to solve two-digit addition problems			9-10	2/2	173-174	p. 173A: AOC 1	10.5	10.5	10.5
11-A.1	To add one- and two-digit numbers with and without regrouping	1 2	3-4 5-6 7-8 9-10	11 12	8/12	179-180 181-182 183-184 185-186	p. 163C: BB p. 177C: PG p. 177D: LCC	11.1 11.2 11.3 11.4	11.1 11.2 11.3 11.4	11.1 11.2 11.3 11.4
11-A.2	To identify information that is not necessary to solve a problem and then solve problems			13-14	2/2	187-188	p. 188A: AOC 1 AOC 2, AOC 3	11.5	11.5	11.5

Key: AOC–Activity Options Column **BB**–Bulletin Board **PG**–Practice Game **LCC**–Learning Center Card **Tech-GSL**–Technology, Grow Slide Level

MATH ADVANTAGE

Individual Record Form

GRADE 2 • Chapters 12-13

Child's Name _____

Test	Chapter 12	Chapter 13	Chapters 12-13	Cum Chs 12-13
Date				
Score				

LEARNING GOALS

Goal #	Learning Goal	CHAPTER TEST — Test Items — Concept	Skills	PSolv	Criterion Scores	REVIEW OPTIONS — Lesson page #	Teacher's Edition	Workbooks P	R	E
12-A.1	To model subtraction of one- and two-digit numbers from two-digit numbers with and without regrouping	1-2 3-4 5-6	7-10		9/10	197-198 199-200 201-202 203-204	p. 195C: BB p. 195D: LCC p. 201A: AOC 2	12.1 12.2 12.3 12.4	12.1 12.2 12.3 12.4	12.1 12.2 12.3 12.4
12-A.2	To choose the operation to solve problems			11-12	2/2	205-206	p. 205A: AOC 1	12.5	12.5	12.5
13-A.1	To subtract two-digit numbers from two-digit numbers with and without regrouping	1-2	3-4 5-8 9-10		9/10	211-212 213-214 215-216 217-218	p. 209C: PG p. 209D: LCC p. 214A: Tech-GSL S	13.1 13.2 13.3 13.4	13.1 13.2 13.3 13.4	13.1 13.2 13.3 13.4
13-A.2	To choose the operation to solve problems			11-12	2/2	219-220	p. 219A: AOC 3	13.5	13.5	13.5

Key: AOC–Activity Options Column   **BB**–Bulletin Board   **PG**–Practice Game   **LCC**–Learning Center Card   **Tech-GSL**–Technology, Grow Slide Level

Grading Sheet

Individual Record Form

GRADE 2 • Chapters 14-16

Child's Name _____

Test	Chapter 14	Chapter 15	Chapter 16	Chapters 14-16	Cum Chs 14-16
Date					
Score					

LEARNING GOALS / CHAPTER TEST / REVIEW OPTIONS

Goal #	Learning Goal	Concept	Skills	PSolv	Criterion Scores	Lesson page #	Teacher's Edition	P	R	E
14-A.1	To record data in tally tables and use the data to solve problems	1-2		3-6 9-12	8/10	229-230 231-232 237-238	p. 227C: BB p. 227D: LCC	14.1 14.2 14.4	14.1 14.2 14.4	14.1 14.2 14.4
14-A.2	To take surveys and record data in tally tables		7-8		2/2	233-234	p. 234A: Reteach	14.3	14.3	14.3
15-A.1	To read and interpret data in picture graphs and pictographs		1-4 5-8		6/8	241-242 243-244	p. 241A: AOC 2	15.1 15.2	15.1 15.2	15.1 15.2
15-A.2	To read and interpret data in bar graphs			9-12	3/4	245-246	p. 239C: PG	15.3	15.3	15.3
15-A.3	To make or use a graph to solve problems			13-16	3/4	247-248	p. 239D: LCC	15.4	15.4	15.4
16-A.1	To determine if an event is certain or impossible, most likely or least likely		1-4 5-8 11-12	13	8/11	253-254 255-256 259-260	p. 254A: Reteach	16.1 16.2 16.4	16.1 16.2 16.4	16.1 16.2 16.4
16-A.2	To interpret outcomes of games		9-10	14	2/3	257-258	p. 251D: LCC	16.3	16.3	16.3

Workbooks columns: P, R, E

Key: AOC–Activity Options Column **BB**–Bulletin Board **PG**–Practice Game **LCC**–Learning Center Card **Tech-GSL**–Technology, Grow Slide Level

Individual Record Form

GRADE 2 • Chapters 17-19

Child's Name _____

Test	Chapter 17	Chapter 18	Chapter 19	Chapters 17-19	Cum Chs 17-19
Date					
Score					

LEARNING GOALS

CHAPTER TEST / REVIEW OPTIONS

Goal #	Learning Goal	Concept	Skills	PSolv	Criterion Scores	Lesson page #	Teacher's Edition	P	R	E
17-A.1	To identify and sort solid figures	5-8	1-4		6/8	269-270 271-272	p. 267C: BB	17.1 17.2	17.1 17.2	17.1 17.2
17-A.2	To look for a pattern and find mistakes in a pattern			9-10	2/2	273-274	p. 273A: AOC 2, AOC 3	17.3	17.3	17.3
17-A.3	To identify plane figures as faces of solid figures		11-12		2/2	275-276	p. 275A: AOC 2	17.4	17.4	17.4
18-A.1	To identify plane figures		1-2		2/2	281-282	p. 281A: AOC 1	18.1	18.1	18.1
18-A.2	To identify the number of sides and corners in plane figures		3-6		3/4	283-284	p. 283A: AOC 1, AOC 2	18.2	18.2	18.2
18-A.3	To separate a plane figure to create different plane figures	7-8			2/2	285-286	p. 285A: AOC 2	18.3	18.3	18.3
18-A.4	To identify and draw congruent figures		9-12		3/4	287-288	p. 286A: Tech-GSL P	18.4	18.4	18.4
19-A.1	To identify lines of symmetry	1-4	5-6		5/6	293-294 295-296	p. 291C: BB p. 291D: LCC	19.1 19.2	19.1 19.2	19.1 19.2
19-A.2	To identify a slide, flip, or turn of a figure		7-8 9-10		3/4	297-298 299-300	p. 298A: Reteach p. 299A: AOC 2	19.3 19.4	19.3 19.4	19.3 19.4

Header note: CHAPTER TEST — Test Items (Concept, Skills, PSolv), Criterion Scores. REVIEW OPTIONS — Lesson page #, Teacher's Edition. Workbooks — P, R, E.

Key: AOC–Activity Options Column **BB**–Bulletin Board **PG**–Practice Game **LCC**–Learning Center Card **Tech-GSL**–Technology, Grow Slide Level

Grading Sheet

Individual Record Form

MATH ADVANTAGE

GRADE 2 • Chapters 20–23

Child's Name _____

Test	Chapter 20	Chapter 21	Chapter 22	Chapter 23	Chapters 20-23	Cum Chs 20-23
Date						
Score						

LEARNING GOALS		CHAPTER TEST				REVIEW OPTIONS					
		Test Items			Criterion	Lesson	Teacher's Edition	Workbooks			
Goal #	Learning Goal	Concept	Skills	PSolv	Scores	page #		P	R	E	
20-A.1	To use nonstandard units to measure length		1-2		2/2	309-310	p. 309A: AOC 2	20.1	20.1	20.1	
20-A.2	To estimate and measure length in inches	3-4	5-6		3/4	311-312 313-314	p. 307C: BB p. 307D: LCC	20.2 20.3	20.2 20.3	20.2 20.3	
20-A.3	To estimate the length of an object as more than, less than, or the same as one foot	7-8	9-10		3/4	315-316	p. 315A: AOC 2	20.4	20.4	20.4	
20-A.4	To use the problem solving strategy *guess and check* to estimate the length of a path			11-12	2/2	317-318	p. 317A: AOC 1, AOC 2, AOC 3	20.5	20.5	20.5	
21-A.1	To measure the length of an object in centimeters		1-4		3/4	323-324	p. 321D: LCC	21.1	21.1	21.1	
21-A.2	To use a decimeter to estimate length of objects and identify objects as more than, less than, or the same as 1 decimeter in length	5-6			2/2	325-326	p. 325A: AOC 2 p. 326A: Reteach	21.2	21.2	21.2	
21-A.3	To determine the perimeter of a figure		7-8		2/2	327-328	p. 327A: Tech-GSL N	21.3	21.3	21.3	
21-A.4	To use the *guess and check* strategy to estimate the area of a figure			9-10	2/2	329-330	p. 321C: PG	21.4	21.4	21.4	
22-A.1	To identify the number of cups that fill a cup, pint, and quart	1-3			2/3	335-336	p. 335A: AOC 2	22.1	22.1	22.1	
22-A.2	To identify whether an object weighs more than or less than a pound	4-6			2/3	337-338	p. 337A: AOC 2, AOC 3	22.2	22.2	22.2	
22-A.3	To read a thermometer and identify the temperature	7-9			2/3	339-340	p. 339A: AOC 1	22.3	22.3	22.3	
22-A.4	To choose the appropriate tool to measure an object	10-11		12	2/3	341-342	p. 341A: AOC 2	22.4	22.4	22.4	

Key: AOC–Activity Options Column **BB**–Bulletin Board **PG**–Practice Game **LCC**–Learning Center Card **Tech-GSL**–Technology, Grow Slide Level

Individual Record Form

GRADE 2 • Chapters 20-23

Child's Name _____

Test	Chapter 20	Chapter 21	Chapter 22	Chapter 23	Chapters 20-23	Cum Chs 20-23
Date						
Score						

LEARNING GOALS

		CHAPTER TEST				REVIEW OPTIONS				
			Test Items		Criterion				Workbooks	
Goal #	Learning Goal	Concept	Skills	PSolv	Scores	Lesson page #	Teacher's Edition	P	R	E
23-A.1	To identify fractions as parts of a whole: halves, fourths, thirds, and sixths	1-2	3-4 5-6 7-8		7/8	347-348 349-350 351-352	p. 345D: LCC p. 350A: Reteach	23.1 23.2 23.3	23.1 23.2 23.3	23.1 23.2 23.3
23-A.2	To identify fractional parts of a group		9-10		2/2	353-354	p. 353A: AOC 1	23.4	23.4	23.4
23-A.3	To solve problems by making or using a model			11-12	2/2	355-356	p. 355A: AOC 1, AOC 2	23.5	23.5	

Key: AOC–Activity Options Column   **BB**–Bulletin Board   **PG**–Practice Game   **LCC**–Learning Center Card   **Tech-GSL**–Technology, Grow Slide Level

Harcourt Brace School Publishers

 MATH ADVANTAGE

Individual Record Form

GRADE 2 • Chapters 24-26

Child's Name _____

	Chapter 24	Chapter 25	Chapters 24-26	Cum Chs 24-26
Test				
Date				
Score				

LEARNING GOALS / CHAPTER TEST / REVIEW OPTIONS

Goal #	Learning Goal	Concept	Skills	PSolv	Criterion Scores	Lesson page #	Teacher's Edition	P	R	E
24-A.1	To identify the number of hundreds, tens, and ones in numbers to 1,000	1-2 3-4	5-6 9-10	7-8	9/10	365-366 367-368 369-370 371-372	p. 363C: BB p. 363D: LCC	24.1 24.2 24.3 24.4	24.1 24.2 24.3 24.4	24.1 24.2 24.3 24.4
24-A.2	To use combinations of coins to build $1.00		11-12		2/2	373-374	p. 373A: AOC 2	24.5	24.5	24.5
25-A.1	To identify which of two numbers is greater or less	1 2	3-4 5-6 9-10	7 8	8/10	379-380 381-382 383-384	p. 377D: LCC p. 379A: AOC 1 p. 382A: Tech-GSL T	25.1 25.2 25.3	25.1 25.2 25.3	25.1 25.2 25.3
25-A.2	To identify numbers that come before, after, or between other numbers		11-14		3/4	385-386	p. 385A: AOC 3	25.4	25.4	25.4
25-A.3	To order sets of numbers from least to greatest		15-16		2/2	387-388	p. 388A: Reteach	25.5	25.5	25.5
26-A.1	To add three-digit numbers	1	3-4 7-8	11	4/6	393-394 395-396	p. 393A: AOC 2	26.1 26.2	26.1 26.2	26.1 26.2
26-A.2	To subtract three-digit numbers	2	5-6 9-10	12	4/6	397-398 399-400	p. 397A: AOC 2, AOC 3	26.3 26.4	26.3 26.4	26.3 26.4
26-A.3	To add and subtract money amounts		13-14	15-16	3/4	401-402	p. 391D: LCC	26.5	26.5	26.5

Key: AOC–Activity Options Column **BB**–Bulletin Board **PG**–Practice Game **LCC**–Learning Center Card **Tech-GSL**–Technology, Grow Slide Level

Individual Record Form

GRADE 2 • Chapters 27-28

Child's Name _____

Test	Chapter 27	Chapter 28	Chapters 27-28	Cum Chs 27-28
Date				
Score				

LEARNING GOALS

CHAPTER TEST

REVIEW OPTIONS

Goal #	Learning Goal	Test Items Concept	Test Items Skills	Test Items PSolv	Criterion Scores	Lesson page #	Teacher's Edition	Workbooks P	R	E
27-A.1	To add equal groups to determine how many	1-2			2/2	411-412	p. 412A: Reteach	27.1	27.1	27.1
27-A.2	To multiply by 2, 3, 4, and 5	3-6 7-10			6/8	413-414 415-416	p. 409C: BB p. 409D: LCC	27.2 27.3	27.2 27.3	27.2 27.3
27-A.3	To draw pictures to solve problems			11-12	2/2	417-418	p. 417A: AOC 3	27.4	27.4	27.4
28-A.1	To identify how many groups or how many in a group	1-2 5-6	3-4 7-8		6/8	423-424 425-428	p. 421D: LCC p. 425A: AOC 1	28.1 28.2	28.1 28.2	28.1 28.2
28-A.2	To choose a strategy to solve a problem			9-10 11-12	3/4	427-428 429-430	p. 429A: AOC 1, AOC 2, AOC 3	28.3 28.4	28.3 28.4	28.3 28.4

Key: AOC–Activity Options Column **BB**–Bulletin Board **PG**–Practice Game **LCC**–Learning Center Card **Tech-GSL**–Technology, Grow Slide Level

Formal Assessment

Class Record Form

School		Inventory	Chapter 1	Chapter 2	Chapters 1-2	Cumulatives 1-2	Chapter 3	Chapter 4	Chapter 5	Chapter 3-5	Cumulatives 1-5	Chapter 6	Chapter 7
Teacher													
Criterion Score			11/16	8/12	8/12	19/28	8/12	8/12	8/12	8/12	14/20	9/14	11/16
NAMES	**Date**												

School Teacher		Chapter 8	Chapter 9	Chapters 6-9	Cumulatives 1-9	Chapter 10	Chapter 11	Chapters 10-11	Cumulatives 1-11	Chapter 12	Chapter 13	Chapters 12-13	Cumulatives 1-13
Criterion Score		7/10	8/12	9/14	16/24	7/10	9/14	7/10		8/12	8/12	8/12	14/20
NAMES	**Date**												

School Teacher	Chapter 14	Chapter 15	Chapter 16	Chapters 14-16	Cumulatives 1-16	Chapter 17	Chapter 18	Chapter 19	Chapters 17-19	Cumulatives 1-19	Chapter 20	Chapter 21
Criterion Score	8/12	11/16	9/14	5/8	12/18	8/12	8/12	7/10	7/10	14/20	8/12	7/10
NAMES　　　　**Date**												